Grades K–3

Everyday Mathematics®

Teacher's Reference Manual

Grades K–3

Everyday Mathematics®

Teacher's Reference Manual

The University of Chicago School Mathematics Project

A Division of The **McGraw·Hill** Companies

Columbus, Ohio
Chicago, Illinois

UCSMP Elementary Materials Component

Max Bell, Director

Authors

Max Bell
Jean Bell
John Bretzlauf*
Amy Dillard*
Robert Hartfield
Andy Isaacs*
James McBride, Director
Kathleen Pitvorec*
Peter Saecker

Technical Art

Diana Barrie*

Second Edition only

Photo Credits

Phil Martin/Photography
Jack Demuth/Photography
Cover: Bill Burlingham/Photography
Photo Collage: Herman Adler Design

www.sra4kids.com

SRA/McGraw-Hill

A Division of The McGraw·Hill Companies

Send all inquiries to:
SRA/McGraw-Hill
P.O. Box 812960
Chicago, IL 60681

Printed in the United States of America.

ISBN 1-57039-847-X

4 5 6 7 8 9 QW 07 06 05 04 03 02 01

Contents

Introduction	1
How to Use this Book	1
The *Everyday Mathematics* Program	2
Program Highlights	4
Mathematical Content	5

Management Guide	7
Managing the Curriculum	8
Daily Routines	8
Explorations	8
Fact Triangles	9
Frames-and-Arrows Diagrams	10
Function Machines	10
Games	10
Home Links	12
Math Boxes	12
Math Messages	13
Mental Math and Reflexes	13
Museums	14
Name-Collection Boxes	14
Number Grids	14
Number Lines	15
Projects	15
Situation Diagrams	16
Slates	16
Substitute Teachers	17
Unit Boxes	18
"What's My Rule?"	18

Organizing Students	18
Cooperative Groupings	18
Group Responses	22
Ideas for "Built-in" Mathematics	22
Children with Special Needs	24
Language Diversity	25
Tools	26
Calculators	27
Other Tools	31
Tool Kits	36
The Importance of Problem Solving	37
Assessment	38
Providing for Home-and-School Communication	38
Home Links and Family Letters	38
Organizing Routines and Displays	39
Attendance Chart	39
Class Calendar	40
Class Data Pad	42
Class Number Line	42
Classroom Jobs	44
Daily Schedule	45
Number-Writing Practice	46
Semipermanent Chalk—A Useful Display Tool	46
Temperature and Weather Records	47

Mathematical Topics	51
Essay 1 Number and Counting	52
1.1 Number Uses	53
1.2 Number Systems	53
1.2.1 Counting and the Whole Numbers	54
1.2.2 Numbers for Measuring: The Positive Rational Numbers	54
1.2.3 The Rational Numbers: Positive, Negative, and Zero	55
1.2.4 The Real Numbers	55
1.2.5 The Ordinal Numbers	56

1.3 Counting: Plain and Fancy   57
   1.3.1 Rote Counting   57
   1.3.2 Rational Counting   58

1.4 Number Grids, Scrolls, and Lines   58
   1.4.1 Number Grids   58
   1.4.2 Number Scrolls   61
   1.4.3 Number Lines   62

1.5 Relations   64
   1.5.1 Equality   65
   1.5.2 Name-Collection Boxes   65

1.6 Fractions, Decimals, and Percents   66
   1.6.1 Uses of Fractions   67
   1.6.2 Rates and Ratios   68
   1.6.3 Percents   68
   1.6.4 Equivalence   69

1.7 Notation   69
   1.7.1 Numeration and Place Value   69
   1.7.2 Notation for Rational Numbers   71

Essay 2 Operations and Facts   72

2.1 Operations and Use Classes   73
   2.1.1 Addition and Subtraction   73
   2.1.2 Multiplication and Division   77

2.2 Number Models and Number Sentences   81
   2.2.1 Arithmetic Symbols   82
   2.2.2 Number Sentences   86
   2.2.3 Variables   88

2.3 Basic Facts   89

2.4 Games for Practice   92

Essay 3 Algorithms and Mental Arithmetic   94

3.1 Algorithms and Procedures   95
   3.1.1 Computational Algorithms   96
   3.1.2 Inventing Algorithms   98
   3.13 Focus Algorithms   99

3.2 Standard and Alternative Algorithms   100
   3.2.1 Addition Algorithms   101
   3.2.2 Subtractions Algorithms   103
   3.2.3 Multiplication Algorithms   106
   3.2.4 Division Algorithms   109

3.3 Mental Arithmetic   111

Essay 4 Data and Chance   114

4.1 Data Collection, Organization, and Analysis   114
   4.1.1 Formulating a Question   114
   4.1.2 Collecting, Organizing, and Recording Data   115
   4.1.3 Organizing and Displaying Data   116
   4.1.4 Data Analysis   119

4.2 Probability   120
   4.2.1 Why Study Probability?   121
   4.2.2 The Language of Chance   121
   4.2.3 Making Predictions   122

4.3 Using Data and Probability   122

Essay 5 Geometry   124

5.1 Dimension   125

5.2 Points   126

5.3 Lines, Segments, and Rays   127

5.4 Plane Figures   127
   5.4.1 Angles and Rotations   128
   5.4.2 Polygons   129
   5.4.3 Circles and Pi (π)   133

6.7	**Weight and Mass**	156
6.8	**Angle Measure**	156
6.9	**Elapsed Time**	157
6.10	**Money**	157
	6.10.1 Money Facts	158
	6.10.2 Money History	160

Essay 7 Reference Frames — 162

7.1	**Temperature**	163
7.2	**Time**	165
	7.2.1 Clocks	166
	7.2.2 Calendars	167
	7.2.3 Timelines	170
7.3	**Maps**	170
	7.3.1 Map Coordinates	171
	7.3.2 Map Scales	173

5.5	**Solid Figures**	135
	5.5.1 Solid vs. 3-D	135
	5.5.2 Spheres	136
	5.5.3 Prisms and Cylinders	136
	5.5.4 Pyramids	137
	5.5.5 Polyhedrons	137
5.6	**Transformations**	138
5.7	**Relations**	139
	5.7.1 Parallel and Perpendicular	139
	5.7.2 Congruence and Similarity	140
5.8	**Symmetry**	141
	5.8.1 Line Symmetry	141
	5.8.2 Other Symmetries	142
5.9	**Coordinate Geometry**	142
5.10	**Teaching Geometry**	143
	5.10.1 The van Hiele Levels	144
	5.10.2 Solid vs. Plane Geometry	144
	5.10.3 Geometric Tools	145

Essay 6 Measurement — 146

6.1	**Personal Measures**	147
6.2	**Measurement Systems**	149
	6.2.1 U.S. Customary System	149
	6.2.2 Metric System	149
	6.2.3 Converting between Measures	150
6.3	**Measurement Tools and Techniques**	150
	6.3.1 Measurements as Estimates	150
	6.3.2 Measuring Sticks and Tapes	151
	6.3.3 Scales and Balances	151
6.4	**Length**	153
6.5	**Area**	153
	6.5.1 Discrete Conception of Area	153
	6.5.2 Continuous Conception of Area	154
6.6	**Volume**	154
	6.6.1 Discrete and Continuous Conceptions of Volume	154
	6.6.2 Capacity	155
	6.6.3 Linking Area and Volume	155

Essay 8 Estimation and Number Sense — 174

8.1	**Why Estimate?**	175
	8.1.1 Estimates Are Sometimes Necessary	175
	8.1.2 Estimates Are Easy to Understand	176
	8.1.3 Estimates Can help in Problem Solving	177
8.2	**Extreme Numbers**	177
8.3	**Estimates in Calculations**	178
8.4	**Rounding**	179
	8.4.1 Rounding Algorithms	179
8.5	**Number Sense and Mathematical Connections**	180

Essay 9 Patterns, Sequences, Functions, and Algebra — 182

9.1	**Visual Patterns**	182
9.2	**Odd and Even Number Patterns**	184
9.3	**Sequences**	184
	9.3.1 Frames and Arrows	185
	9.3.2 Incomplete Number Lines	187
	9.3.3 Teaching with Sequences	188

9.4 Functions 189

  9.4.1 Function Machines 190

  9.4.2 "What's My Rule?" 191

  9.4.3 What Is a Function? 192

  9.4.4 Functions and Representations 193

9.5 Algebra 195

Essay 10 Problem Solving 196

10.1 What Is Problem Solving? 196

10.2 Problem Representations 197

10.3 Mathematical Modeling 199

10.4 Teaching Problem Solving 201

  10.4.1 Learning Mathematical Modeling 201

  10.4.2 Number Stories 202

  10.4.3 Sharing Children's Strategies and Solutions 204

  10.4.4 Problem Solving Strategies for Beginners 205

Glossary 209

Index 255

K–3 Games Correlation Chart 262

Table of Measures 264

Introduction

How to Use This Book

This *Teacher's Reference Manual* has three main parts: a Management Guide, a collection of ten Mathematical Topics essays, and a Glossary. The Management Guide includes suggestions about how to implement the *Everyday Mathematics* program; ideas for organizing the curriculum, your students, and program materials; and descriptions of some of *Everyday Mathematics's* features. The Mathematical Topics essays are a good source of reliable information on the mathematics in the K–3 *Everyday Mathematics* curriculum. The essays are followed by a detailed Glossary of mathematical and special terms used in *Everyday Mathematics*. Many glossary entries include references to related portions of the Mathematical Topics.

You may want to read through the Management Guide section of this book before you begin teaching with *Everyday Mathematics* in order to familiarize yourself with the program's features and routines and to help you decide on some organizational strategies for your classroom. As the school year progresses, you may want to refer to some sections again in order to gain further insights.

The Mathematical Topics section of this book provides the essays as background. The essays do not have to be read in their entirety or in any particular order. At the beginning of each essay, you will find a table of contents that outlines the presented material. You can skim an essay, consult its table of contents for a specific topic, or read the essay straight through.

Alternatively, you can look up a term in the glossary and then follow the reference to a related essay or section. For example, the glossary defines *fact power* as "the ability to recall basic number facts automatically, without having to figure them out." Included is a reference to Section 2.3 of the Operations and Facts essay. This section is an extended discussion of how *Everyday*

Mathematics approaches the basic facts, why they are so important, and how the program works to ensure that all children achieve fact power. You may elect to read Section 2.3, or perhaps the entire essay.

Every effort has been made to make this manual easy to use. We hope you find it worthwhile. Please send us any suggestions on how we can improve it.

A brief introduction to *Everyday Mathematics* follows. The Management Guide begins on page 7, the Mathematical Topics essays on page 51, and the Glossary on page 209.

The Everyday Mathematics Program

Everyday Mathematics is a complete K–6 mathematics curriculum embracing many of the traditional goals of school mathematics as well as two ambitious new goals:

• To substantially raise expectations with respect to the amount and range of mathematics that children can learn

• To provide materials for children and support for teachers that enable them to meet these higher expectations

Philosophy

The children of the 21st Century need a mathematics curriculum that is both rigorous and balanced:

• a curriculum that emphasizes conceptual understanding while building a mastery of basic skills

• a curriculum that explores the full mathematics spectrum, not just basic arithmetic

• a curriculum based on how children learn, what they're interested in, and the future for which they must be prepared

We must change both the mathematics we teach and how we teach it if our children are to measure up to the ever-increasing demand for mathematics competence and problem-solving agility. *Everyday Mathematics* makes these changes by introducing children to all the major mathematical content domains—number sense, algebra, measurement, geometry, data analysis, and probability—beginning in Kindergarten. The program helps teachers move beyond basic arithmetic and nurture higher-order and critical-thinking skills in their students, using everyday, real-world problems and situations—while also building and maintaining basic skills, including automatic fact recall.

Everyday Mathematics differs from textbook-centered instruction in a number of ways. The program has been created so that it is consistent with the ways children actually learn mathematics, building understanding over a period of time, first through informal exposure and then through more formal and directed instruction.

Since learning proceeds from the known to the unknown, new learning needs to be connected to and built upon an existing knowledge base.

Children using *Everyday Mathematics* are expected to master a variety of mathematical skills and concepts, but not the first time they are encountered. Mathematical content is taught in a repeated fashion, beginning with concrete experiences. It is a mistake to proceed too quickly from the concrete to the abstract, or to isolate concepts and skills from one another or from problem contexts. Children also need to "double back," revisiting topics, concepts, and skills, and then relating them to each other in new and different ways.

Pacing is important. Children learn best when new topics are presented briskly and in an interesting way. Most children will not master a new topic the first time it is presented, so *Everyday Mathematics* allows children to revisit content in varied contexts, integrating new learning with previous knowledge and experiences. If newly learned concepts and skills are not periodically reviewed, practiced, and applied in a wide variety of contexts, they will not be retained.

It is important to note how the differences between *Everyday Mathematics* and other programs may affect your day-to-day planning and teaching. Daily routines and games are a necessary part of the program, not optional extensions. Routines and games are designed to build conceptual understanding and ensure mastery of basic skills in authentic and interesting contexts. Another way in which *Everyday Mathematics* differs from other programs is that it is designed for the teacher, rather than being centered on a student textbook, offering materials that provide children with a rich variety of experiences across mathematical content strands.

Because language, communication, social interaction, tools, and manipulatives all play important roles in helping children acquire skills, *Everyday Mathematics* employs cooperative learning activities, Explorations, and Projects. The classroom needs to be set up to accommodate group work, and students must be able to work together without direct supervision. To facilitate this learning process, the authors have provided a section about Cooperative Groupings on page 18 of this Management Guide.

In *Everyday Mathematics,* assessment is closely linked with instruction. While some formal assessment is necessary, a balanced approach including less formal, ongoing methods will provide a more complete picture of each child's progress. A number of assessment tools are built into the *Everyday Mathematics* program to help you create an assessment program that will give you feedback about your students' instructional needs and information you can use to assign grades. For more information, see the section on Assessment in the Management Guide, as well as the *Assessment Handbook*.

Everyday Mathematics assumes that virtually all students are capable of a much greater understanding of and proficiency in mathematics than has been traditionally expected. The program establishes high expectations for all students and gives teachers the tools they need to help students meet, and often exceed, these expectations. *Everyday Mathematics* is committed to establishing world-class mathematics standards for our nation's schools.

Program Highlights

Key features of the *Everyday Mathematics* program include:

• *Problem solving for everyday situations.* Research and experience show that children who are unable to solve problems in purely symbolic form often have little trouble with these problems when they are presented in everyday contexts.

• *Developing readiness through hands-on activities. Everyday Mathematics* offers many suggestions for Explorations and Projects for children to work on together. These activities pave the way for the introduction of new mathematical ideas.

• *Establishing links between past experiences and explorations of new concepts.* Ideas that have been explored with concrete materials or pictorial representations are revisited through oral descriptions and symbolic representations. Children learn to shift comfortably among various representations and to select models that are most appropriate for given situations.

• *Sharing ideas through discussion.* Children gain important insights about mathematics by building on one another's discoveries; one idea leads to another or to refinements of a child's own understanding. Discussion promotes good listening habits and fosters a receptive attitude to the ideas of classmates. Because verbalization often clarifies concepts, talking about mathematics is an important part of thinking about mathematics.

• *Cooperative learning through partner and small-group activities.* Children discover that working together is usually more enjoyable and stimulating than working independently. Moreover, as children learn to work as a team, cooperation replaces competition, and the less skilled benefit by drawing support from the more skilled.

• *Practice through games.* Frequent practice is imperative for a student to attain mastery of a skill. Unfortunately, drills tend to become monotonous and gradually lose effectiveness over time. Games, however, (1) relieve the tedium of rote repetition, (2) reduce the use of worksheets, and (3) offer an almost unlimited source of problem material, because, in most cases, numbers are generated randomly.

- *Ongoing review throughout the year.* It is rare that students master something new the first time they encounter it. For this reason, repeated exposures to key ideas presented in slightly different contexts are built into the *Everyday Mathematics* program.

- *Daily routines.* The program suggests routines that children can perform on a regular basis. Tasks such as keeping the daily schedule, class calendar, weather and temperature records, and attendance chart are learning experiences in themselves. Other regular classroom tasks help children develop a sense of order, initiative, and responsibility while reinforcing numerous mathematical concepts.

- *Informal assessment.* In addition to independent review exercises, *Everyday Mathematics* provides many suggestions for small-group activities to help you assess children's progress. Through your interactions with small groups of children, you will obtain a clearer understanding of individual strengths and weaknesses.

- *Home-and-school partnership.* Optimal learning occurs if it involves the child, the teacher, and the home. *The Home Connection Handbook* (included in the program) offers many suggestions for this. Family Letters help inform parents and guardians about each unit's topics and terms, offering ideas for home-based mathematics activities that supplement classroom work. Also, parents or others at home are invited to participate in each child's mathematics experiences through the Home Links included in most lessons.

Mathematical Content

Everyday Mathematics Grades K–3 is organized into the following content strands:

- Data and Chance
- Geometry
- Measurement and Reference Frames
- Numeration
- Operations and Computation
- Patterns, Functions, and Algebra

Woven throughout the content strands are several key mathematical themes:

- Algorithmic and Procedural Thinking
- Estimation Skills and Number Sense
- Mental Arithmetic Skills and Reflexes
- Problem Solving

Special emphasis is placed on:

- Establishing links from past experiences, activities with concrete materials, pictures, oral statements, and symbolic arithmetic statements. For example, children might act out a problem or talk about it to get a feel for what is happening. Or they could draw simple pictures or diagrams, or do some mental arithmetic, which would eventually lead them to write a number model.

- Discussing and sharing ideas. (Can you tell us how you do that? Why do you think so? Does everyone agree?)

- Using and comparing equivalent expressions. (What other ways can we say or write . . . ?)

- Expressing quantities and measurements in context by including labels or units. (Five what?)

- Learning about the reversibility of most things: put in, take out; add, subtract; take apart, put together; go away, come back; expand, shrink; spend money, get money; positive, negative; and so on.

- Using calculators as a tool for counting, displaying numbers, developing concepts and skills, and solving problems—especially real-life problems.

By becoming a part of everyday work and play, these lessons, exercises, and concepts will gradually shape children's ways of thinking about mathematics and foster the development of children's mathematical intuition and understanding.

Management Guide

The following sections offer suggestions for making *Everyday Mathematics* "work" in your classroom. This Guide explains how to use the program's features and materials and presents ideas for organizing students during instruction, as well as for reaching students of all abilities.

outline

Managing the Curriculum 8
  Daily Routines 8
  Explorations 8
  Fact Triangles 9
  Frames-and-Arrows Diagrams 10
  Function Machines 10
  Games 10
  Home Links 12
  Math Boxes 12
  Math Messages 13
  Mental Math and Reflexes 13
  Museums 14
  Name-Collection Boxes 14
  Number Grids 14
  Number Lines 15
  Projects 15
  Situation Diagrams 16
  Slates 16
  Substitute Teachers 17
  Unit Boxes 18
  "What's My Rule?" 18

Organizing Students 18
  Cooperative Groupings 18

  Group Responses 22
  Ideas for "Built-in" Mathematics 22
  Children with Special Needs 24
  Language Diversity 25

Tools 26
  Calculators 27
  Other Tools 31
  Tool Kits 36

The Importance of Problem Solving 37

Assessment 38

Providing for Home-and-School Communication 38
  Home Links and Family Letters 38

Organizing Routines and Displays 39
  Attendance Chart 39
  Class Calendar 40
  Class Data Pad 42
  Class Number Line 42
  Classroom Jobs 44
  Daily Schedule 45
  Number-Writing Practice 46
  Semipermanent Chalk—A Useful Display Tool 46
  Temperature and Weather Records 47

Managing the Curriculum

Perhaps the single greatest difference between *Everyday Mathematics* and other programs is that *Everyday Mathematics* is written for the teacher rather than focused on a student textbook. Student materials are designed as supplements to facilitate the teacher's use of the program. This section discusses program features and describes materials that support the program design.

Daily Routines

Children learn a great deal of mathematics through the daily routines they perform independently and as a class. Most of the routines in *Everyday Mathematics* should be introduced in the first unit and then maintained throughout the year. Although these routines require special attention and extra time at the beginning of the year, you will find that investing this time will make teaching easier in the long run. Once routines have been established, they become self-sustaining, as much by the children's energy as by the teacher's effort. Learning becomes much more efficient and effective. For more information on routines, see the Organizing Routines and Displays section on p. 39 of this Management Guide.

Explorations

In *Everyday Mathematics,* the term *Explorations* means time set aside for independent, small-group activities. In addition to providing the benefits of cooperative learning, small-group work lets all children have a chance to use manipulatives (such as the pan balance and base-10 blocks) that are limited in supply.

If there are enough materials for everyone, you may decide to have the whole class work on one Exploration at a time. It is more likely, though, that you will want to have small groups of children working on several Explorations simultaneously. Thus, you will need to plan how you will manage several different activities at the same time. Parent volunteers can be very helpful in these situations.

The Explorations have been designed so that you can position the various activities at different stations around the room and have groups rotate among the stations (or rotate the materials among the groups).

Whenever possible, you might find it helpful to organize the materials for each Exploration by keeping them together in a small plastic tub, pan, bin, bucket, or box. After the Explorations have been completed, you can make the materials available for review and free-time activities.

Each Explorations lesson suggests three activities, with the option of adding others. Decide how many stations you will need to accommodate groups of three to five children each. Each station should have one kind of material for children to share. To ensure you have enough stations for all of your groups, you may want to set up two stations for each Exploration activity or set up additional familiar activities or games for children to complete independently while other groups are working on Explorations.

Of all the Exploration activities suggested in the lesson, the first one, Exploration A, contains the main content of the lesson and requires the most teacher involvement at the outset. Try to spend most of your time at this station, although you will likely need to circulate as well, especially if parent volunteers are not available and particularly at the beginning of the year, when children are less independent. If you remain at one station as the children rotate through it, this will enable you to work with every child in a small group and to use the task at that station as an informal assessment opportunity.

To promote a cooperative environment, the authors suggest that you make and display a poster of Rules for Explorations, such as the one shown in the margin.

Discuss these rules, and any others that you or the children want to add, prior to each Explorations lesson until children become accustomed to working this way.

Beginning in second grade, *Everyday Mathematics* supplies instruction masters (found in the *Math Masters* book) for the Exploration activities. These masters aim to make the groups more independent and to incorporate reading into the Explorations process. The groups will need more help and attention at the beginning of the year. But as the year progresses and children become stronger readers, and as they familiarize themselves with some of the activities, they will become increasingly independent. You may want to mount the instruction sheets on tagboard and/or laminate them so you will be able to use them over the course of the school year.

You should set aside enough class time so that all of your students can experience the Explorations. Do not set up the Explorations stations solely as optional centers for children to use when they have finished their other work. If you do that, the children who need these experiences the most will get fewer opportunities to participate in Explorations activities.

Fact Triangles

Fact Triangles help children develop their mental arithmetic reflexes. You might think of them as the *Everyday Mathematics* version of flash cards. Fact Triangles are more effective than flash cards in helping children memorize facts, however, because they emphasize fact families and the relationships between operations.

Rules for Explorations

1. Cooperate with others.
2. Move about quietly.
3. Keep voices low.
4. Treat materials as tools, not as toys.
5. Give everyone in the group a chance to use the materials.
6. Straighten up when finished. Put materials back where they belong.
7. Try to settle disputes quietly within the group. If necessary, one person can go to the teacher for help.

For more about Fact Triangles, see Section 2.3 of the Mathematical Topics in this book.

Sample Fact Triangles are shown below, one for an addition/subtraction fact family and one for a multiplication/division fact family.

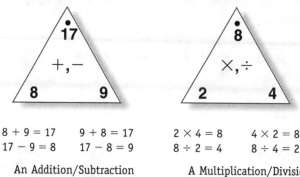

| 8 + 9 = 17 | 9 + 8 = 17 | 2 × 4 = 8 | 4 × 2 = 8 |
| 17 − 9 = 8 | 17 − 8 = 9 | 8 ÷ 2 = 4 | 8 ÷ 4 = 2 |

An Addition/Subtraction Fact Triangle   A Multiplication/Division Fact Triangle

Frames-and-Arrows Diagrams

Frames-and-Arrows diagrams provide children with a way to organize work with sequences. Each frame contains a number in the sequence; each arrow represents a rule that determines what number goes in the next frame.

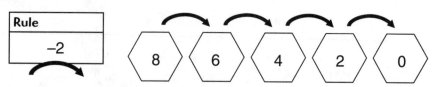

Function Machines

A function machine is an imaginary machine programmed to process numbers according to a certain rule. An input number is put into the machine, it is then transformed into an output number through the application of the designated rule.

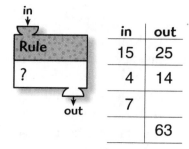

in	out
15	25
4	14
7	
	63

Games

Many parents and educators make a sharp distinction between work and play. They tend to "allow" play only during prescribed times. However, children naturally carry their playfulness into all of their activities. This is why *Everyday Mathematics* sees games as enjoyable ways to practice number skills, especially those that help children develop *fact power*.

Games are an integral part of the *Everyday Mathematics* program, rather than an optional extra as they are traditionally used in many classrooms. Make sure that all children have time to play games, especially those who work at a slower pace or encounter more difficulty than their classmates. Just as with the Explorations, if children play the games only after finishing other work, many of the children who need these experiences most will get fewer opportunities to have them.

See Section 9.3.1 of the Mathematical Topics for more information.

See "What's My Rule?" on p. 18 of this section and Section 9.4.2 of the Mathematical Topics for more information.

For more on using games to develop fact power, see Section 2.4 in the Operations and Facts essay.

management guide

Games can also be played frequently without the same mathematical problems repeating because the numbers in most games are generated randomly. The game format eliminates the tedium typical of most drills. You may want to set up a Games Corner using some of your students' favorite games. That way, students can get additional practice while playing games of their own choosing during free time. Rotate games often to keep the Games Corner fresh and interesting.

There will be times when certain games do not offer sufficient practice with a concept. On these occasions, you may want to employ traditional drill problems. In some instances, you may also wish to use timed drills. Always strive for balance in your approach to drills and practice. Too much monotonous, rote pencil pushing has helped produce generations of people who see mathematics as little else.

Competition

One issue frequently raised concerning the inclusion of games in the curriculum is competition. Many teachers do not want young children to compete against each other. As one teacher writes, "I prefer to have children work in cooperative groupings, staying away from win-or-lose games. I can't think of a quicker way to turn a child off to the concept one is trying to teach than to inject the emotional disaster of 'I've lost!' into the experience."

It is true that many of the games in the *Everyday Mathematics* program are competitive. Fair and friendly competition can generate many good things: excitement, determination, independence, and challenge. Game rules may also be changed to fit the players' needs for fairness, harmony, and equality. It is possible to modify most of the games so that children practice the same number skills while working cooperatively. The challenge and excitement will come from working together, making joint decisions, doing one's best, having fun.

We can use *Multiplication Top-It* to demonstrate how a competitive game can be modified to make it non-competitive. In *Multiplication Top-It,* children use a deck of 1–10 number cards, consisting of four cards of each number, for a total of 40 cards. Each child turns over two cards and calls out the product. The player with the highest product takes all the cards played in that turn. The player with the most cards at the end of the game wins.

Suppose, however, that two or three children are asked to play the same game, but are given a group objective: "Play until all 40 cards are used, putting all the used cards into a single discard pile. Time the game. Play again until all 40 cards are used. Try to beat your best time to play the whole deck."

This modified game allows practice of the same multiplication skills but does not declare "winners" and "losers." Instead, the focus is on the group objective of achieving a faster time.

Many of the games, as they are, identify the winner as the player with the highest total after a certain number of turns. Here are some strategies for converting these games to relatively non-competitive games:

- Have the children take turns (as usual), but ask them to record their results for each round on the same sheet of paper. Each game total will then represent the combined efforts of all group members.

- Redefine the game objective. For example, ask groups to play a sequence of games and "report the highest and lowest single game totals." This modification may inspire some measure of healthy competition among groups, but the one-on-one competitive nature of the standard game will be reduced.

These are only examples. The best ideas for modifying games will probably come from your own classroom experiences. Involve your children in the revisions. If they realize that their input will result in improved games, they will become more eager players—and learners.

The Everything Math Deck

The Everything Math Deck is a deck of 54 number cards used for a variety of *Everyday Mathematics* games and activities. The deck can be purchased through the publisher. It has four of each card for the numbers 0 to 10, and one of each card for the numbers 11 to 20. On the reverse of the 0–10 cards are fractions represented in a variety of ways.

You can transform an ordinary deck of 54 playing cards to function like an Everything Math Deck (whole number side), as follows:

- Change the four queens to 0s.
- Remove the four jacks, four kings, and two jokers. Label each of these ten cards with one of the numbers from 11 to 20.
- Change the four aces to 1s.
- All number cards represent their face value.

Home Links

 Home Links are the *Everyday Mathematics* version of homework assignments. Each lesson has a Home Link, which can be found in the *Math Masters* book. The next lesson has a follow-up to the previous Home Link. Home Links consist of active projects and ongoing review problems that show parents what the children can do in mathematics. A blank Home Link form has also been provided for you to create your own.

See "Providing for Home-and-School Communication" on page 38 in this section for more information.

Math Boxes

Math Boxes, originally developed by *Everyday Mathematics* teacher Ellen Dairyko, are an excellent way to review material on a regular basis.

In *Everyday Mathematics,* Math Boxes are one of the main components of review and skills maintenance. Once this routine has been introduced, almost every lesson includes a Math Boxes page in the *Math Journal* as part of the Ongoing Learning and Practice section.

Math Boxes problems are not intended to reinforce the content of the lesson in which they appear. Rather, they provide continuous distributed practice of all skills and concepts in the program. The Math Boxes page does not need to be completed on the same day as the lesson, but it should not be skipped.

Math Boxes are designed as independent activities. Expect that your guidance will be needed, especially at the beginning of the school year when some problems review skills from prior years. If children struggle with a problem set, it is not necessary to create a lesson to develop these skills. You can modify or skip problems that you know are not review for your children. Lesson activities revisit skills throughout the year. Math Boxes also provide useful assessment information on review skills.

NOTE: Although Math Boxes are designed primarily as independent activities, at times it may be useful to have children work with partners or work through some problems as a class.

Math Messages

A Math Message is provided at the beginning of each lesson, beginning with Unit 4 in first grade. The Math Message usually leads into the lesson for the day; sometimes it reviews topics previously covered. Children should complete the Math Message before the start of each lesson.

You can display Math Messages in a number of ways. You may want to write them on the board, the Class Data Pad, overhead transparencies; or post them on the bulletin board; or duplicate them ahead of time on quarter-sheets as handouts.

Many teachers find it attractive to have children record their answers to the Math Message. In some classrooms, children keep a daily Math Journal where they enter Math Message questions and answers. In other classrooms, children record their answers on quarter- or half-sheets, which teachers collect from time to time.

Although the *Teacher's Lesson Guide* contains many suggestions for Math Messages, you are encouraged to create your own, designed around the needs of your children and on the activities that take place in your classroom. You may also want to provide a Suggestion Box into which children can put their own Math Message ideas as well as number stories.

Mental Math and Reflexes

The term Mental Math and Reflexes refers to exercises, usually oral, designed to strengthen children's number sense and to review and advance essential basic skills. Mental Math and Reflexes sessions should be brief, lasting no more than five minutes. Numerous short interactions are far more effective than fewer prolonged sessions.

There are several kinds of Mental Math suggestions provided in the *Teacher's Lesson Guide*. Some involve a choral counting routine;

See Section 3.3 of the Mathematical Topics for more information on Mental Arithmetic.

many are basic-skills practice with counts, operations, or measures; and some are problem-solving exercises.

For Mental Math and Reflexes exercises that require children to record their answers on slates, see "Slates" on page 16 of this section for one possible procedure as well as suggestions for alternatives if you do not have slates.

The *Teacher's Lesson Guide* suggests Mental Math and Reflexes exercises for almost every lesson. You are encouraged to use these exercises based on your children's needs and your classroom activities. If the suggested exercises do not meet the needs of your class, feel free to provide an alternate set.

Museums

Everyday Mathematics encourages the development of classroom museums—using a bulletin board or table where related items can be collected, categorized, and labeled. The first example of such a museum might be the Numbers All Around Museum that is assembled in first grade as children bring examples of uses of numbers from home. Other museums could include the following:

- *Fractions Museum* Children bring halves, fourths, and other fractions of nonperishable things from home.

- *Hundreds Museum* Children collect sets of 100 things for display, such as one-hundred-piece jigsaw puzzles or one hundred baseball cards.

- *3-D Shapes Museum* Children collect 3-dimensional shapes and pictures of 3-D shapes.

Everyday Mathematics museums are often supplemented with posters of 2-dimensional representations of items. Along with helping to connect concepts between solid objects and 2-D pictures, the posters help summarize categories of objects that children are likely to have identified in their concrete manipulations.

If you take your class to a museum in your community, encourage the children to look for the uses of mathematics that abound there. Examples include statistics about objects in exhibits and different ways of categorizing those objects—ways that often have some underlying frame of reference, such as size or time.

Name-Collection Boxes

A name-collection box is a diagram of an open-top box with a label attached to it. It is used to structure work with equivalent names for numbers. The name on the label identifies the number whose names are collected in the box. For example, the box shown in the margin is a 16-box, a name-collection box for the number 16.

Number Grids

A number grid is a matrix which consists of rows of boxes, ten to each row, containing a set of consecutive whole numbers. Children

16
XVI
dieciséis
10 less than 26
20 − 4
4 + 4 + 4 + 4
(2 × 5) + 6
sixteen
116 − 100
half of 32
8 twos
32 ÷ 2

16-box

See Section 1.5.2 of the Mathematical Topics for more information.

use number grids to explore number patterns, reinforce place-value concepts, and calculate sums and differences.

See Section 1.4.1 of the Mathematical Topics for more information.

									0
1	2	3	4	5	6	7	8	9	10
11	12	13	14	15	16	17	18	19	20
21	22	23	24	25	26	27	28	29	30
31	32	33	34	35	36	37	38	39	40
41	42	43	44	45	46	47	48	49	50
51	52	53	54	55	56	57	58	59	60
61	62	63	64	65	66	67	68	69	70
71	72	73	74	75	76	77	78	79	80
81	82	83	84	85	86	87	88	89	90
91	92	93	94	95	96	97	98	99	100
101	102	103	104	105	106	107	108	109	110

Number Lines

A number line is a line on which points correspond to numbers. There is one point for every number and one number for every point. Children use number lines when counting and skip counting, performing measuring activities, and adding and subtracting. Number lines are also used as the axes in coordinate graphing systems.

See Section 1.4.3 of the Mathematical Topics for more information.

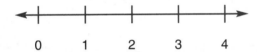

Projects

The Projects suggested in *Everyday Mathematics* cover a wide array of mathematics activities and concepts, and are created around themes that interest children. Project ideas are found in the Projects Appendix of the *Teacher's Lesson Guide* for each grade. Project Masters are found in the Teaching Masters Section of the *Math Masters* book.

The Projects are cross-curricular, drawing on and developing skills and concepts in reading and language arts, social studies, art, and especially science. They often include the following science processes:

- Observing
- Communicating
- Identifying
- Collecting, organizing, and graphing data
- Using numbers
- Measuring
- Determining patterns and relationships

Total	
?	
Part	Part
12	15

Parts-and-total diagram

You can consider many Projects and other activities suggested in the *Everyday Mathematics* program as part of your science curriculum.

Projects especially appropriate at particular points during the school year are suggested in various Unit Organizers in each *Teacher's Lesson Guide.* Since many ideas have been included in the Projects—more than can usually be used—choose those that interest your children, and feel free to add your own. Unlike the short activities in the Explorations, projects may take a day or more to complete. Projects, however, are an important part of the curriculum and are memorable to children, so please take the time to have your class work on them.

Situation Diagrams

In *Everyday Mathematics,* various diagrams are used to help children organize information in simple one-step problem-solving situations. Parts-and-total diagrams, comparison diagrams, change diagrams, and rate diagrams are some examples:

Quantity	
12	
Quantity	**Difference**
8	?

Quantity	
12	
Quantity	Difference
8	?

Comparison diagrams

Start	Change	End
35	−6	?

Change diagram

children	cards per child	cards
4	?	24

Rate diagram

Slates

Most children and teachers genuinely enjoy using slates. They afford an excellent opportunity for everyone to quietly answer a question at the same time, and they help you to see at a glance which children may need extra help. They also save paper. Two kinds of slates are particularly easy to use:

- *Plastic Write-on/Wipe-off Slates* Children write on these small, white slates with dry-erase markers. They can store both the markers and the slates in their tool kits or stack them on a counter or shelf for easy distribution when needed.

- *Chalkboard Slates* Chalk may be kept in old socks that can also be used as erasers. Small rug scraps or pieces of cloth also make good erasers. One teacher recommends small, cosmetic, cotton-quilt pads.

management guide

Establish a routine for using slates. You might want to use one-word cues, such as *Listen, Think, Write, Show, Erase.* The following procedure, if used consistently, helps prevent confusion:

• Explain each exercise aloud. Tell children to *Listen.* If children find the problems too challenging, you may want to write them on the board or overhead.

• Have the children work the problems mentally. Be sure to give them time to *Think.*

• Instruct the children to *Write* their answers on their slates and keep them covered.

• When most children have written their answers, tell them to *Show* their slates at the same time by holding them up facing you. Afterward, when appropriate, take a few minutes to have the children share their strategies.

• Have the children *Erase* their slates.

There are, of course, alternatives to slates. Children can fold a piece of paper into fourths, which will give them eight cells in which to write answers. Another alternative is to use laminated tagboard and dry-erase markers.

Instead of doing oral and slate assessments with the whole class, another strategy would be to work with small groups of children, one group at a time, over several days. While you do this, the rest of the class can work on Assessment Masters. When using slates, it is not necessary to record every child's performance on every problem. Instead, you need keep a record of only those children who are struggling. You can go back later and enter positive comments for students you know are doing well.

Substitute Teachers

The *Everyday Mathematics* approach may be unfamiliar to some substitute teachers, so you may want to provide additional materials for those times when you must be absent. Many lessons can be handled by substitutes, especially if they let the children think things through for themselves. Here are some suggestions:

• Reserve the Math Boxes from several lessons or create extra Math Boxes of your own. Routines like Frames and Arrows and "What's My Rule?" can also be included.

• Set aside several engaging games for children to play. Game days are always a favorite, and yet it can sometimes be difficult to find time for them.

• Prepare suggestions for practice with Fact Triangles. Children can sort the facts by strategy or into facts that they know and those they still need to practice. Partners can take turns quizzing each other. Known facts can be recorded in the *Math Journal.*

• Make an "emergency box" with activities to be done on days when your absence is unexpected. As you teach, identify activities from *Everyday Mathematics* that could be included.

Unit box

See "Function Machines" on page 10 in this section and Section 9.4.2 of the Mathematical Topics for more information.

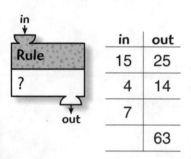

in	out
15	25
4	14
7	
	63

Unit Boxes

A unit box is a rectangular box displayed next to a problem or a set of problems. Unit boxes contain the labels or units of measure used in the corresponding problem(s). Unit boxes help children to think symbolically by encouraging them to see numbers as quantities or measurements of real objects.

"What's My Rule?"

"What's My Rule?" is an activity in which children analyze a set of number pairs to determine the rule that relates the numbers in each pair. The data are often presented in the form of a function table generated by a function machine. "What's My Rule?" problems appear from time to time in Mental Math and Reflexes, lesson activities, and Math Boxes.

Organizing Students

The previous sections contain suggestions for managing features of the *Everyday Mathematics* program. The following sections outline hints for managing your classroom as you do mathematics.

Cooperative Groupings

Cooperative learning improves attitudes toward learning and academic achievement; improves social skills and time on task; and helps develop speaking, listening, and writing skills. Cooperative learning also creates an atmosphere in which children can share ideas and ways of thinking as they solve problems. One benefit is that children are exposed to strategies they may not have discovered on their own. Cooperative learning also prepares students for real life situations. On the job, people share responsibilities with others, cooperate, and work together toward common goals.

Since children will be working together much of the time, it is important that they understand your expectations with respect to working in partnerships and small groups.

Consider making and displaying a poster of Partner Principles, listing rules for working with a partner.

Groups and Partnerships

For simplicity, the word *group* is used to refer both to partners and small groups. In group activities, learning becomes a dynamic process in which interaction among group members encourages an inquisitive spirit and introduces new avenues for exploration, while instilling a spirit of teamwork.

Because *Everyday Mathematics* is filled with group activities, both teacher-directed and independent, you may want to plan seating arrangements accordingly. That way, children can make the transition from whole-class work to group work with minimal disruption.

Partnership Principles

1. Guide
2. Check
3. Praise

To maximize success, thought and planning must be given to setting up groups. The best lessons can fail if groups are not properly formed. Having children work with their best friends does not always create an ideal learning environment. And if teams are formed at random, children with the lowest or highest skill levels could end up in one group. Along with your personal knowledge of each child's respective skill level, the following strategies suggested by teachers may be helpful:

- Groups should be heterogeneous in terms of skill, gender, and race or ethnicity. The mixed achievement levels within groups allows for peer tutoring. Random groups or special-interest groups can be formed to vary the learning experience, but heterogeneous groupings usually work best.

- To arrange the class into groups, list your children from high to low according to skill or achievement level. Take one student from the top of the list, one from the bottom, and two from the middle to form each group. When it is necessary to break a team into partners, match high-medium and medium-low.

- A good size for small groups is four children, which also allows for pairs working together within the group. If the class does not divide by four equally, place one or two remaining students in a group that will best fit their needs. If there are three remaining, form another group.

- Keep groups together for about six weeks. If situations develop that impede a group's progress, make changes as necessary.

Team Building and Group Etiquette

For children to work cooperatively in groups, there often needs to be a team-building process that establishes the team's identity, spirit, and responsibility to one another. If children don't know one another, "getting to know you" activities will help. For example, have children make lists of likes and dislikes and then have them look for differences and common interests.

Even though children have worked in groups before, it is important that you take time during the first few weeks of school to review partner and small-group etiquette. The value of group study is diminished if social interaction replaces purposeful learning.

Post the three basic principles of constructive partner and group interaction: Guide, Check, and Praise. Then, during the first few days of the year, have children share what they think these terms mean. Guide the discussion to cover the following points:

Guide
- Help and demonstrate what to do without telling or doing everything yourself.
- Take turns.
- Only one student should get help from the teacher if the group needs it.

Check

- Pay attention and listen to others.
- If someone makes a mistake, respond positively and in a helpful way. (Make a list of helpful phrases such as "Try again," "Good try," "Close," and so on.)
- Help fellow group members find correct responses.

Praise

- Let others know they are doing a good job.
- Praise others. (Help children compile a list of appropriate praise words and phrases.)

To establish a positive learning environment, it is also worthwhile to have children brainstorm with you about a good set of general rules. You then might post these rules on the bulletin board so that children can refer to them as needed. Such rules might include the following:

- Do not let others do all of the work.
- Use quiet voices.
- Move quietly.
- Share materials.
- Talk about problems, but don't argue.
- Be polite to one another.

Duties of Group Members

Each group member may be assigned a specific role that changes daily or weekly. Some roles can be eliminated or modified depending on the activity and grade level.

Recorder Writes group answers and strategies used; can also act as the reporter for the group.

Reader Reads problems, text selections, directions, and so on.

Facilitator Makes sure everyone is on task and encourages participation from each group member. Uses positive phrases such as the following:

- "We need to work on problem three."
- "Which step is next?"

Gatekeeper Makes sure one person does not monopolize the activity and ensures equal participation. Uses positive phrases, such as the following:

- "Denise, how would you do this?"
- "Do you agree, Eric?"
- "What do you think, Shawna?"

Materials/Supply Handler Gathers and returns all materials needed for group activities.

Summarizer Sums up group solutions, opinions, or findings.

Duties of the Teacher

- Explain the activity.
- Monitor groups to make sure they are working in the right direction, and that behavior is appropriate.
- Answer group questions and provide assistance as necessary.
- Assess group/individual skills.
- Provide closure for each lesson or activity.

Group Structures

The following group structures are recommended by Spencer Kagan and other cooperative-learning experts:

Numbered Heads Together This is a simple structure for reviewing basic facts and general information.

- Children in each group are numbered 1 to 4.
- The teacher asks a question.
- Children put their heads together and discuss possible solutions.
- The teacher calls a number at random. The child in each group with that number reports his or her group's findings.

Pairs-Check This structure works well for learning a new skill.

- Groups of four children break into pairs.
- One child in each pair works a problem while the other coaches as necessary.
- The coach checks the solution. If a pair does not agree on an answer, they may ask the other pair in their group. If the whole group does not agree, the teacher then helps the group.
- Children continue in this manner, changing roles after each problem.

Inside-Outside Circle Children make two circles, one inside the other. Children in the inside circle face the children in the outside circle so each child on the inside has a partner on the outside.

The teacher asks a question and partners discuss a solution. If they can't find an answer, they may confer with children on either side of them. The teacher calls for a response from either the inside or outside circle of children.

Inside-Outside Circle: Variation with Flash Cards Children have flash cards with questions on one side and answers on the other. They rotate in their circles so they practice with a new partner for each rotation.

Think-Pair-Share The teacher asks a question. Children are given a specified amount of time to think about the answer. Once the time has elapsed, children share their ideas, opinions, answers with teammates or partners. The teacher then asks for volunteers to share their solutions with the class.

> **in perspective** The "Expert Jigsaw" strategy for cooperative grouping, developed in the upper elementary grades, involves the initial use of larger groups (8 to 10 students). It is used in fifth grade specifically to learn computation tricks. The class is divided into three groups. Each group learns and practices a different computation trick. Each member of the group must be able to perform and explain the trick. The three groups then "jigsaw" to form new, smaller groups consisting of three students, each an expert on one of the tricks. Each student performs and explains his or her trick to the other two students in the group.

Group-Related Resources

Adrini, Beth and Spencer Kagan. *Cooperative Learning and Mathematics.* San Juan Capistrano, California: Kagan Cooperative Learning, 1992.

Johnson, David W. and Roger T. Johnson. *Learning Mathematics and Cooperative Learning.* Edina, Minnesota: Interaction Book Company, 1991.

Johnson, David W., Roger T. Johnson, and Edythe Johnson Holubec. *The Nuts and Bolts of Cooperative Learning.* Edina, Minnesota: Interaction Book Company, 1994.

Kagan, Spencer. *Cooperative Learning.* San Juan Capistrano, California: Kagan Cooperative Learning, 1992.

Group Responses

Just as choral readings have proven beneficial for beginning readers, group-response techniques such as plain and fancy counting, calculator counting, and fact reviews can be equally beneficial for primary grade mathematics learners. Many Mental Math and Reflexes activities require group responses.

Group-response activities allow all children to participate at their own levels without being put on the spot. More skilled children will have the opportunity to lead while others hear them and are thereby strengthened in the concepts in which they are weak.

Establish a brisk rhythm, with responses given simultaneously and clearly. Keep group-response activities brief. If you have children work in small groups or sit around tables, you can focus on one group at a time, even if the whole class is responding. This will help you identify children who may need extra help.

Ideas for "Built-in" Mathematics

The following suggestions were contributed by teachers who piloted the *Everyday Mathematics* program:

- When disputes between two children arise that could be settled in either one's favor, have each disputant choose a number between 1 and 100. Pick a number yourself and tell it to a third party or write it down secretly. Explain that the one who guesses closest to your number will be the "winner." After settling the issue, ask questions such as, "Is this fair? What makes it fair?" You can extend or limit the range of numbers as appropriate for the situation or the grade level.

- Whenever the opportunity to choose an option presents itself, have the children vote. Tell them to vote for what they want, and tell them that they can only vote once. Be sure they understand that the option receiving the most votes is the one by which they all must abide. Children can then tally, count, and compare totals. In case of ties, ask the children to suggest a fair way to proceed.

- When you give directions, quantify as often as you can. *For example,* say, "Six children may use the Reading Corner, and five may use the Math Center."

- Whenever possible, have children line up according to specified categories, such as: "everyone wearing something red," "everyone wearing a belt," or "everyone wearing brown shoes."

- Alternatively, have children line up without revealing the category to them. For this version of "What's My Rule?" determine a category and then call out the names of children who fit the category. Then ask the class to explain why you chose those particular children. Don't insist on your rule if children see one that is equally valid. *("What I had in mind was . . . , but yours works, too," or "I didn't think of yours.")*

- Lining-up activities can also be used to help teach ordinal numbers. For example, have children line up and then give them directions such as: "The first, second, and third children may walk to the door. The seventh child may walk to the door. The fourth child who walked to the door may sit down."

- During the first few days of school, when books and supplies are distributed, you can use these distribution tasks to have children practice counting, matching one-to-one correspondence, and doing simple mental arithmetic operations. For example, ask someone to count the children in a row, at a table, or in a group, and then ask how many of each item being passed out will be needed so that every child will have one. Or you could ask a member of the group to figure out how many items their group will need before each distribution. Another idea is to give more or less than required of an item to a small group of children. After they have distributed the items among themselves, ask each group to describe the results. Encourage them to verbalize any problems: "We needed ___, but you gave us ___. That's ___ too many."

- Dice and spinners are good random-number generators. You can make nonstandard dice by putting self-stick number labels on standard dice or on wooden cubes. Vary the numbers to make new games.

- When minor decisions need to be made or when you can't quite think of a way to perform a particular task, take a few minutes to have children think about the problem. Discuss their ideas— sometimes they can be great! This also gives children a chance to solve real problems.

- If you have a Math Center, don't let it get too cluttered. Introduce new items and remove old ones to maintain children's interest.

Children with Special Needs

Everyday Mathematics is a hands-on curriculum that builds on children's interests and experiences, reinforcing content over time. These and other key features make it an accessible and effective program for all children, even those with a wide range of special needs.

Pacing is important in the overall schematic of the *Everyday Mathematics* curriculum. Since the program is designed to continually build on children's prior experiences, topics and concepts are revisited in a number of ways throughout the year and in the years that follow. Do not dwell on one skill area or concept, even if some have yet to master it. *Everyday Mathematics* provides many opportunities for children to master the content. Staying too long with a topic may help some children attain temporary mastery, but for maximum long-term retention, it is best to follow the basic structure of the curriculum as it is written.

When changes to lesson content or instruction *do* need to be made in order to accommodate specific children, the authors recommend an approach of modification, rather than supplementation. Modify lessons only when there is a mismatch between the learner and the type of instruction or materials, or within the task assigned. Focus on the simplest change possible and be sensitive to the social aspects of modification.

The lessons in the *Teacher's Lesson Guide* include specific information about modifying content and/or instruction to meet the needs of particular children. The "Options for Individualizing" component, which can be found at the end of almost every lesson, suggests optional activities for extra practice, reteaching, and/or enrichment to reinforce, extend or fine-tune the main content of that lesson. Additionally, "Adjusting the Activity" suggestions provide ideas for making particular activities more or less challenging.

Be sure that students have plenty of time to investigate the Explorations that are a part of the program and pay close attention to see that all students have a chance to participate in learning games. Modify the games to best meet students' needs, if necessary, or model game strategies prior to playing games. Many important concepts and skills are taught through Explorations and games in *Everyday Mathematics*. Students at all levels can participate and gain from these experiences.

As you assess students' progress, examine and analyze individual responses through a variety of activities, varying the types of cues given and responses required (visual, auditory, tactile, verbal, written, drawing a diagram, and so on). Ask the following questions to determine what types of modification may be needed:

- Is the task developmentally too difficult?
- Is there a mismatch between instructional and learning styles or between required and preferred response modes?
- Is the task too lengthy?
- Is there a pattern to the errors?
- Are there environmental barriers to learning such as distractions, inappropriate seating, and so on?
- What are this child's strengths?

If children are involved in gifted or special education programs, network with other teachers, counselors, or program leaders. Share information, objectives, and strategies within the Individual Education Plan (IEP) to best meet the needs of each child. Monitor the IEP objectives to determine whether they need to be modified when tasks, assessments, or assignments are changed.

Involve the children in helping themselves and one another. Promote student accountability by involving children in setting goals, monitoring progress toward their goals, planning practice activities, and seeking and receiving help from peers, staff members, or parents. Explain to children what they should do when they get stuck on a task. For example:

- Think about the problem or task carefully.
- Use a predetermined signal to indicate the need for assistance from a peer or an adult.
- Work on another activity or task until help is available.

Provide opportunities for peer tutoring as well as cross-age peer tutoring. Use math buddies from upper grades to practice math strategies, or play math games.

When sending Home Links home, provide completed examples, definitions, or further explanations to help children have a successful experience at home. Read and discuss the directions with children prior to sending the Home Links home. Also send home games for children to play with parents. Use parent volunteers in the classroom who can play math games and assist during guided practice. Utilize other available adults in the building during math time by arranging opportunities for children to play math games with the principal, custodians, cooks, specialists, and so on.

Language Diversity

Good instruction in mathematics and ESL education share many teaching strategies. *Everyday Mathematics* supports an effective learning environment in mathematics for the ESL student by incorporating group work into daily lessons, teaching English through content that is relevant to students' experiences, and developing mathematical language proficiency through the use of manipulatives, models, and demonstrations.

Daily group work is strongly encouraged. *Everyday Mathematics* provides opportunities for children to use and hear language through games and activities in student journals. In small groups, students have more opportunities to express ideas, ask questions, and clarify their thinking. Procedures for working in groups ought to be established early in the year. Group work is complemented by whole-class instruction, in which the teacher models and uses mathematical language to reinforce skills and concepts addressed during group work.

English, as with any foreign language, is learned through content and contact that is relevant to the students. With *Everyday Mathematics* there are opportunities for children to experience mathematics in many contexts. Attention is paid to teaching vocabulary in contexts relevant to the children. Concrete examples, visual aids, and diagrams from students' experiences and backgrounds are all provided.

Developing mathematical language proficiency in *Everyday Mathematics* is accomplished through written and oral activities within a problem-solving context. Conceptual development is enhanced through the use of concrete aids, models, and discussion.

Children have many opportunities to explain their reasoning in their journals, on slates, and orally. They may represent their thinking in multiple ways. If they lack the skills to explain their thinking in writing, their text can be supplemented with drawings, diagrams, or models.

Tools

Tools are extremely important in the *Everyday Mathematics* program. The authors define tools broadly, to include anything that can be used to facilitate mathematical thinking and problem-solving. Calculators, rulers, and manipulatives (such as pattern blocks or geoboards) can be employed as tools, as can paper and pencil, slates, and reference books, to name a few. *Everyday Mathematics* strives to develop children's skills in effectively using a variety of tools and in choosing the proper tool for each particular problem.

By emphasizing the power of tools and helping children learn how to employ them intelligently, *Everyday Mathematics* is working to make the mathematics in school resemble mathematics of the real world. Without this type of approach, school math risks becoming abstract and disconnected from everyday life—a complaint that many adults make about their own mathematics education!

The following sections, focus on tools that are often used in *Everyday Mathematics*. More information about these and other mathematical tools can be found in some of the Mathematical Topics essays, which include discussions of specific tools that are useful for the teaching, learning, and application of particular topics.

Calculators

In the quarter-century that electronic calculators have become widely available, many researchers have studied their effects on how children learn. The majority of evidence from these studies suggests that the proper use of calculators can enhance children's understanding and mastery of arithmetic, promote good number sense, and improve problem-solving skills.

Two summaries of this research are "Research on Calculators in Mathematics Education," by Ray Hembree and Donald J. Dessart, and "A Meta-analysis of Outcomes from the Use of Calculators in Mathematics Education," by Brian A. Smith. (For details on these and other calculator studies, see the sources cited at the end of this section.) Smith's study also concludes that calculator usage does not hinder the development of paper and pencil skills. Moreover, both teacher experience and educational research show that most children develop good judgment about when to use and when not to use calculators. Students need to learn how to decide when it is appropriate to solve an arithmetic problem by estimating or calculating mentally, by using paper and pencil, or by using a calculator. The evidence indicates that children who use calculators are able to choose appropriately.

Calculators are useful teaching tools. They make it possible for young children to display numbers before they are skilled at writing. Calculators can be used to count forward or backward by any whole number or decimal—a particularly important activity in the primary grades because counting is so central to number and operations at this level. Calculators also allow children to solve interesting, everyday problems requiring computations that might otherwise be too difficult for them to perform, including problems that arise outside of mathematics class. There is no evidence to suggest that this will cause children to become dependent on calculators or make them unable to solve problems mentally or with paper and pencil.

Everyday Mathematics encourages children to think about developing algorithms as they solve problems. To develop this habit, students need to study particular algorithms, but once the algorithms are understood, repeated use will become tedious. Another reason that calculators are so helpful in the mathematics curriculum is that they free both children and teachers from having to spend so much time on dull, repetitive, and unproductive tasks.

For more information about measurement tools see Section 6.3 of the Measurement Essay.

For more information about Geometry tools see Section 5.10.3 of the Geometry Essay.

management guide

For more information on developing algorithms, see Essay 3, Algorithms and Mental Arthmetic.

Before the availability of inexpensive calculators, the elementary school mathematics curriculum was designed primarily so that children would become skilled at carrying out algorithms. Thus, there was little time left for children to learn to think mathematically and solve problems. Calculators enable children to think about the problems themselves, rather than only on carrying out algorithms without mistakes.

Sources:

Groves, Susie and Kaye, Stacey. "Calculators in Primary Mathematics: Exploring Number before Teaching Algorithms." In *The Teaching and Learning of Algorithms in School Mathematics,* edited by Lorna J. Morrow, pp. 120–129. Reston, VA: National Council of Teachers of Mathematics, 1998.

Hembree, Ray and Donald J. Dessart. "Research on Calculators in Mathematics Education." In *Calculators in Mathematics Education: 1992 Yearbook,* edited by James T. Fey and Christian R. Hirsch, pp. 23–32. Reston, VA: National Council of Teachers of Mathematics, 1992.

National Research Council. *Everybody Counts: A Report to the Nation on the Future of Mathematics Education,* pp. 46–48, 61–63. Washington, D.C.: National Academy Press, 1989.

Smith, Brian A. "A Meta-analysis of Outcomes from the Use of Calculators in Mathematics Education." *Dissertation Abstracts International* 58 (1997):787A.

Calculator Basics

Children begin using calculators in *Kindergarten Everyday Mathematics* both to display numbers and to count. If your class has had no previous experience with calculators, you may want to begin with a period of free exploration and then use some of the introductory exercises provided in the next section as a warm-up.

As with any tool, proper and effective use of a calculator requires instruction. Research has shown that children using calculators who have had no instruction in their use do not do calculations any better than children not using calculators. Whenever an operation that can be performed on a calculator is introduced, *Everyday Mathematics* includes an activity that introduces new calculator key(s). It is recommended that you draw the new key(s) on the board or on an overhead transparency.

The order in which keys need to be pressed to perform a calculation is called a *key sequence.* In *Everyday Mathematics,* keys that perform functions, such as [+] and [−], are written with square brackets in key sequences. Numbers are not. For example, to show how to solve 12 − 3 + 5 on a calculator, we write 12 [−] 3 [+] 5 [=]. Encouraging children to "discover" an appropriate key sequence is a suitable activity at any grade level and fits well into the *Everyday Mathematics* approach.

NOTE: Before you begin using calculators, they should be marked in some way. For example, mark children's names on calculators that they supply and children's tool kit identification numbers on those that the school supplies.

management guide

Using calculators may require children to learn alternative symbols for operations. For example, [/] means division on some calculators, but is used to enter fractions on others. Some calculators follow the conventional order of operations discussed in Section 2.2.2 of the Operations and Facts essay (parentheses, exponentiation, multiplication, division, addition, and subtraction), but others, especially many four-function calculators used in the primary grades, simply perform operations in the order they are entered. Testing a calculator with a problem like $5 + 3 \times 4$ will reveal if it has the order of operations built in: If the answer is 17, it does; if the answer is 32, it doesn't. It's always advisable to try calculator activities ahead of time using the same model calculator your students have, so that you will be familiar with all symbols and key sequences involved.

Introductory Exercises

Children who have had previous experience with calculators are wonderful resources for helping inexperienced students. Use the following exercises with first-time users, or with small groups of children who have never used calculators.

The Clear Keys The key marked [ON/C] or [CE/C] or [C] functions like an erase key. ("C" on these keys means "Clear;" "CE" means "Clear Entry.") Ask children to imagine that they are erasing a chalkboard so they can begin again. Explain how the [CE/C] key works: the first press clears the most recent number entered; the second press clears the calculator completely. On some calculators the "on" key reads [ON/AC]. In this case, AC means "All Clear" and serves the same purpose as pressing [CE/C] twice. It is important for children to get into the habit of clearing the calculator at the beginning of each new calculator exercise. If they do not, they may obtain incorrect results.

Displaying and Reading Numbers One way to introduce calculator exploration is to ask: "What if . . . ?" questions. For example:

- What will happen if you do not press [CE/C] before you start a new calculation?
- What number will be in the display window if you press 3? *(3)*
- What number will be in the display if you press 3 again without first clearing the calculator? *(33)*
- What number will appear if you press 3 again? *(333)* And again? *(3333)*

Children can enter numbers they are able to read and then ask classmates to read the numbers in the displays. Some children may also want to display large numbers that they are unable to read; help them read some of these large numbers.

On many inexpensive calculators, the [=] key acts as both an "equals" key and a "repeat" key. It serves as a repeat key as long as

in perspective

The four basic arithmetic keys [+], [−], [×], and [÷], along with the number, decimal, and clear keys, are introduced by *Third Grade Everyday Mathematics*. In Grades 4–6, students learn about squaring [x^2], powering [^], [x^y], or [y^x], square root [$\sqrt{}$], and the inverse key [x^{-1}] or [$1/x$].

management guide

an operation key is pressed first. The repeat function is especially useful for counting by 1s or other numbers, either forward or backward. The *Everyday Mathematics* program uses [R/=] to symbolize the dual role of the [=] key.

- To count up from 0 by any whole number *k:*
  Press [CE/C] [CE/C] [+] k [R/=] [R/=] [R/=] …
  For example, to count up from 0 by 9s,
  press [CE/C] [CE/C] [+] 9 [R/=] [R/=] [R/=] …
  Displays: 9, 9, 18, 27, …

- To count up from any number *n* by any whole number *k:*
  Press [CE/C] [CE/C] n [+] k [R/=] [R/=] [R/=] …
  For example, to count up from 27 by 3s,
  press [CE/C] [CE/C] 27 [+] 3 [R/=] [R/=] [R/=] …
  Displays: 27, 3, 30, 33, 36, …

- Counting back from any number *n* by any whole number *k:*
  Press [CE/C] [CE/C] n [−] k [R/=] [R/=] [R/=] …
  For example, to count back from 27 by 3s,
  press [CE/C] [CE/C] 27 [−] 3 [R/=] [R/=] [R/=] …
  Displays: 27, 3, 24, 21, 18, …
  What happens if you count back past 0?
  (Displays: −3, −6, −9, …)
  Do the numbers continue to get smaller? *(yes)*

NOTE: On the more expensive "scientific" calculators, a "K" (constant) key is sometimes used for repetitive operations. See your calculator's manual.

Interpreting the Display

Calculators compute with internally programmed algorithms; they do not solve problems. The user must know which keys to press, and how to interpret what those results mean.

One difficulty is that calculators often display more digits than are necessary, or as mathematicians say, significant. In fourth through sixth grade *Everyday Mathematics,* children study significant digits formally, but the basic idea is straightforward: The answer that results from a mathematical procedure can be no more exact than the numbers that went into the procedure. For example, if the ages of a group of children are 9, 12, 7, 13, 8, 6, and 10 years, then reporting the average age as 9.7142857 years is silly—reporting the average as "about 10" would be more reasonable. For the primary grades, it's enough for children to be aware that not all the digits that the calculator displays are meaningful. A rule of thumb is that answers usually have no more meaningful digits than the original numbers. So if the numbers you enter have two digits each, probably only two of the digits in the calculator display are significant.

Another difficulty is that calculators sometimes display fewer digits than are expected. For example, suppose a calculator is used to find the value of 36 nickels. The key sequence 36 [×] 0.05 [=] leads to a window display of 1.8—not 1.80. This cutting off, or truncating, of trailing zeroes to the right of the decimal point can be disconcerting for the novice.

The biggest obstacle with calculators is that sometimes the display in the window is nonsense. Reasons for this include: the calculator wasn't properly cleared; a number or operation was miskeyed; the analysis of the problem was faulty. For whatever reason, sometimes the calculator's answer just doesn't make sense, and the user must determine whether an answer is reasonable by asking whether it makes sense in terms of the original problem situation or by using mental arithmetic to estimate what the answer should be.

Other Tools

Children in *Everyday Mathematics* use a wide variety of non-electronic tools. Although not every tool used in *Everyday Mathematics* is discussed below, some of the major ones are highlighted and explained in the following sections.

Rulers and Tape Measures

Children are introduced to standard units of measurement in Kindergarten, and rulers and tape measures are among the first tools children use. If your children are using retractable tape measures, teach and enforce the "2-inch or 5-centimeter no-zap rule:" do not "zap" the tape measure until no more than 2 inches or 5 centimeters show. Following this rule will extend the life of the tape measures and make your life quieter and easier. Just as doctors, carpenters, and others respect and take care of the tools they use, children should learn to respect and care for the tools in their tool kits.

Scales

A scale is a tool for measuring how heavy something is according to a standard weight. There are three types of scales: balance, mechanical and electronic.

Everyday Mathematics provides activities calling for children to weigh and then order objects by weight using pan balances, bathroom scales, and spring scales. Children balance objects primarily in Explorations because of the limited supply of such tools. Activities begin with informal play in kindergarten, where children first compare weights with their own hands, and then with pan balances.

In first grade, pan balances are used to introduce the symbols for relations ($<$, $>$, $=$, and so on). Through third grade, children write number models using these symbols.

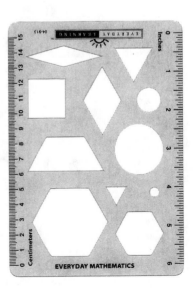

Pattern-Block Template

Pattern-Block Templates are used for exploring plane figures. Children are encouraged to use the templates to make designs in Explorations, Projects, and some lessons. In Kindergarten, for example, children are asked to estimate how many triangles, squares, or other figures it will take to "fill up" a piece of paper. They check their guesses by drawing the shapes using the templates. This informal introduction to area develops valuable background for formal definitions later. Children in Kindergarten through third grade also use their Pattern-Block Templates, rather than compasses, to draw circles.

in perspective Beginning in fourth grade, students use a Geometry Template (which might be more accurately called a geometry and measurement template). The number and variety of shapes are increased (compared to Pattern-Block Templates) in order to help students with more detailed explorations of categories of triangles and quadrangles. The measuring devices on the Geometry Template include inch and centimeter scales, a percent circle for making circle graphs, and two protractors.

Pattern Blocks and Geometric Solids

Kindergarten Everyday Mathematics introduces children to measurement, in part, through the use of building blocks. Children use both metric and U.S. customary rulers to measure the lengths of of block edges and the heights and lengths of structures they build using several blocks. Such uses of models of geometric solids continue as a basis for the study of 1- and 2-dimensional geometry through third grade.

Pattern blocks help children learn the names and features of geometric objects. In Kindergarten and first grade, children identify categories of shapes, colors, and weights of pattern blocks. Beginning in first grade, children are encouraged to find different ways of categorizing blocks on their own—that is, to create multiple perspectives of a given set of blocks. This ability to think about the same things in different ways is important for many problem-solving activities. Science educators also identify classification as one of the most important processes of science.

Straws and Twist-Ties

Constructing 2- and 3-dimensional objects with straws and twist-ties are popular activities, beginning in *First Grade Everyday Mathematics*. This section includes several suggestions to help you manage these activities. Since these activities result in representations of geometric shapes, we include a few words about the true nature of such shapes.

Two-dimensional shapes such as polygons and circles are defined as boundaries of flat regions without the interiors. For example, a polygon is made up of line segments; the region inside a polygon is not part of the polygon. Similarly, 3-dimensional shapes, such as prisms, pyramids, and cylinders, are made up of flat or curved surfaces, but do not include the interiors. For example, a rectangular prism is a box of cereal minus the cornflakes. Polygons constructed with straws are true representations of such shapes—the straws actually show the line segments. On the other hand,

in perspective

Building-block activities provide children with background for a methodical approach to making 2-dimensional maps of 3-dimensional structures in fourth through sixth grades.

3-dimensional straw constructions only suggest the actual shapes—the straws are the edges of the 2-dimensional shapes that make up the faces of the 3-dimensional object.

For more information on plane and solid figures, see Sections 5.4 and 5.5 of the Geometry essay.

Materials and Advance Preparation The *Everyday Mathematics* authors have found that straw constructions work best if plastic straws are used with twist-ties as connectors. Drinking straws are usually about 8 inches long; some coffee-stirrer straws also work well but are shorter, so directions for some exercises need to be adjusted if they are used. Straws with small diameters work much better than those with larger diameters. About 1,000 straws and 2,000 twist-ties are ample for a class of 30 children. Eight-inch, small-diameter drinking straws are available (and inexpensive) in bulk boxes of 500 at party, restaurant-supply, or paper-goods stores. The supplier for your school lunchroom may be able to obtain the appropriate straws, but lunchroom straws themselves probably will not be suitable. Avoid large-diameter and individually wrapped straws.

Four-inch twist-ties that are often used as fasteners for plastic bags work well as connectors. Craft pipe cleaners, cut in halves, also make good connectors, but twist-ties work better and cost far less. Bulk packages of the twist-ties may be available through your grocery store, bakery, or produce market, or at the same party or paper-goods stores that stock small-diameter straws. Some businesses respond to requests from schools and may be happy to order additional twist-ties for you at their cost. Both straws and connectors are reusable. Except for figures that you or the children wish to keep, shapes can be dismantled and the straws and connectors returned to their storage containers for use at other times.

Preparation for Activities Using scissors, straws can be easily cut to different lengths by you or the children. For cutting many straws at one time, some paper cutters work well. For most exercises specified in Explorations and lessons, three sizes suffice: the standard 8" length, 4" length, and 6" length. You might want to prepare an initial supply of straws in these three sizes. Don't worry about small variations in length. For a few exercises, children may cut full-length straws to meet special conditions. For example, children may be told to construct triangles with no two sides the same length (scalene triangles).

Management of Materials Keep straws and twist-ties in small open boxes or bins so that children can use them as directed (often in a Math Message). Lessons often call for straws of various lengths. Try to keep straws with the standard equal lengths together and a special box for straws of assorted lengths. Work out a routine with the children so that straws and ties are returned to their proper boxes or bins at the end of a lesson or when shapes are dismantled. Such sorting and clean-up routines have value in and of themselves, in addition to making materials for the next shape-construction exercise easily accessible.

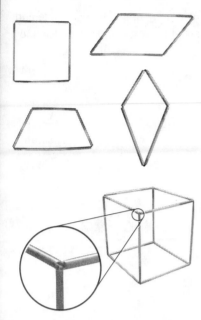

Straw constructions

Teaching with Straws and Twist-Ties Teachers find that most children have little trouble constructing polygons with straws and connectors. The ends of the ties may need to be pinched a little to slide into the straws. If you have to use large-diameter straws, fold back an inch or so of the end of the connector for a tighter joint. To keep the size of polygons with more than five sides to sensible limits, use shorter straws. Except for triangles, polygons are easily twisted so they don't lie "flat." When they are not laying flat, they are no longer in a plane, thus they are no longer 2-dimensional figures. Have children make polygons on flat surfaces and encourage them to try to keep the polygons flat when picking them up.

For 3-dimensional figures, begin by putting two connectors, or one folded connector, into one end of each straw, so that each can be connected to two other straws. When more than three straws need to be connected, insert additional connectors as needed. Or you could connect pairs of straws and bundle them all together using an additional connector.

Tools for Exploring Data and Chance

Everyday Mathematics uses a variety of devices to generate random outcomes. These tools are integral to the success of many games. Often these devices do not generate perfectly random outcomes, but they are good enough for most purposes. Several tools for helping children generate random outcomes are listed below.

The Everything Math Deck This deck of cards consists of four sets of number cards 0–10 and one set of number cards 11–20. Fractions are on the reverse side of the 0–10 cards. You can limit the range of numbers to be generated simply by removing some of the cards from the deck. If the whole deck is used, you have an increased chance of drawing a 0–10 card than a 11–20 card. To use the cards, simply shuffle and draw. The better the shuffle, the more unpredictable the draw will be.

Standard Playing Cards Use the 2–9 cards, the aces for 1s, and the queens for 0s. Draw one card to get a 1 in 10 chance of a digit 0–9. Draw two cards to make double-digit numbers, and so on. (If more than one card is drawn, you will need to decide whether to replace it before another card is drawn. If the first card is replaced in the deck and the deck is reshuffled, the probability will remain the same for each draw. If the card is not replaced, the chance of pulling that digit decreases.)

Dice Use a regular die to generate numbers 1 through 6. Use a polyhedral die (with 12 or 20 sides) to extend the range of numbers to be generated. Note that rolling more than one die and adding the resulting number of dots produces a nonuniform distribution of possible outcomes. For example, if you roll two standard dice, there are 36 possible ways for them to land. Only one of the 36 has a sum of 2 (two 1s), but six of the 36 have a sum of 7 ([1,6], [2,5], [3,4], [4,3], [5,2] and [6,1]). (See below.) Therefore, the chance of rolling a

management guide

7 is much greater than the chance of rolling a 2. This is what is meant by a "nonuniform distribution." Shaking a die in a cup may lead to slightly more random results than throwing the die by hand.

2	3	4	5	6	7	8	9	10	11	12
					6+1					
			5+1	5+2	6+2					
		4+1	4+2	4+3	5+3	6+3				
	3+1	3+2	3+3	3+4	4+4	5+4	6+4			
2+1	2+2	2+3	2+4	2+5	3+5	4+5	5+5	6+5		
1+1	1+2	1+3	1+4	1+5	1+6	2+6	3+6	4+6	5+6	6+6
2	3	4	5	6	7	8	9	10	11	12

Sums of Two Dice

Egg Cartons Label each egg carton cup with a number. For example, you might label the cups 0–11. Place one or more pennies, beans, or centimeter cubes inside the carton, close the lid, shake the carton, and then open it to see in which cups the objects have landed. Randomness depends on how thoroughly the carton is shaken. This is probably the least random method of the list.

Spinners Spinners are used throughout *Everyday Mathematics,* usually in games. They are extremely useful for helping children visualize chances. There are many commercially available spinners, though it is not necessary to purchase them. Children can use a pencil and paper clip as shown in the margin. Use either a large (2") or standard (1") paper clip for the part that spins. The larger size is preferred because it spins more easily. Make a mark, as a pointer, at one end of the paper clip, using a permanent felt-tip pen.

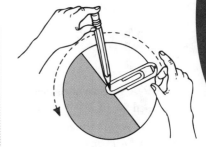

The spinning mat may be drawn on cardstock or paper. Sometimes a mat is supplied as a master or journal page. If you make your own mat, start with a circle or square big enough for the paper clip. Mark the center of the circle, choose the number and size of the divisions, and then measure the appropriate angles. For example, six equal wedges would be 360° divided by 6, or 60° each. Of course the wedges do not have to be the same size, as in the *Money Game* spinner mat shown in the margin. You can make the edge of the mat any shape you wish.

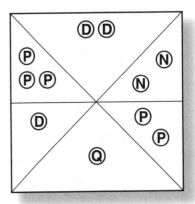

Money-Game Spinner

Before spinning, tape the mat to a level surface. You need only two small pieces of tape, one at the top and one at the bottom. To spin, place the tip of a pen or pencil on the center of the circle and within the paper clip (as shown in the diagram). Flick the paper clip about halfway between the center of the circle and the tip of the paper clip. (Flicking the paper clip near the pointer end will generate less of a spin.)

Base-10 Blocks

In *Everyday Mathematics,* children use base-10 blocks starting in first grade. They build structures and count cubes to check estimates of height or length. They also make exchanges to investigate place value. In the *Money Exchange* game, children work on exchanges up to 100 (100 pennies in a dollar). To extend beyond 100, base-10 blocks are used for the *Ones, Tens, Hundreds Game*.

First graders may also use base-10 blocks to solve number models. For example, to solve the number model 41 – 18 = n, children might match two sets of base-10 blocks one-to-one and then count the unmatched blocks, or they might count out 41 blocks, remove 18, and count the number left. The blocks also may be used on pan balances instead of weights to represent number sentences.

In third grade, base-10 blocks are used for decimal exchanges. For example, a long rod may represent the ONE, and unit cubes represent tenths. Or a flat may represent the ONE, and unit cubes represent hundredths. The hundredth model is quickly made pictorial as children color or shade hundredths of a 10-by-10 grid to represent decimals. Children also work in the other direction— writing decimals for partially-shaded grids.

Sometimes you may want to make a written record of work with base-10 blocks. The system of shorthand shown below works well. This shorthand is handy for drawing quick pictures of base-10 blocks. Such pictures are often more convenient than the actual blocks, especially for the larger blocks, and can be useful for explaining and recording solutions.

Name Block Shorthand		
Name	**Block**	**Shorthand**
cm cube		▪
long		│
flat		▢
big cube		

Tool Kits

For Grades K–3, it is recommended that every child have a tool kit in which to store a calculator, measuring tools, and the manipulatives that are used throughout the year, many of which were described in the previous section. The tool kits may be the zippered bags which were especially designed for the *Everyday Mathematics* program (and may be purchased from Everyday Learning Corporation) or some other container, such as a wooden box or a recloseable plastic bag. The tool kit is designed to give children a sense of independence by

IN **perspective**

In fourth and fifth grades, the shaded grids are used to develop fraction sense and to represent percents.

□ □ ‖‖ .....

2,045 in 'base-10 shorthand'

NOTE: A variety of names are used for base-10 blocks. The following names are used in *Everyday Mathematics*: *cube* for the smaller 1-cm cube, *long* for the block consisting of 10 cm cubes (1 × 10), *flat* for the block consisting of 100 cm cubes (10 × 10), and *big cube* for the larger cube consisting of 1000 1-cm cubes (10 × 10 × 10).

giving them immediate access to basic tools. Use a permanent marker to write identification numbers on tool kits and on the non-consumable items in the tool kits.

Distribute a few needed items along with the tool kits early in the year. Pass out other items later, when they are first used in classroom activities. Eventually, the tool kit may contain a tape measure, ruler, calculator, play money, real coins, Pattern-Block Template, clock face, tangrams, dice, and other small items.

Encourage children to take care of their tool kits and to store each tool after use so that it is always there when needed. In this way, children will develop a sense of responsibility that may be carried over to other activities. A periodic check of the contents might be a good idea, especially before vacation periods. You might also want to keep a classroom "lost-and-found box."

The Importance of Problem Solving

In *Everyday Mathematics,* problem solving is much more than solving word problems. Problem solving is a process of building a mathematical model of a situation and then reasoning with the model to draw conclusions about the situation. The process typically involves some or all of the following steps, not necessarily in the order presented.

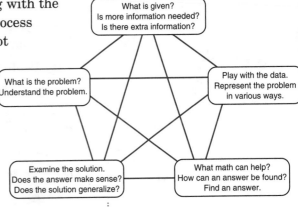

- Identifying precisely what the problem is
- Analyzing what is known and seeking out further data as necessary
- Playing with the data to try to discover patterns and meaning
- Identifying mathematical techniques that can help in finding a solution
- Looking back and asking, "Does the solution make sense?"

Everyday Mathematics regards problem solving as an approach applied to all topics rather than as a topic unto itself. In every strand in the curriculum, children solve a wide range of problems. Some require children to apply their current mathematical knowledge; others stretch children's skills and understanding. Problems for which children have no method of solution immediately at hand are often the most productive. Children are encouraged to solve all problems in many different ways; sharing and comparing solution methods is a prominent feature of the *Everyday Mathematics* program.

Traditional word problems have a place in *Everyday Mathematics*—such problems have value as exercises—but problem solving permeates the entire curriculum. Each unit organizer in the *Teacher's Lesson Guide* has a section that identifies activities where problem solving is particularly prominent, but many other opportunities for problem solving will present themselves as children grapple with the rich material in the program.

For further information about mathematical modeling and the *Everyday Mathematics* approach to problem solving, see the Problem Solving essay (Section 10) in the Mathematical Topics section of this book.

Assessment

Everyday Mathematics encourages a balanced approach to student assessment, one that tracks the development of a child's mathematical understanding while giving the teacher useful feedback about instructional needs. The assessment information also provides adequate documentation for assigning grades.

A variety of assessment techniques are already built into the program. These include ideas for using lesson activities and components for **ongoing assessment,** something the authors call "kid-watching"; suggestions for collecting work samples for **product or portfolio assessment;** and tools for conducting more formal **periodic assessment.** Assessment suggestions are incorporated into the lesson descriptions, compiled for each unit in the Unit Organizers, and discussed in the *Assessment Handbook*. Feel free to pick and choose from the assessment tools and techniques suggested to design your own balanced assessment plan.

The following simple rubric can be used to categorize progress with any of the assessment activities:

General Rubric

Beginning (B)

Children cannot complete the task independently. They show little understanding of the concept or skill.

Developing (D)

Children show some understanding. However, errors or misunderstandings still occur. Reminders, hints, and suggestions are incorporated with understanding.

Secure (S)

Children can apply the skill or concept correctly and independently.

Other rubrics are suggested in the *Assessment Handbook*.

Providing for Home-and-School Communication

Dialogue and discussion, as well as experimentation and discovery, are at the heart of *Everyday Mathematics*. Parents accustomed to conventional mathematics programs may think that because children are not bringing home daily arithmetic drill sheets, they are not learning or doing mathematics. The Home Links and Family Letters (see below) reassure them that this is not the case. In addition, the *Home Connection Handbook* can help you inform parents about the *Everyday Mathematics* curriculum.

Home Links and Family Letters

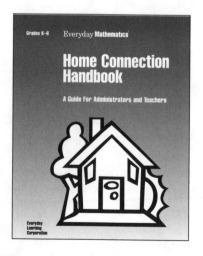

 Home Links activities serve three main purposes: They (1) promote follow-up, (2) provide enrichment, and (3) involve parents or guardians in their children's mathematics education.

Other reasons for using Home Links throughout the year include the following:

- The assignments encourage children to take initiative and responsibility.
- The activities help reinforce newly learned skills and concepts.
- Many of the assignments relate what is learned in school to the children's lives outside of school, tying mathematics to their everyday world.
- The assignments can serve as informal assessment tools.

Many Home Links require children to interact with parents, other adults, or older children. Since primary caregivers or those likely to help with the homework are not necessarily "parents," Home Links instruct children to complete the activity with someone at home. At the beginning of the year, you might send home the introductory Family Letter. Continue to involve families throughout the year by sending home unit-specific letters that explain the content that will be covered. *Everyday Mathematics* also provides some Family Letters that are meant to be sent home with particular Home Links (both the letters and the Home Links are labeled with the lesson numbers). These letters explain an idea or an activity that parents might not be familiar with. All Family Letters and Home Links are included in the *Math Masters* book.

Think of the Home Links suggestions as a beginning. As you and your students become familiar with the program, you may want to send home activities of your own as Home Links. You may also want to use the Home Links format to extend various Explorations and Projects. Blank Home Links forms have been provided for these purposes in the *Math Masters* book.

Organizing Routines and Displays

Most classrooms have routines for daily activities such as taking attendance or keeping track of the date. *Everyday Mathematics* strongly suggests that students take an active part in these routines, which provide numerous opportunities to show mathematics in everyday contexts. The following sections contain general advice and tips from fellow teachers.

Attendance Chart

Even if keeping a daily attendance record is not required in your school, good mathematics activities can result from keeping track of which children are present and absent. Interesting activities can also be built around tracking lunch or milk counts. There are many ways to set up an attendance chart so that children can record their own arrival each day.

- Use a poster or wall chart with pockets containing name cards to be turned over by children when they arrive.
- Set up a grid on which children sign in daily with an X, as shown on the next page. Children's names can be numbered with the

Attendance Chart

1. John	✗	✗	✗	✗	✗
2. Gloria		✗	✗	✗	✗
3. Sara	✗	✗		✗	✗
4. Dave	✗	✗	✗	✗	✗

same numbers used to identify their tool kits and their non-consumable tool-kit items. A stack of identical weekly sheets can be hung up and the used sheet torn off to start each new week.

- The designated attendance person can pass around a sheet on which children mark off their names.

You might also want to have attendance data available in sentence form on a poster such as the one shown in the margin. Another variation is to include lunch options in the posted materials. As the year progresses, vary the manner in which the data for the poster are collected. Here are some suggestions:

- After the class is gathered, have children count off, or have them count the class members to determine the number present (also tally lunch options). Help children determine how many children are absent. You may want to use a parts-and-total diagram to represent this problem.

Attendance Data

25 children are in our class.

21 children are here today.

4 children are absent today.

Total	
26	
Present	**Absent**
23	?

Total	
29	
Present	**Absent**
?	4

- Later in the year, have children do this without help. In schools that require taking attendance, this responsibility can be extended to having children help fill out the daily attendance slips.

- If you save daily attendance information, children can use the data later in the school year. For example, they might make graphs to investigate whether certain weekdays or certain months have substantially more absences than others. This may lead to interesting discussions about possible reasons.

- Work with children to create number stories using the information on the attendance chart.

Class Calendar

Using the calendar every day is the best way for children to acquire calendar skills. To this end, *Everyday Mathematics* recommends that you buy or construct a large, reusable calendar and post it in your classroom. If you make your own calendar, use posterboard and then, if possible, laminate it. Make a grid of six rows with seven cells in each row. Write the days of the week across the top; reserve spaces in which to write or post the month and the year.

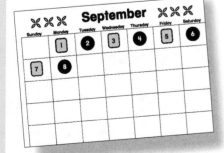

September

Sunday	Monday	Tuesday	Wednesday	Thursday	Friday	Saturday
	1	2	3	4	5	6
7	8					

Some teachers have a calendar in place at the beginning of each month, and children mark off the days with some kind of movable frame. Other teachers fill in the calendar as the month progresses, assigning the job of placing a new number on the grid each school day to one child. On the first school day after a weekend or holiday, that child also adds those missing days to the calendar.

You can place a number on the grid in several ways. Write the number directly on the laminated grid using a water-based marker, or write all the numbers 1–31 on cards or slips of paper that can be taped or tacked to the calendar. You might even cut these cards into shapes appropriate for the month and scatter them around for children to find and place on the grid.

In addition to recording the date, children can also record data such as weather conditions, temperatures, and special days and events.

At the beginning of each month, the class as a whole can work to dismantle the calendar for the previous month. Have children remove the different days of the month by identifying such things as:

- the 23rd day of the month
- pairs of dates whose sum is 20
- the date in the fourth row and second column
- dates with a 4 in the ones place or a 2 in the tens place
- the date equal to 1 ten and 4 ones or 1 ten and 14 ones
- the date that is 10 more (or 10 less) than 16
- the date that comes one week after the 8th of the month

The possibilities for removal criteria are endless! Adjust them according to the abilities and interests of your class.

There is a blank blackline calendar master in the *Math Masters* for Grades 1–3. (*Everyday Mathematics* expects children to master calendar skills by fourth grade.) At the beginning of each month, make enough copies so that each child can have one. (You might want to partially fill in the master before copying it.)

Beginning with Lesson 1.4 in first grade, date lines are provided on journal pages. Dating written work may be difficult for some children in the beginning but will become a habit over time. It helps to have the date posted daily on the board as either "October 3, 2001," or "10/3/01." Teachers have reported that following this procedure results in a tremendous payoff for younger children: Their understanding of days and months is greatly improved.

Some teachers have the class fill in the days during a whole-group, interactive problem-solving session, by asking such questions as:

- How many days are in this month?
- If the first day is on a Monday, what day will the 8th day be?
- If the 7th is on a Saturday, what day is the 14th on? The 28th?
- If the second Tuesday is the 9th, what are the dates of the other Tuesdays?

Class Data Pad

Throughout the year, you and the children will have opportunities to collect information that will greatly enrich the content of the program. Such information might include data collected in and outside the classroom to be analyzed and graphed, and interesting facts and information to be used in making up number stories.

Much of this information can be used several times over the course of the year. For example, children might find the middle number for a collection of data; graph the data at some other time; and compare it with a related set of data at still another time. In order to save this information for repeated use, we suggest that you record it on a Class Data Pad—a large pad of newsprint. Although you could set aside a portion of a bulletin board or the board to record data, this might be inconvenient, because both have limited surface area. With the Class Data Pad you can save sheets on the pad for later use. If you label large, self-stick notes and position them so that they extend over the edges of pages, you can easily index and retrieve stored data.

Class Number Line

A class number line has many uses, from tracking the school days in a school year to providing a large visual display for rote-counting exercises to focusing on specific numbers as they are introduced. In Kindergarten, the authors recommend building a *growing number line* as the year progresses. In subsequent grades it is recommended that you display a number line from the beginning of the school year.

The following sections include a description of the growing number line, which introduces the idea of a number line as a time line; some practical suggestions for making number lines in later grades; and an optional application of the number line to help second graders learn about Roman numerals.

Growing Number Line

A growing number line should begin on the first day of Kindergarten. Each day, write the number of that school day and add it to a number line that grows around the room and is used throughout the whole year. Three-by-five file cards are easy to use. Post the cards in consecutive order, high enough for the class to see. As you put up the "1" for the first day of school, you may want to discuss with the class the fact that, since yesterday there was no school, "0" represents the day before school started.

Many ideas evolved from using this growing number line during the field-testing of *Kindergarten Everyday Mathematics.* You may be able to adapt some of these ideas for other grades as well.

- As one class reached school day number 101, a child observed that the number 101 was also on their classroom door! This led to a whole new activity of finding the numbers on other classroom doors and trying to figure out a pattern for that numbering.

- As another class began working with 10s, the teacher marked all the 10s on the number line with a different color, and then let the children figure out the pattern for all those colored numbers.

- One teacher started asking, "What number should we put up today?" The class was learning to anticipate number order past 100. Many classes had "100 Day" celebrations, with children bringing in 100 of some object, such as buttons, candy, shells, or popcorn. The items were then displayed, weighed, measured, and discussed.

- Yet another class estimated what number would be on the number line when it turned the corner of the wall—a possible activity for any fixed location in the room.

A Prefabricated Number Line

Beginning in first grade, it is worth preparing a number line before school starts with at least the number of days in your school year—usually about 180. You can make such a number line by putting together a pair of commercial, classroom-sized number lines; and writing the missing digits for numbers greater than 100. Everyday Learning Corporation also sells number lines printed from –30 to 180. Mount the number line on a wall at a height that children can reach easily when standing on a sturdy chair (with you or another "spotter" holding the chair steady and standing by, ready to help if necessary). An alternative is to lower current 10-day sections of the line to a height convenient for children. If the number line has to go across windows or over door frames, that's fine. One teacher made a number line by attaching the numbers to a string with paper clips, and then stringing the line around her room.

The school-day number line lends itself to many teaching opportunities. Besides being useful for numbering the school days, it can serve as a time line for recording special or memorable school events. The time line can be the basis of one of the ongoing class jobs, that of class historian, whose responsibilities would include:

- Marking off the current day on the number line

- Choosing something noteworthy about that day or week

- Drawing a picture or writing about the special event (with your help at first) and putting the picture or report on the number line (This activity generates a time line of the entire school year.)

The number line can serve as a frame of reference for counting and numeration activities throughout the year. *For example:*

- Find or read a number, and then add or subtract 10 (or 100) to or from it.

- Skip count to or count on from any given number by 2s, by 10s, and so on.

- Tell what number comes before or after a given number.

- Determine how many days until day n or from day n.

You can also use the number line as a starting point for discussions about specific numbers. On day 31, for example, ask questions such as these:

- Where and when might the number 31 be used?
- What items or objects might you need 31 of?
- What will 31 cents buy?

For second grade, we suggest using the number line to learn the Roman numeral system. The elements of the system are shown in the table below:

Roman Numerals

I = 1	XX =	20 (2 tens)	CC	=	200
II = 2	XXX =	30 (3 tens)	CCC	=	300
III = 3	XL =	40 (50 less 10)	CD	=	400
IV = 4	L =	50	D	=	500
V = 5	LX =	60 (50 plus 10)	CM	=	900
VI = 6	LXX =	70 (50 plus 2 tens)	M	=	1,000
VII = 7	LXXX =	80 (50 plus 3 tens)	$\overline{X}$	=	10,000
VIII = 8	XC =	90 (100 less 10)	$\overline{C}$	=	100,000
IX = 9	C = 100		∞	=	100,000,000
X = 10					or infinity

You can assign one or more children the job of figuring out and attaching the appropriate Roman numeral for the day to the number line. The numerals can be written on large, self-stick notes.

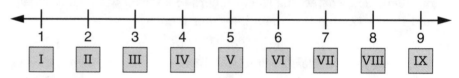

From time to time, discuss and review the patterns found in the Roman numeral system.

Classroom Jobs

A good deal of mathematics can be learned by children who perform classroom jobs. Many jobs present opportunities for practice in estimating, counting, measuring, and other mathematical skills. As an added benefit, children become increasingly independent and responsible, freeing you to devote your time and energy to where they are most needed.

Although organizing these jobs requires special attention at the beginning of the year, you will find that taking the extra time to organize and explain the jobs then will pay off handsomely in the long-run.

Begin with two or three jobs. You can add jobs as needed throughout the year. Classroom jobs might include taking attendance, marking off days on the number line and calendar, recording the temperature, passing out needed materials, leading

Job Chart

the line, delivering messages, and keeping learning centers in good order, as well as whatever else might meet your classroom needs.

Job Chart

You can keep track of job assignments with the help of a job chart. Staple or tape a card pocket for each child to a large posterboard. Write a child's name on each pocket. On cards that fit into the pockets, write job titles (or pictures) or the words "day off." Insert the cards into the pockets. Change jobs by moving the cards across the rows of pockets in some regular pattern so that the children can anticipate their job assignments. Some suggestions:

- Some teachers use library-card envelopes and file cards.
- One teacher kept a tally on each child's card of the number of times that child had a job assignment.
- Another teacher held an election once a month to assign jobs.

Jobs can be rotated weekly or daily. And changing the job chart itself can be an assigned job.

Daily Schedule

A good way to acquaint children with each day's schedule is to post a daily schedule or time chart, such as the one in the margin. You can post small clock faces, rebuses, or sentence strips that can be changed as needed. Save one or more blank spaces for special activities. Of course, the schedule could also be displayed informally on the board or bulletin board.

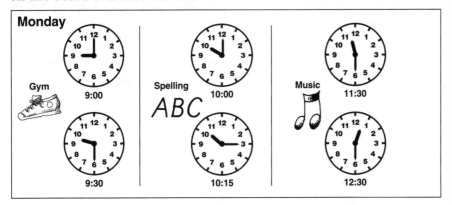

The daily schedule provides frequent opportunities for children to practice telling time. Whenever new opportunities arise, use the daily schedule and classroom clock to ask questions such as the following (Question difficulty, of course, will depend on the experience of your children.):

- Does the classroom clock match *(a scheduled activity)* time? Is it *(a scheduled activity)* time?
- Where will the hour hand be for *(a scheduled activity)*? The minute hand?
- (Show a time on a demonstration clock.) What activity takes place at this time?
- If art class starts at 9:35 and ends at 10:15, how long is art class?
- How long is it from now until recess?

Number-Writing Practice

Research has shown that young children who receive direct instruction as they practice the strokes for writing each number and letter progress more readily in developing their own readable handwriting styles. If children are not instructed, they may develop an inefficient or illegible script that is often difficult to change as they move to cursive handwriting.

At the beginning of first grade, children's motor skills and experience with writing will vary greatly, so you will need to use your own best judgment to determine how rapidly to move through the number-writing activities that begin in *First Grade Everyday Mathematics.* When number-writing is part of a handwriting program, numbers are often put off until later in the year. But since children begin writing numbers early in *Everyday Mathematics,* it is beneficial to begin with the correct forms immediately. (If you choose to teach your own handwriting program instead of the forms indicated in our materials, tell the children to ignore the arrows shown on their journal pages.)

Along with writing numbers in their journals and on blackline masters, children practice number-writing on slates. (See page 16 in this section for more information.)

Semipermanent Chalk—A Useful Display Tool

There will be times when you will want to write or draw things on the board that cannot be erased with a standard board eraser. You can do this by using "semipermanent" chalk. For example, you might want to draw a picture of a geoboard by making an array of dots using the semipermanent chalk—and then use regular chalk to draw a figure on the board geoboard. If you then want to draw a new figure, you can erase the old figure with a board eraser, while leaving the geoboard dots intact. The semipermanent drawing can be washed off later using a damp cloth or sponge.

Here is one way to make "semi-permanent" chalk:

• Dissolve sugar in some hot water until the water can no longer absorb any additional sugar. Drop a piece of porous chalk into the sugar solution and let it stand overnight. The chalk will soak up the sugar solution and become resistant to erasure. When not in use, keep the chalk in a sealed container so that it will not dry up completely.

When you make a mark on the board with this chalk, the mark may not be visible at first. It will become visible once the chalk mark has dried. Once dried, the marks cannot be erased with a board eraser, but can be easily erased with a wet cloth or sponge.

Another semipermanent chalkboard drawing option:

• To make a semipermanent drawing on the chalkboard, thoroughly wet the area where you want it. Draw with regular chalk while the board is wet. Wait for it to dry completely. Now you will be able to write on the base drawing and erase a number of times without losing the base drawing. To remove the base drawing, simply wash it off with water.

Temperature and Weather Records

Keeping daily temperature and weather records are regular routines in both Kindergarten and first grade. In second and third grades, children may continue to collect temperature and weather data in optional activities.

Temperature Record

At about the same time each day during the school year, a child should record the outside temperature. Pinpointing and reading the exact number of degrees on a temperature scale can be very difficult, so the following system for color-coding temperature ranges on the thermometer is suggested, at least for the beginning of the year: Color-code a large outdoor thermometer (one with both Celsius and Fahrenheit scales) by using permanent markers, crayons, or colored plastic strips to mark off temperature ranges. *Everyday Mathematics* suggests the following code.

Color Codes for a Classroom Thermometer		
Below –20°Celsius	Below –4°Fahrenheit	no color/very frigid
–20° to –10°Celsius	–4° to 14°Fahrenheit	purple/frigid
–9° to 0°Celsius	16° to 32°Fahrenheit	blue/cold
1° to 10°Celsius	34° to 50°Fahrenheit	green/cool
11° to 20°Celsius	52° to 68°Fahrenheit	yellow/warm
21° to 30°Celsius	70° to 86°Fahrenheit	orange/hot
Above 30°Celsius	Above 86°Fahrenheit	red/very hot

NOTE: If you live in a region that never has negative temperatures, see "Temperature Maps" later in this section.

Having both scales not only gives children an informal introduction to each scale, it will also stimulate discussion about why we often see temperatures recorded both ways.

At the beginning of each day, the child whose job it is to record the temperature should note the color zone on the thermometer and record it. Two ideas for recording:

• Put self-adhesive colored dots directly on a number line.

• Draw colored dots or put self-adhesive colored dots on a paper strip such as adding-machine tape.

You or the child should also note the date. If you use paper strips, these eventually can be taped together and children can use this yearlong temperature record to observe seasonal trends. This task often leads to discussion about the drop in temperature in the fall and the rise in the spring.

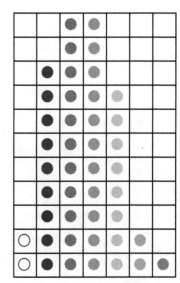

You might also want to construct a bar graph representing different temperature colors. Each day have a child fill in a bar with the appropriate color. By midyear your graph should look quite impressive.

As the year progresses, help children read the number of degrees Celsius or Fahrenheit and record this information as well as the appropriate color. The first day "below zero" will give you an opportunity to talk about the numbers that are less than zero (negative numbers). At that time, you might want to add a few negative numbers to the class number line.

Because the temperature changes during each day, later in the year the children might start taking second readings at lunch time or before school lets out. This information is a source for "real-life" subtraction and comparison problems. The information will also be data that children can use throughout the year for graphing and making comparisons.

Temperature Maps

Another possible source of data is the weather map from a daily newspaper. These maps often use a color scheme similar to that described in the Temperature Record section above. The maps are a wonderful way of showing the temperature changes across the country (and introducing children from warmer climates to negative temperatures). These weather maps also help children become familiar with the geography of the United States.

You might want to use a weather map on a monthly basis. If you do, children can observe that temperatures change greatly in some parts of the country and remain fairly constant in others. If possible, mount each map as it is used or keep the maps on the Class Data Pad so the entire 9-month school period can be displayed and all the data compared.

If appropriate for your class, it might be interesting to find out what parts of the country different children travel to. Do more go to warm areas or cold areas, the mountains or the seashore?

Weather Record

As with temperatures, general weather conditions can be observed and recorded. Make it the weather person's job to observe the weather outside and to tally it in the appropriate place. (In at least one classroom, this child is called the *meteorologist*.)

Choose symbols (perhaps with the children's help) to pictorially represent the kind of weather your area experiences. You might use some of the symbols shown at the left.

Sunny	Cloudy	Rainy	Snowy	Partly Cloudy	Foggy
卌 卌 /	//	///		卌 //	/

There are many ways to set up this kind of record so that tally marks can be made to indicate the frequency of each type of weather. One way is to hang cards below the symbols on a chart, wall, or bulletin board, and then mark tallies on the cards.

Tally marks can periodically be counted by 5s as a skip-counting exercise. By the end of the year, the class will know about how many days there have been of each type of weather. If the chart paper is marked off on a grid with each square large enough for 5 tally marks, it will be easier for children to record the tallies accurately. It is also fun to find out if the total number of tallies of the different weather types corresponds to the total number of school days so far in the year.

Weather often changes during the day. You may want to take this into account later in the year by having children take two readings per day and record by half-days. The data children collect can be saved and used later in the year for graphing and comparing activities.

Mathematical Topics

contents

Essay	Title	Page
1	Number and Counting	52
2	Operations and Facts	72
3	Algorithms and Mental Arithmetic	94
4	Data and Chance	114
5	Geometry	124
6	Measurement	146
7	Reference Frames	162
8	Estimation and Number Sense	174
9	Patterns, Sequences, Functions, and Algebra	182
10	Problem Solving	196

ESSAY

1

Number and Counting

outline

1.1 Number Uses   53

1.2 Number Systems   53
  1.2.1 Counting and the Whole Numbers   54
  1.2.2 Numbers for Measuring: The Positive Rational Numbers   54
  1.2.3 The Rational Numbers: Positive, Negative, and Zero   55
  1.2.4 The Real Numbers   55
  1.2.5 The Ordinal Numbers   56

1.3 Counting: Plain and Fancy   57
  1.3.1 Rote Counting   57
  1.3.2 Rational Counting   58

1.4 Number Grids, Scrolls, and Lines   58
  1.4.1 Number Grids   58

1.4.2 Number Scrolls   61
1.4.3 Number Lines   62

1.5 Relations   64
  1.5.1 Equality   65
  1.5.2 Name-Collection Boxes   65

1.6 Fractions, Decimals, and Percents   66
  1.6.1 Uses of Fractions   67
  1.6.2 Rates and Ratios   68
  1.6.3 Percents   68
  1.6.4 Equivalence   69

1.7 Notation   69
  1.7.1 Numeration and Place Value   69
  1.7.2 Notation for Rational Numbers   71

Children often already know a lot of mathematics when they begin school. They are fluent in the practical geometry of everyday life: they enjoy patterns of sound, shape, and movement; they can reason a little. But probably their most important mathematical skill is counting. Counting provides a foundation for understanding our number system and the basic operations of arithmetic. Arithmetic operations with counting numbers lead, in turn, to other kinds of numbers—such as positive rational numbers (fractions and decimals), and negative numbers and eventually to algebra and higher mathematics.

Numbers and counting are integral to most of the topics in this book. This essay addresses noncomputational aspects of numbers, including number systems and uses of numbers. Numbers are also discussed at length in the essays on Operations and Facts; Estimation and Number Sense; and Patterns, Sequences, Functions, and Algebra.

1.1 Number Uses

If you're looking for only one phrase to capture the overall philosophy of *Everyday Mathematics,* it might be "Numbers All Around." In Kindergarten, children explore magazines and other media in search of numbers. In first grade, children create a "Numbers All Around Museum" and collect numbers about themselves. In second grade, children collect numbers about their worlds and curate another Numbers All Around Museum. Similar lessons using numbers and mathematics from children's everyday experience continue through *Sixth Grade Everyday Mathematics.*

The numbers that surround us in today's world are not all the same. Some are measurements, some are counts, and others still are used for identification. The developers of *Everyday Mathematics* have identified five basic categories, or use-classes, that cover 90% of number uses:

- counts
- measures
- locations
- ratio comparisons
- codes

Counts and *measures* are straightforward: 6 eggs, 3 pounds, and so on. *Locations* are a bit trickier: 9:05 a.m. expresses a location in time; 72°C is a location on a temperature scale; pairs of numbers such as 42°N, 87°W mark a location on the Earth's surface. See Essay 7, Reference Frames, for more information about this use of numbers and how it differs from measurement.

A *ratio comparison* is a number like 3 times as much or $\frac{1}{2}$ as many. *Ratio comparisons* are less common in primary grade mathematics than are *counts* and *measures,* but become increasingly important in later grades.

Codes are numbers used as identification tags, which often also include letters. *Codes* are used for credit cards, Social Security numbers, phone numbers, and so on. Often a code has several parts. For example, in the zip code 60637:

6   refers to Illinois, Missouri, Nebraska, or Kansas

06 refers to Chicago

37 refers to the neighborhood in Chicago that includes the University of Chicago

1.2 Number Systems

Thousands of years ago people got by without numbers or with only the numbers: 1, 2, 3, ... Eventually, however, these numbers were found to be inadequate for certain purposes, and other number systems were invented. The inventions of these new number systems were motivated either by the everyday needs of people, or by mathematical needs, or both. In this section, we discuss various number systems, including whole numbers, positive and negative rational numbers, and real numbers. In Section 1.7.1, Numeration and Place Value, we discuss systems for writing numbers.

1.2.1 Counting and the Whole Numbers

The first numbers people used were for counting: 1, 2, 3, and so on. These numbers were the beginning of mathematics. Zero was invented both to express "none" as a count and to make writing numbers easier. The numbers {0, 1, 2, 3, . . .} are known as the whole numbers.[1]

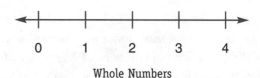

Whole Numbers

1.2.2 Numbers for Measuring: The Positive Rational Numbers

The whole numbers are adequate for counting, but measurement requires numbers between the whole numbers. A pencil, for example, might be more than five inches long but less than six inches long. The "measure numbers"—the positive rational numbers—fill this need. The positive rational numbers include both fractions and decimals[2] and the numbers {1, 2, 3, . . .}. The efficient and convenient notations we have today for these numbers—fractions and decimals—evolved later, but the numbers themselves were invented thousands of years ago.

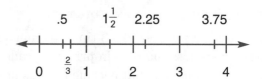

Zero and some Positive Rational Numbers

The whole numbers are always enough for addition and multiplication of whole numbers: The sum of any two whole numbers is a whole number, and the product of any two whole numbers is a whole number. But not all differences and quotients of whole numbers are whole numbers. For example, $7 \div 2$ and $3 - 5$, do not have whole-number answers. With the positive rational numbers, however, all division problems with whole numbers (except for divisions by 0) have answers. (See Section 3.2.4 for more information on division by 0.)

NOTE: The term "rational number" is confusing. Rational numbers are not more reasonable than other numbers. Rational numbers are called rational because they can be written as ratios of integers.[3] Any positive rational number can be expressed as a ratio (or fraction) where the numerator is a whole number and the denominator is a non-zero whole number. For example, the rational number 7.5 can be expressed as the ratio $\frac{75}{10}$.

---

[1] You may encounter the terms *natural numbers* and *counting numbers*. Usually these are synonymous and are defined to be the numbers {1, 2, 3, . . .} or, sometimes, {0, 1, 2, 3, . . .}.

[2] Strictly speaking, only decimals that terminate or repeat are rational numbers (such as 1.5 and 0.1231123 . . .). Decimals that go on forever without repeating are not rational (such as 3.14159 . . .).

[3] The integers are the whole numbers {0, 1, 2, 3, . . .} and their opposites {0, −1, −2, −3, . . .}. Note that 0 is its own opposite. 0 is neither positive nor negative.

1.2.3 The Rational Numbers: Positive, Negative, and Zero

For many purposes, the positive rational numbers and 0 are sufficient. Anything that can be counted, for example, can be counted with positive numbers. Similarly, positive numbers are all we need for measures. When we add, multiply, or divide positive numbers, the answer is always a positive number: $4 + 3$, 5×6, $7 \div 2$, all have positive answers.

Positive rational numbers are not enough for subtraction. When we subtract one positive number from another, sometimes the answer is a positive number (for example, $15 - 7$), but sometimes the answer is not positive (for example, $8 - 17$). In order for problems like $8 - 17$ to have answers, we need negative numbers.

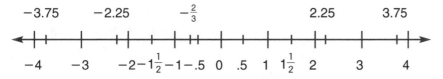

Rational Numbers

Many common situations can be used to help children understand negative numbers. Such situations illustrate that negatives are *opposites* of positives. Positives and negatives always come in pairs, and familiarity with negatives can be improved by comparing them with positive opposites. For example, if Asha gives Bert 3 dollars, Asha's cash is 3 dollars less ($-\$3$) and Bert's cash is 3 dollars more ($+\$3$). Number lines are also useful for representing negative numbers and their relationships to positive numbers.

Real Situations with Positive and Negative Numbers			
Situation	**Negative**	**Zero**	**Positive**
Temperature (°C)	below freezing	water freezes	above freezing
Weight	weight loss	no change	weight gain
Bank account	withdrawal	no change	deposit
Time	before	now	after
Games	behind	even	ahead
Business	loss	break even	profit
Elevation	below sea level	sea level	above sea level

1.2.4 The Real Numbers

Rational numbers suffice for addition, subtraction, multiplication, and division of any whole numbers (except, of course, division by 0), but they are not enough for many other applications. For example, in taking square roots,[4] sometimes the square root of a whole number is another whole number: the square root of 9 is 3; the

---

[4]The square root of a number is the number that multiplied by itself equals that number. The square root of 81, for example, is 9 because $9 \times 9 = 81$.

square root of 100 is 10. But many square roots are not whole numbers. The square root of 2, for example, is more than 1 but less than 2.

One might hope that the square roots that "don't come out even" were rational numbers, but this is not the case. Over two thousand years ago, the followers of the Greek philosopher Pythagoras proved that the square root of 2 is not rational. Numbers that are not rational are called irrational. When the irrationality of the square root of 2 was first proved, it caused a sensation among the Pythagoreans. The discoverer is said to have been thrown from a ship because Pythagorean dogma held that all numbers were rational.

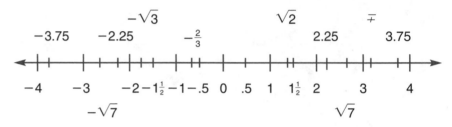

Real Numbers

The name *irrational* for these numbers does not mean these numbers are unreasonable. It simply means that they cannot be written as ratios of two integers. The square root of 2, for example, cannot be written as a fraction where the numerator and denominator are both whole numbers. To write an irrational number in ordinary notation would require writing an infinitely long decimal. Usually special symbols are used instead, for example, $\sqrt{2}$ for the square root of two.

The irrational numbers and the rational numbers together make up what mathematicians today call the *real numbers*. For practical purposes, we don't really need the real numbers; even scientists use rational-number approximations for real numbers whenever they perform calculations. (Calculations with infinite decimals are not very convenient.) In a mathematical system, however, real numbers are extremely important.

In many ways, the real numbers are the end of the number-system story. For example, every point on the number line corresponds with exactly one real number, and every real number matches exactly one point on the number line—there are no gaps. Real numbers are more than adequate for everything we do in *Everyday Mathematics*. One thing the real numbers cannot do, however, is name square roots of negative numbers. Mathematicians have invented other numbers for that, *complex numbers*, but that's another story.

1.2.5 The Ordinal Numbers

The counting numbers tell how many: 5 apples, 3 books, 2 birds. To tell the order of objects in a sequence, a different kind of number is used: first, second, third, and so on. These are called the ordinal numbers.

The ordinal numbers are not as simple as they seem. Suppose, for example, we have an apple, a pear, a peach, a banana, and a plum. Counting these pieces of fruit is easy: There are five of them. But assigning ordinals is not so easy. The apple is listed first, but it could easily be listed third or fifth instead. Indeed, the apple might be first in alphabetical order and fifth in weight. Also, 5 refers to the entire collection of fruit, but *fifth* refers only to the last piece in some sequential ordering of the five fruits. Fortunately, children can learn to use ordinal numbers without having to bother about these rather abstract issues.

1.3 Counting: Plain and Fancy

Recent research shows that very young children, as well as certain animals, have rudimentary nonverbal counting abilities. These counting foundations appear to be hard-wired in our makeup. Building on these fundamental nonverbal capabilities, verbal counting is one of the most useful ways to introduce young children to numerous important mathematical concepts. Just as one needs to be familiar with the progression of notes in a musical scale before one can play a piece of written music, children need a secure grasp of counting before they can understand our number system and develop arithmetic competence. Throughout *Everyday Mathematics,* you are encouraged to incorporate the many varied and playful rote-counting and rational-counting activities into your lesson plans.

1.3.1 Rote Counting

Children first learn to count aloud by reciting a string of number words by rote, without understanding the significance behind what they are saying. At first, they make mistakes ("one, two, three, six, nine, eleven, threeteen, . . ."), though they usually make the same mistakes every time. Eventually, they learn to recite the number sequence correctly to 10 or 20 or beyond; but generally without full numerical understanding, especially for higher numbers.

Rote, oral counting is important for learning about our number system. As children count, they hear, and then later see, the order and number-word patterns of the base-ten system. Types of rote counting include the following:

- counting on from numbers other than 0 or 1
- counting backward from a number
- skip counting by 2s, 5s, 10s, and so on, from 0 at first, and then later from other numbers

All these types of counting help children develop the skills and understandings that are used to solve problems. Counting on, for example, is a good way for Kindergarten or first grade students to solve simple addition problems.

A variation on any of the above rote-counting activities is what is called interrupted oral counting. This includes having one group of children count so far, stopping them, and then having another group continue. A more advanced version of interrupted counting is having children stop in the middle of a counting activity (counting backward, skip counting by 2s, and so on) and then giving them a new starting number from which they continue using the same activity.

1.3.2 Rational Counting

Reciting number words by rote is just the beginning. Children also need to learn to count collections of objects correctly. This involves coordinating the spoken number words with pointing to or touching the objects being counted. The children must also avoid skipping objects or counting some twice, and they must come to realize that the order in which objects are counted makes no difference. Such meaningful counting is called "rational counting" and is achieved only after a great deal of practice.

1.4 Number Grids, Scrolls, and Lines

"Grid" is short for "gridiron," an old English word for a framework of metal bars or wires used to grill meat or fish. Generally, a grid is any set of equally spaced parallel lines or squares used to help establish locations of objects.

In *Everyday Mathematics,* children use grids in many ways, including number grids, coordinate grids, grids for estimating area, and grids for interpreting maps. The tick marks on a number line form perhaps the most primitive grid structure. Lattices and arrays are organizations of objects into gridlike formations—a calendar is a common example. Here we discuss what we call number grids and number scrolls. Coordinate grids are discussed in Sections 5.9 and 7.3.1.

1.4.1 Number Grids

A number grid consists of rows of boxes, usually ten boxes in each row, containing consecutive whole numbers. In *First Grade Everyday Mathematics,* children are introduced to the number grid on page 59.

									0
1	2	3	4	5	6	7	8	9	10
11	12	13	14	15	16	17	18	19	20
21	22	23	24	25	26	27	28	29	30
31	32	33	34	35	36	37	38	39	40
41	42	43	44	45	46	47	48	49	50
51	52	53	54	55	56	57	58	59	60
61	62	63	64	65	66	67	68	69	70
71	72	73	74	75	76	77	78	79	80
81	82	83	84	85	86	87	88	89	90
91	92	93	94	95	96	97	98	99	100
101	102	103	104	105	106	107	108	109	110

Number Grid

in perspective

Identifying number patterns in grids can help children understand divisibility rules, prime numbers, and factoring in later grades.

Number grids have many wonderful features that help children with pattern recognition and place value. Their original use, however, was simply to solve the problem of number lines being unmanageably long. Number lines can be cumbersome even when stretched along a classroom wall, and it is nearly impossible to print them in children's books without breaking them into chunks. Number grids may be considered number lines that fit nicely on a page or a classroom poster. Number scrolls (discussed in greater detail in Section 1.4.2.) are number grids that extend into the hundreds or thousands.

The number grid lends itself to many activities that reinforce understanding of numeration and place value. By exploring the patterns in rows and columns, for example, children discover that any number on the number grid is:

1 more than the number to its left
1 less than the number to its right
10 more than the number above it
10 less than the number below it.

In other words, as you move from left to right, the ones digit increases by 1 and the tens digit remains unchanged. As you move down, the tens digit increases by 1 and the ones digit remains unchanged.

In the primary grades, *Everyday Mathematics* includes many counting activities that use number grids: Count by 10s, starting at

Number-grid puzzle

17; count backward by 10s, starting at 84; and so on. Children also solve puzzles based on the number grid. These puzzles are pieces of a number grid in which some, but not all, of the numbers are missing. For example, in the puzzle at the left, the missing numbers are 356 and 358. Number-grid puzzles are used through third grade, mostly for numbers in the hundreds and thousands.

Number grids can be used to explore number patterns. For example, children can color boxes as they count by 2s. If they start at 0 and count by 2s, they will color the even numbers; if they start at 1, the odd numbers. If they count by 5s, starting at 0, they will color the boxes containing numbers with 0 or 5 in the ones place.

									0
1	2	3	4	5	6	7	8	9	10
11	12	13	14	15	16	17	18	19	20
21	22	23	24	25	26	27	28	29	30
31	32	33	34	35	36	37	38	39	40
41	42	43	44	45	46	47	48	49	50
51	52	53	54	55	56	57	58	59	60
61	62	63	64	65	66	67	68	69	70
71	72	73	74	75	76	77	78	79	80
81	82	83	84	85	86	87	88	89	90
91	92	93	94	95	96	97	98	99	100
101	102	103	104	105	106	107	108	109	110

Number grids are also useful for addition and subtraction. For example, one way to find the difference between 84 and 37 is to first count the number of tens from 37 to 77 (4 tens) and then count the number of ones from 77 to 84 (7 ones). The difference between 84 and 37 is thus 4 tens plus 7 ones, or 47. This difference corresponds to the distance between the points 37 and 84 on a number line. Another way to solve 84 − 37 on the number grid is to start at 84 and count back to 37, noting as before how many numbers have been counted. Still another way is to count back 37 from 84: 74, 64, 54, 53, 52, 51, 50, 49, 48, 47. Addition problems can also be solved on the number grid using similar methods. Clearly, the number grid simplifies "double counting"—counting the number of numbers counted—that is required in many of these addition and subtraction procedures.

									0
1	2	3	4	5	6	7	8	9	10
11	12	13	14	15	16	17	18	19	20
21	22	23	24	25	26	27	28	29	30
31	32	33	34	35	36	(37)	38	39	40
41	42	43	44	45	46	47	48	49	50
51	52	53	54	55	56	57	58	59	60
61	62	63	64	65	66	67	68	69	70
71	72	73	74	75	76	77	78	79	80
81	82	83	(84)	85	86	87	88	89	90
91	92	93	94	95	96	97	98	99	100
101	102	103	104	105	106	107	108	109	110

One way to find the difference between 84 and 37

Number grids can also be extended to negative numbers. This is especially useful as a tool for finding differences or to illustrate, for example, that -17 is less than -6.

−19	−18	−17	−16	−15	−14	−13	−12	−11	−10
−9	−8	−7	−6	−5	−4	−3	−2	−1	0
1	2	3	4	5	6	7	8	9	10
11	12	13	14	15	16	17	18	19	20

1.4.2 Number Scrolls

Number scrolls are simply an extension of number grids. They are made by adding single sheets of 100 numbers to existing sheets—either forward (positively) or backward (negatively). Among other things, scrolls give children the chance to experience the ongoing repetitive patterns of our base-ten number system beyond 100: "101, 102, 103, . . ." instead of continuing, as children often do, with "200, 300, 400, . . ." Teachers have found that many children get excited when they discover these patterns and realize they are capable of writing bigger and bigger numbers based on their discoveries. Meanwhile, they are practicing their handwriting as well as their counting skills.

1.4.3 Number Lines

A number line is a line with numbers marked on it. Normally, these numbers are marked at regular intervals from a starting point called the origin, or 0.

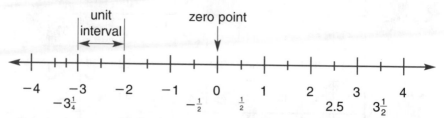

Like any line, a number line extends without end in both directions. Any drawing of a number line is just a model of part of the line. Where you place the 0-point is arbitrary, and how you space the numbers depends on the situation you wish to illustrate. You might, for example, mark every other unit-interval point and label by 2s, or you may mark every half-interval point and label by halves. In *Everyday Mathematics,* children are often asked to solve incomplete-number-line problems that help them understand these concepts.

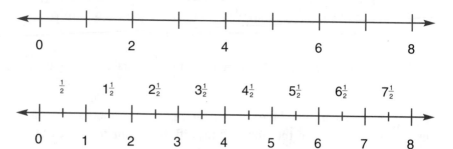

An ordinary ruler is a number line for measuring length, with inch unit intervals, centimeter unit intervals, or other unit intervals. The number line below, for example, can be used for measuring distances in inches and fractions of inches.

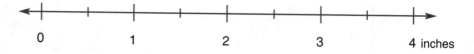

This number line has tick marks at all unit and half-unit intervals. You may recognize the similarities between the scale on this line and the one on a U.S. customary foot-ruler. This line has fewer fraction-of-unit intervals marked. In contrast, foot-rulers are usually marked every sixteenth of an inch. See Section 6.4 for more about measuring length.

You can assign any scale you wish to a number line. For example, a unit interval on a map scale might represent one mile on the map. Such a line would not be used to measure distances directly in the real world but instead to translate distances on the map into distances in the real world.

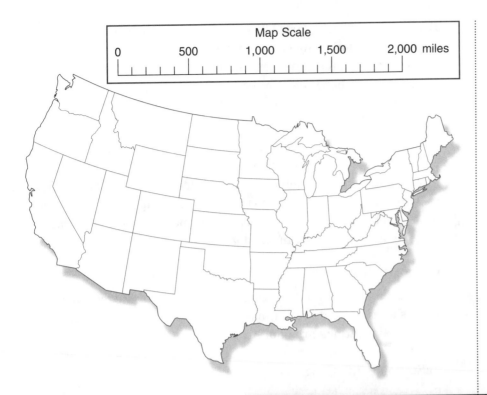

Map Scale

| 0 | 500 | 1,000 | 1,500 | 2,000 miles |

Number lines can also have nonlinear scales, meaning that the distances between the numbers are not proportional to the differences between the numbers. The distance between 10 and 20, for instance, might be the same as the distance between 1 and 2. Radio dials are based on logarithmic scales, one type of nonlinear scale.

Photograph courtesy of Bill Lettow, 1999

A number line always has a 0-point, even when it doesn't show. In the first number line below, the 0-point is understood to be off to the left. Sometimes you see a broken-line symbol as in the second number line below. This symbol indicates that a piece of the line between 0 and 330 has been omitted. The device is often used in technical drawings to show important details while still indicating that something is missing.

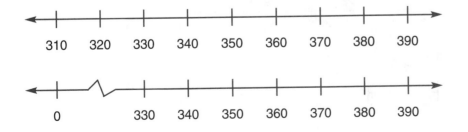

Number-line ideas are
expanded upon and treated
more formally in Grades 4–
6. Number lines continue to
serve as one or more of the
axes in data displays, such
as scatter plots, bar graphs,
and line plots.

Beginning in *Kindergarten Everyday Mathematics*, children use number lines for many counting activities. They use both horizontal and vertical number lines for counting and skip counting. A "Growing Number Line" can be kept on the classroom wall, with a new number added every day or whenever a new landmark in counting is achieved.

In first and second grades, children use a number line to keep track of the number of school days in the school year. They also use number lines on thermometers (two different scales: Fahrenheit and Celsius) and on linear measuring tools. "Incomplete Number Line" problems begin in first grade. Number lines in coordinate graphing systems are introduced in third grade.

1.5 Relations

In mathematics, a relation tells how one thing compares to another. In this section we discuss numerical relations. The most important numerical relations are equality ($=$) and inequality ($<$ and $>$), but there are others. Geometric relations are discussed in Section 5.7.2, Congruence and Similarity.

Even preschool children have some idea of "more" and "less." They may be deceived by appearances but, under the right conditions, they can judge bigger/smaller, shorter/taller, heavier/lighter, and so on. This capacity for judging more/less is the basis for understanding numerical relations.

Table 1. Symbols for Numerical Relations		
Symbol	**Meaning**	**Examples**
$=$	"equals" "is equal to" "is the same as"	$3 = \frac{6}{2}$ 3.0 seconds $=$ 3 seconds $\frac{1}{2} = 50\%$
$>$	"is greater than"	$12 > 4$ $1.23 > 1.2$ 6,000 ft $>$ 1 mi
$<$	"is less than"	8 million $<$ 12 million $0.1 < 1.1$ $\frac{5}{2} < 4$
$\geq$	"is greater than or equal to"	attendance $\geq$ 250 people $2 + 2 \geq 4$ the temperature $\geq$ 32°F the area $\geq$ 2 acres
$\leq$	"is less than or equal to"	the rent $\leq$ \$700 $2 + 2 \leq 4$ the fee $\leq$ \$25 the time $\leq$ 2 hours
$\neq$	"does not equal" "is not equal to" "is not the same as"	$10 \neq 100$ $\frac{10}{120} \neq \frac{1}{2}$ 85% $\neq$ 85

As children begin to attach counts and measures to objects, they learn ways to write those objects' relations symbolically. Table 1 shows the most common symbols for expressing numerical relations.

1.5.1 Equality

Although the concept of equality seems straightforward, children who have been through several years of schooling often have difficulty using the "$=$" symbol. Research studies show that many older children reject such number sentences as $5 = 5$ (they say there is no problem), $4 = 2 + 2$ (they say that the answer is on the wrong side), and $4 + 3 = 5 + 2$ (they say there are two problems, but no answers).

The origin of these errors seems clear. Children in school usually see number sentences written only with a problem on the left-hand side of the equal sign and the answer on the right-hand side: $5 + 7 = 12$. The cure is obvious: Deliberately write $12 = 5 + 7$ as often as $5 + 7 = 12$, and encourage children to say "means the same as" or "looks different, but is really the same as" when the equal symbol appears.

In large part, arithmetic consists of simply replacing numbers or expressions with equivalent (equal) numbers or expressions.[5] We replace $7 + 8$ with 15, or substitute 27 for $459 \div 17$. When it suits us, we use $\frac{1}{2}$ in place of $\frac{1}{3} + \frac{1}{6}$ and vice versa. Number sense and arithmetic skill consist largely of being aware of the many possibilities for equivalent names for numbers and being able to exploit them flexibly.

For most collections of equivalent names, one name is often recognized as the "simplest" and serves to identify the entire collection. But simplest doesn't necessarily mean best—$\frac{50}{100}$ (as in 50 per 100) may convey more information in a given situation than its simpler cousin $\frac{1}{2}$ and also serves as a better bridge to understanding that 50% is equivalent to $\frac{1}{2}$. Unfortunately, much of the traditional mathematics curriculum has made the "simplification" of numbers synonymous with mathematics itself. Students of *Everyday Mathematics* will not have this sterile experience.

1.5.2 Name-Collection Boxes

Beginning in first grade, children use name-collection boxes to manage equivalent names for numbers. These devices offer a simple way for children to experience the idea that numbers can be expressed in many different ways. In Kindergarten through third grade, a name-collection box is an open-top box with a label identifying the number whose names are collected in the box. For example, the box shown in the margin is a 16-box, a name-collection box for the number 16.

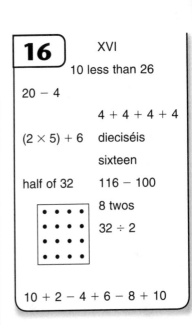

16 | XVI
10 less than 26
20 − 4
4 + 4 + 4 + 4
(2 × 5) + 6 | dieciséis
sixteen
half of 32 | 116 − 100
8 twos
32 ÷ 2
10 + 2 − 4 + 6 − 8 + 10

---

[5]The French mathematician Henri Poincaré (1865–1912) went even further. He once remarked that "Mathematics is the art of giving the same name to different things." For example, mathematicians give the name "polygon" to many different shapes, including squares, triangle, and pentagons.

14
1,400%
2 * 7
$\frac{56}{4}$
20 − 6
1 + 13
700/50
$3^3 - 13$
0.028 * 500
XIV
(3 * 7) − 7

in perspective Beginning in fourth grade, *Everyday Mathematics* introduces a more compact name-collection box.

Names can include sums, differences, products, quotients, the results of combining several operations, words in English or other languages, tally marks, arrays, Roman numerals, and so on.

1.6 Fractions, Decimals, and Percents

The real world is made up of lengths, weights, and other measures that cannot be expressed using only whole-number marks on rulers, scales, measuring cups, and the like. Dealing with numbers in the modern world involves much more than counting with whole numbers. Money transactions are expressed in decimal form; fractions arise as soon as we share a pizza; both fractions and decimals are routinely used in measurement.

Fractions can be confusing, in part because the procedures for adding, subtracting, multiplying, and dividing them at first seem arbitrary and unpredictable. For example, many people really don't understand the "invert and multiply" rule for the division of one fraction by another. These mysterious manipulations, often taught without meaningful real-life situations, have helped convince many adults that mathematics is impossible to understand and that getting "correct" results is more a matter of "good luck" than good thinking and management.

Another reason people have trouble with fractions is that many school programs avoid them for years while children work exclusively with whole numbers. When children are finally introduced to fractions, many find them confusing because results often run counter to their expectations from having worked only with whole numbers. A product involving fractions may be smaller than its factors; a quotient may be larger than the thing being divided; and "repeated addition" has little meaning in the multiplication of two fractions.

Much of the content of the traditional primary grade mathematics curriculum is concerned with whole-number addition, subtraction, multiplication, and place value. K–3 *Everyday Mathematics* goes significantly beyond this traditional work. The curriculum introduces negative numbers in Kindergarten (with temperatures, timelines, and number lines); fractions (with measures and "part of" situations) and decimals (mainly with money) in first grade; and easy percents as alternatives to easy fractions ("one-tenth of . . ." and "ten percent of . . .") in second grade.

Children can understand these new numbers when they are presented as part of their everyday experiences. For example, several years before the authors began to develop *Everyday Mathematics,* they conducted interviews with 5- and 6-year-olds

in perspective

In *Everyday Mathematics,* most paper-and-pencil arithmetic with fractions is delayed until fourth grade and beyond. The primary grades focus instead on helping children develop a conceptual basis for learning computations and other operations with fractions later.

that showed that young children respond quickly and accurately when asked for "half of" something—probably as a result of sharing things equally with siblings and friends. Building on these observations, the primary grade *Everyday Mathematics* program includes a healthy dose of fractions, decimals, negative numbers, and percents. These numbers are used mainly to convey information. The authors did find, however, that "multiplication" with such fractions as "half of . . ." or "a tenth of . . ." is readily accepted by children, especially in contexts that pair "two of . . ." with "half of . . ." or "ten of . . ." with "one-tenth of . . . ."

1.6.1 Uses of Fractions

One reason fractions are confusing is that they have many different meanings. The fraction $\frac{1}{4}$, for example, can have any of the following meanings:

- a part of a whole: $\frac{1}{4}$ of a pizza
- a part of a collection: $\frac{1}{4}$ of a group of children
- a measurement: $\frac{1}{4}$ mile
- a division: $1 \div 4$
- a rate or ratio: 1 part vinegar to 4 parts oil
- a probability: 1 chance in 4
- a pure number: the number halfway between 0 and $\frac{1}{2}$

The idea of a unit whole is essential in the first two of these meanings. How big $\frac{1}{4}$ of a pizza is, for example, depends on how big the whole pizza is. To know how many children are in $\frac{1}{4}$ of a group, one needs to know how big the whole group is. In order to understand such "part-whole" fractions, children must appreciate the role of the unit whole. They should also understand that the denominator tells how many parts are in the whole and that the numerator tells how many parts are included in the fraction. In *Everyday Mathematics* the unit whole is called the ONE. Part-whole fractions are perhaps the easiest to understand, and many primary grade activities in *Everyday Mathematics* involve them.

In fractions and in measurements, the unit is also vitally important: $\frac{1}{4}$ mile is quite different from $\frac{1}{4}$ inch. Using fractions makes possible more precise measurements. With a ruler marked only in whole inches, for example, it is possible to measure precisely only to the nearest inch. But if the spaces between the whole-number marks are subdivided into equal intervals, then more precise measurements become possible. Other measuring tools like graduated cylinders, measuring cups, and kitchen scales also subdivide the spaces between whole numbers of units. A significant part of learning to use such tools is learning to interpret the marks on the scales correctly.

In most other uses of fractions, there is no clear unit whole. In ratios, for example, there is no unit whole. A ratio like $\frac{1}{4}$ (which can also be written 1:4 or "1 to 4") might mean one tablespoon of vinegar to

NOTE: The notation a ÷ b is used only in elementary school textbooks. $\frac{a}{b}$ and a/b, which have identical meanings to $a \div b$, are used everywhere else. Because of calculators and computers, the a/b notation is more important than ever. The link between fractions and division is the key to converting fractions to decimals and percents. Therefore, Grades 4–6 *Everyday Mathematics* uses the symbol "/" to indicate division.

in**perspective**

Fractions as equal parts of unit wholes and fractions on measurement scales and number lines get a lot of attention in Grades 1–3. These kinds of fractions, along with fractions for division and fractions for rates and ratios, appear often in Grades 4–6 in a variety of applications.

four tablespoons of oil in a salad dressing. There is no unit whole in such fractions, nor is there in fractions that indicate division.

1.6.2 Rates and Ratios

In both higher mathematics and technical work, perhaps the most common use of fraction notation is to express rates and ratios.

Speed is the basic model for rates. Speed is distance traveled per length of time. Therefore, 20 inches/4 days is a speed, for example, of the growth of a bamboo plant. Speeds are usually expressed as distance per one unit of time: 5 inches/1 day.

Rates can also involve quantities other than distance per time. Prices, for example, can be thought of as rates: Bananas at 33¢/lb or gasoline at $1.50/gal are rates that involve cost per unit. In general, rates express comparisons of pairs of quantities by multiplication or division. The counts or measures in the numerator and denominator may have different units, resulting in a rate with compound units such as miles per hour or dollars per pound.

Ratios compare quantities that have the same unit; in effect, the units cancel, and the resulting fraction has no unit. For example, $\frac{2}{20}$ could mean that 2 out of 20 people in a class failed a test, or that 2 out of 20 pears are ripe. The ratio $\frac{2}{20}$ may even be a simplified fraction to express the fact that 20,000 out of 200,000 people voted for a certain candidate in an election.

Another use of ratios is to indicate relative size or scale. In a picture of an object in a book drawn to $\frac{1}{10}$ scale, for example, every length is $\frac{1}{10}$ the length of the actual object. In the language of transformations, the picture in the dictionary is a size-change image of the object by scale factor $\frac{1}{10}$. Such size-change ratios are also used in mapping and geometry.

1.6.3 Percents

A percent is a ratio comparison based on hundredths. The word *percent* comes from the Latin *per centum,* meaning "for each 100." Essentially, a percent is just a number—15% is $\frac{15}{100}$, 75% is $\frac{75}{100}$, and so on. Because percents are often used in complicated situations, the underlying meaning is often obscured. The percent symbol (%) can be interpreted in several ways:

times 0.01	$5\% = 5 \times 0.01 = 0.05$
times $\frac{1}{100}$	$5\% = 5 \times \frac{1}{100} = \frac{5}{100}$
divided by 100	$5\% = \frac{5}{100} = 0.05$

The payoff for repeated, early and informal experiences with decimals, fractions, and percents comes later in the program, when seeing relationships among the numbers allows children to use mental computation and estimation with a high degree of sophistication. Here is an example: "How much is 10% of 30 peaches?" Knowing that 10% is equal to $\frac{1}{10}$ makes this problem easy to do mentally by taking $\frac{1}{10}$ of 30.

1.6.4 Equivalence

Fractions have many equivalent names. Every fraction, in fact, is just one of an infinite set of equivalent fractions. The fraction $\frac{2}{3}$, for example, is a member of the set $\{\frac{2}{3}, \frac{4}{6}, \frac{6}{9}, \frac{8}{12}, \frac{10}{15}, \ldots\}$. One fraction from such a set has no common factors in the numerator and denominator—it is in "simplest form"—and that fraction is a convenient label for the entire set. But this simplest-form fraction is not always preferable to all other equivalent names. In fact, flexibility in arithmetic is gained by freely using whichever form is most convenient or appropriate for the purpose at hand. Truly numerate people artfully use one form for a number rather than another to express what they want or need to say. Also, "reducing" fractions to simplest form may result in important information being lost. For example, saying that the fraction of people voting for a candidate was $\frac{7,500}{10,000}$ conveys more information than form the proportion $\frac{3}{4}$ or 75%.

Everyday Mathematics promotes flexibility in using numbers, including fractions. Standard forms have their place, but to demand their use as the only acceptable alternative is counterproductive to learning.

1.7 Notation

In the discussion thus far we have not distinguished numbers from how they are written. In the next section, we discuss the main system for representing whole numbers. In the final section, we briefly discuss the three main systems for representing rational numbers.

1.7.1 Numeration and Place Value

Today, people everywhere write whole numbers in the same way.[6] The system of numeration we all use was invented in India more than a thousand years ago and came to Western Europe via the Middle East and North Africa. This highly efficient system, known as Hindu-Arabic numeration, has contributed significantly to the tremendous advances in mathematics and science in the past 500 years.

Hindu-Arabic numeration uses 10 digits to represent whole numbers. The digits are placed according to one basic rule: that the value of a digit increases 10 times for every place to the left it is in the number. Thus the 2 in 72 is worth just 2, but the 2 in 27 is worth ten times as much, or 20; and the 2 in 275 is worth a further ten times as much, or 200. The system is called a *place-value* system because the value of a digit depends on its place in the number. The system is also called a base-ten system because the values of the places increase by a factor of 10 for each shift to the left.

---

[6]In Arabic the shapes of the digits differ from those used in most other languages, but the underlying system of numeration is the same.

in perspective

One goal of *Everyday Mathematics* is for students completing sixth grade to instantly recognize decimal and percent equivalents for many common fractions. These include halves, fourths, eighths, fifths, tenths, and thirds. In fourth grade, students explore strategies for finding equivalencies among fractions, decimals, and percents. In fifth grade, students use decimal division to convert fractions into decimals and percents. They also practice recognizing different forms by playing *Frac-Tac-Toe*. Throughout Grades 4–6, students practice operations with fractions, decimals, and percents in real-world contexts.

Mastering Hindu-Arabic numeration is a major goal of primary grade *Everyday Mathematics*. The process begins in Kindergarten when children count up to and beyond 110 by both 1s and by 10s and observe what happens to the written numbers as the count passes landmarks like 100. Children in Kindergarten also work with number lines and number grids, both including numbers beyond 100. At this stage, most children have no understanding of the place-value structure of numbers—writing the number 57 is more like spelling than mathematics—but these activities at least provide children a familiarity with 2- and 3-digit numbers that they can build on in later grades.

In first grade, children group objects by 10s and 100s and make exchanges across places. For example, they may trade 3 tens for 2 tens and 10 ones. First graders extend their counting beyond 1,000, including counts by 1s, 10s, and 100s, and continue to work with number lines and number grids. They also begin exploring ideas of place value and make connections between written numbers and manipulatives like base-10 blocks. The idea that numbers have equivalent names—1,000 = 10 hundreds, and so on—is also stressed in first grade. Realizing that numbers have equivalent forms is essential for understanding written procedures for whole-number computation.

Place value is studied more formally in second grade. Children rename 2- and 3-digit numbers in various ways and investigate place value to 10,000s. Much of this work is integrated with learning how to add and subtract multidigit numbers because most computational algorithms depend heavily on place value. (One of the main reasons Hindu-Arabic numeration has been so widely accepted is that it makes computation so much easier—just try multiplication with Roman numerals!)

By third grade, children begin to extend their understanding of place value both to numbers through the millions and to decimals. Again, much of the place-value work is integrated with learning various procedures for whole-number addition and subtraction. Indeed, one reason to study paper-and-pencil computation with multi-digit numbers is that the algorithms are an excellent context for learning about numeration and place value.

Through all of this number work in Grades K–3, children use a variety of manipulatives—base-10 blocks, counters, coins, straws, number lines, digit cards, and dominoes. Particular attention is paid to helping children make connections between various representations of numbers, including symbols, words, pictures, manipulatives, and real objects. See Section 10.2 for a discussion of how proficiency with multiple representations can help children solve problems.

1.7.2 Notation for Rational Numbers

The importance of alternate notations for numbers is emphasized throughout *Everyday Mathematics*. All three notations for rational numbers—fractions, decimals, and percents—can help children see connections between rational numbers and whole numbers.[7] Fractions build on ideas of equal sharing and whole-number operations; decimals extend the whole-number place-value system; and percents connect to important ideas of ratio and proportion.

Decimals, fractions, and percents are technically interchangeable, but many common situations use one or the other as "standard notation." For example, fractions are standard in stock market reports, but decimals are used in most other financial applications. Measures are commonly expressed as fractions in carpentry and other building trades, but decimals are used for virtually all measures in science and industry. Percents are used in interest rates and as well as in many advertisements and statistics.

The story of the historical development of fractions is a fascinating one. See *The Norton History of the Mathematical Sciences* by Ivor Gratten-Guinness (New York: W. W. Norton, 1997) or *Number Words and Number Symbols: A Cultural History of Numbers* by Karl A. Menninger (New York: Dover, 1992) for a more detailed history. Fractions were developed in prehistoric times, probably in response to the need for more precise "measures" of various things that could not be accommodated solely by whole-number units. The ancient Egyptians used unit fractions—fractions with a numerator of 1 like $\frac{1}{2}$, $\frac{1}{3}$, and $\frac{1}{8}$—almost exclusively. More complicated fractions were then expressed as the sums of unit fractions (for example, $\frac{1}{2} + \frac{1}{4}$ for $\frac{3}{4}$). Even in modern times, unit fractions are sufficient for the everyday needs of many people. The development of decimal notation for rational numbers, which occurred many centuries after fraction notation was first used, has a similarly rich history.

---

[7]You may sometimes encounter the terms *common fraction* and *decimal fraction*. While these terms emphasize that these are two different notations for the same numbers, the authors prefer the simpler terms *fraction* and *decimal*.

Operations and Facts

outline

2.1 Operations and Use Classes   73
  2.1.1 Addition and Subtraction   73
  2.1.2 Multiplication and Division   77
2.2 Number Models and Number Sentences   81
  2.2.1 Arithmetic Symbols   82

2.2.2 Number Sentences   86
2.2.3 Variables   88
2.3 Basic Facts   89
2.4 Games for Practice   92

For many adults, elementary school mathematics consisted of little more than learning to add, subtract, multiply, and divide whole numbers, fractions, and decimals. Unfortunately, this is still the experience of many children today. The authors of *Everyday Mathematics* hope that your acquaintance with our texts and your reading of this manual have convinced you that elementary school mathematics must be far more than arithmetic with the four basic operations.

Nevertheless, the importance of understanding arithmetic for success in mathematics as well as in everyday life cannot be denied. By combining activities that focus on understanding the basic operations with activities that apply arithmetic in geometry, data exploration, measurement, and other contexts, *Everyday Mathematics* ensures that children receive ample practice with arithmetic skills and that they will be better able to make use of those skills to solve problems. And rather than encountering only addition and subtraction in first and second grades, with multiplication and division delayed until third grade or later, children in *Everyday Mathematics* see many uses of all the operations from the beginning and build upon these uses year after year.

Many adults who associate school mathematics with arithmetic also tend to think that an arithmetic operation is what you "do" to get the answer. Division, for example, is carrying out the traditional long-division algorithm. In *Everyday Mathematics,* how one "does"

an operation is referred to as "applying an algorithm" or "carrying out a computation." (See Essay 3, Algorithms and Mental Arithmetic, for descriptions of various algorithms.) Although *Everyday Mathematics* recognizes the importance of knowing algorithms and introduces a variety of algorithms for each operation, *Everyday Mathematics* also recognizes that children need to understand the meanings behind each operation. Choosing the proper algorithm and interpreting the result correctly depends on understanding the operation itself. Grasping the meanings of the operations and proficiency at carrying out algorithms are both required for successful problem solving.

The next section of this essay discusses how the four basic arithmetic operations are used and what they mean. Later sections deal with number sentences, basic facts, and drill and practice. Mental arithmetic and algorithms for calculation with the four basic operations are discussed in Essay 3.

2.1 Operations and Use Classes

One way to understand something is to examine how it is used. A hammer is used for pounding nails. An umbrella is used for keeping dry in the rain. This is how *Everyday Mathematics* approaches the basic operations of arithmetic. At a certain stage formal definitions can be valuable, but in the elementary grades it is better to approach the operations indirectly, by looking at how they are used.

The basic operations of arithmetic—addition, subtraction, multiplication, and division—can be applied in many different situations, but most of those situations can be sorted into just a handful of categories. In *Everyday Mathematics,* the three basic categories for addition and subtraction are called *parts and total, change,* and *comparison.* Depending on what is known and what is unknown, each kind of situation can lead to either addition or subtraction problems. Multiplication and division situations are harder to sort out, but several basic categories can be distinguished: *equal groups, arrays and area, rate and ratio, scaling,* and *Cartesian product.* Again, each kind of situation can lead to either multiplication or division problems depending on what is unknown.

Everyday Mathematics uses special diagrams to help sort out these various kinds of problem situations. These situation diagrams help children organize the information in simple one-step number stories. (The diagrams in *Everyday Mathematics* are adapted from work done by Karen Fuson at Northwestern University.)

2.1.1 Addition and Subtraction

Most situations that lead to addition and subtraction problems can be categorized as *parts and total, change,* or *comparison.*

In a parts-and-total situation, there is a total quantity that can be broken into two or more parts. For example, the total number of

total children on the bus	
?	
4th graders	**1st graders**
12	15

?	
12	15

Parts-and-total diagrams

Total	
35	
Part	**Part**
20	?

Parts-and-total diagram

children in a class can be broken into the number of girls and the number of boys. Or the total distance from Chicago to St. Louis can be broken into the distance from Chicago to Springfield and the distance from Springfield to St. Louis.

In *Everyday Mathematics,* a parts-and-total diagram has a large rectangle on top for the Total and two or more smaller rectangles below for the Parts. The rectangles are filled in with numbers for particular problems.

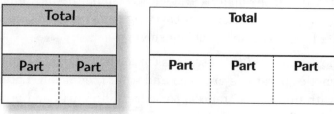

Parts-and-total diagrams

If all the parts are known but the total is unknown, then the problem can be solved by adding the parts.

Example: Twelve fourth graders and 15 first graders are on a bus. How many children in all are on the bus?
The parts are known. You are looking for the total.

Possible number model:

$$12 + 15 = \_\_$$

If the total is known but one of the parts is unknown, then subtraction can be used to find the unknown part.

Example: Thirty-five children are riding on the bus. Twenty of them are boys. How many girls are riding on the bus?
One part and the total are known. You are looking for the other part.

Possible number models:

$$20 + \_\_ = 35$$
$$35 - 20 = \_\_$$

A second kind of addition/subtraction situation is *change.* In a change situation there is a starting quantity, a change, and then finally an ending quantity. For example, a plant 15 cm tall might grow 5 cm in a week and end up being 20 cm tall. Or you might start with a certain amount of money, spend some, and then have less money at the end. Change situations can lead to either addition or subtraction problems, depending on the direction of the change (change to more or change to less) and what is known or unknown.

A change diagram has a rectangle on the left for the starting Quantity, then an arrow above a blank for the Change, and finally a rectangle on the right for the ending Quantity.

Example 1:   Twenty-five children are riding on the bus. At the next stop, 5 more children get on. How many children are on the bus now?

This is a change-to-more situation. The ending quantity is unknown.

Possible number model:

$$25 + 5 = \underline{\ \ }$$

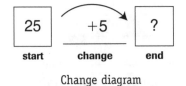

Example 1

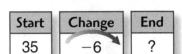

Change diagram

Example 2:   A bus leaves school with 35 children. At the first stop, 6 children get off. How many children are left on the bus? This is a change-to-less situation with the ending quantity unknown.

Possible number models:

$$35 - 6 = \underline{\ \ }$$
$$6 + \underline{\ \ } = 35$$

Start	Change	End
35	−6	?

Example 2

Example 3:   Tom had some money. He bought a magazine for $1.50. Then he had $6.50. How much money did Tom have to start with?

This is a change-to-less situation with the starting quantity unknown.

Possible number models:

$$\underline{\ \ } - \$1.50 = \$6.50$$
$$\$1.50 + \$6.50 = \underline{\ \ }$$

Start	Change	End
?	$1.50	$6.50

Example 3

The third main kind of situation that leads to addition or subtraction is *comparison*. In a comparison situation, there are two separate quantities and the difference between them. For example, one person might be 60 inches tall and another 70 inches tall; the difference in heights would be 10 inches. Or one person might be 25 years old, another 6 years old, and the difference in ages 19 years. As with change and parts-and-total situations, comparison situations can lead to addition or subtraction depending on what is known and what kind of comparison is being made.

A comparison diagram has a large rectangle on top for the larger of the Quantities being compared and smaller rectangles below for the smaller Quantity and for the Difference.

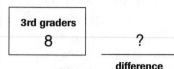

difference

Example 1

Quantity
40

Quantity	Difference
?	4

Vicky
40

Amelia	
?	4

difference

Comparison diagrams for
Example 2

Example 1: There are 12 fourth graders and 8 third graders.
How many more fourth graders are there than third graders?
Here both quantities being compared are known and the difference
is unknown.

Possible number models:

$$12 - 8 = \_\_$$
$$8 + \_\_ = 12$$

Example 2: Vicky is 40 inches tall. Amelia is 4 inches shorter.
How tall is Amelia?
Here one of the quantities being compared and the difference are
known. The other quantity being compared is to be found.

Possible number models:

$$40 - 4 = \_\_$$
$$\_\_ + 4 = 40$$

It is important to remember that these diagrams are simply devices
to help organize problem solving; they are not ends in themselves.
Some children do not need to organize their thinking on paper, and
to require them to do so would not be constructive.

For those children who do find diagrams useful, *Everyday
Mathematics* suggests that they follow these steps, though not
necessarily in this order:

• Choose a diagram that fits the problem situation.
  Sometimes more than one diagram can fit a given situation. One
  person might think of a situation as parts-and-total while another
  person might see the same situation as change. Don't be too
  inflexible about which diagram is the most appropriate for a given
  situation, and remember that many situations are not suitable for
  any diagram. Multi-step problems, for example, do not easily fit
  into these diagrams.

• Write the known quantities and a question mark for the unknown
  quantity in the appropriate parts of the diagram.

• Use the diagram to help decide how to solve the problem.
  Most problems can be solved in more than one way. A change-to-
  more problem, for example, might be solved by addition, by
  counting up mentally or on a number grid, by acting out with
  counters, by drawing pictures, or in any number of other ways.

• Find the answer.

• Write a number model that fits the problem.
  The number model need not reflect how the problem was solved: A
  child might write "8 + 3 = 11" for a change-to-more problem that
  she solved by using counters. Often several number models can fit
  a single situation. Connecting number models to situations can

help children understand both the arithmetic operations and the symbols for those operations.

- Write the answer. Be sure to include a measurement unit or other label.
- Check to see if the answer makes sense.

The importance of including a label in the answer cannot be emphasized enough. Numbers, symbols, and other mathematical abstractions make the most sense to children when they are thought of in real-world contexts. Encourage children to attach appropriate units of measure and other labels, such as cents, lions, and feet, to the numbers they are using.

Because labeling each number can become tedious, *Everyday Mathematics* suggests that you and the children use *unit boxes* for addition and subtraction problems. These rectangular boxes can be displayed beside the problem or at the top of a page of problems. Unit boxes contain the labels or units of measure used in the problem(s). Unit boxes help children organize their mathematics while keeping a particular context in mind.

You might consider posting a unit box for the day on the chalkboard so that children will think of all abstract numbers used in the day's activities (for example, facts practice) in some context. Or children can supply the context themselves; they can choose topics of current interest or, if they prefer, fanciful or silly labels.

2.1.2 Multiplication and Division

Multiplication and division arise in many different situations, but most of these situations can be sorted into just a few categories. These are equal groups, arrays and area, rate and ratio, scaling, and Cartesian product.

Everyday Mathematics uses diagrams to organize the information in many of these situations. The diagrams have two rows of rectangles. The top row is for the units; the bottom row is for the numbers. As with the diagrams for addition and subtraction situations, these diagrams are meant as problem-solving tools, not as ends in themselves. If using a diagram is not helpful, try some other approach, such as making a table or acting the problem out with objects. See Essay 10 for a discussion on problem solving.

Much of the multiplication and division work in primary grade *Everyday Mathematics* involves *equal groups*. In an equal-groups situation, there are several groups of objects with the same number of objects in each group. Depending on what is unknown, equal-groups situations can lead to either multiplication or division problems.

If the total is unknown in an equal-groups situation but the number of groups and the number of objects in each group are known, then the problem can be solved by multiplication.

Unit
cents ¢

unit box

Example: A vase holds 5 flowers with 6 petals on each flower. How many petals are there in all?

Possible number model:

$$5 \times 6 = \underline{}$$

Flowers	Petals per Flower	Total Petals
5	6	?

If the number of groups and the total number of objects are both known, then the problem is to find the number in each group. In *Everyday Mathematics* these are called *equal-sharing* problems. Many children solve equal-sharing problems by "dealing out" the objects to be shared.

Example: Twenty-eight baseball cards are shared equally by 4 children. How many cards does each child get?

Possible number models:

$$4 \times \underline{} = 28$$
$$28 / 4 = \underline{}$$
$$28 \div 4 = \underline{}$$

Children	Baseball Cards per Child	Total Cards
4	?	28

(Equal-sharing division is also known as *partitive division,* a term not used in the *Everyday Mathematics* vocabulary and mentioned here only as a convenience, since it is sometimes used by others.)

If the number in each group and the total number of objects are known, then the problem is to find the number of groups. In *Everyday Mathematics,* we call these *equal-grouping* problems. Many children solve *equal-grouping* problems by making as many groups of the correct size as possible and then counting the number of groups.

Example: Twenty-four Girl Scouts are going on a canoe trip. Each canoe can hold 3 scouts. How many canoes are needed?

Possible number models:

$$3 \times \underline{} = 24$$
$$24 / 3 = \underline{}$$
$$24 \div 3 = \underline{}$$

Canoes	Scouts per Canoe	Total Scouts
?	3	24

Equal-grouping problems are also called *measurement division* or *quotitive division,* terms not used in the *Everyday Mathematics* vocabulary, but sometimes employed in research literature and other programs. The term *measurement division* comes from thinking about using the divisor to "measure" the dividend. For example, consider the problem like 26 ÷ 6. The question is, How many 6s would it take to make 26? Imagine measuring off 6-unit lengths on a number line:

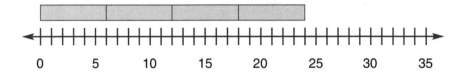

The figure shows that there are 4 6-unit lengths in 26, with 2 left over. Thus 26 ÷ 6 is 4 with remainder 2.

Arrays are closely related to equal-groups situations. If the equal groups are arranged in rows and columns, then a rectangular array is formed. As with equal-groups situations, arrays can lead to either multiplication or division problems.

Example: There are 6 rows with 15 chairs in each row. How many chairs are there in all?

Possible number model:

$$6 \times \underline{\hspace{1cm}} = \underline{\hspace{0.5cm}}$$

Rows	Chairs per Row	Total Chairs
6	15	?

If you think about it, arrays are closely related to *area.* An array of square centimeter tiles with no gaps between the tiles will have an area in square centimeters equal to the number of tiles.

Example: The area of a rectangle is 48 square cm. The rectangle's length is 8 cm. What is its width?

Possible number models:

$$8 \times \underline{\hspace{1cm}} = 48$$

$$48 \div 8 = \underline{\hspace{0.5cm}}$$

cm	cm	square cm
8	?	48

Rate and *ratio* situations are prevalent in higher mathematics and real-world applications. The basic model for rates and ratios is speed, which is the rate of distance per time, but many other situations can also be thought of as rates or ratios as well. When you buy apples, for example, the total cost depends on the amount you purchase and the price per pound, a rate. See Section 1.6.2 for a further discussion of rates and ratios.

Example: The 8 people on the pep squad worked a total of 20 hours preparing for the school assembly. What was the average number of hours per person?

Possible number models:

$$20 / 8 = \underline{\quad}$$
$$20 \div 8 = \underline{\quad}$$
$$8 \times \underline{\quad} = 20$$

People	Hours per Person	Total Person Hours
8	?	20

Scaling is another kind of situation that leads to multiplication or division. The scale factor tells how much larger something becomes. When you double a recipe, for example, you are scaling by 2. If the scale factor is less than 1, then the scaling makes the object smaller.

Example 1: Hector weighed 6 lb at birth. At one year, he weighed 3 times his birth weight. What was his weight at one year?

Possible number model:

$$3 \times 6 = \underline{\quad}$$

Scale Factor	Birth Weight	One-Year Weight
3	6	?

Scale factors, also known as scalars, can also be expressed as fractions or percents. Scaling problems can involve either multiplication or division, depending on what is known and what is to be found.

Example 2: A store has a $\frac{1}{2}$ off (or 50% off) sale. What was the original price of an item that cost $30 on sale?

Possible number models:

$$\frac{1}{2} \times \underline{\quad} = 30$$
$$30 \div = \frac{1}{2} = \underline{\quad}$$

Scale Factor	Original Price	Sale Price
$\frac{1}{2}$	?	30

The last kind of multiplication and division situation is called a *Cartesian product*. Despite the fancy name, the idea is not too difficult to follow. The Cartesian product is the number of pairs that match one item from each of two sets. For example, suppose someone has 3 skirts (black, white, gray) and 5 blouses (black, white, gray, checked, striped). The Cartesian product, 3×5, tells how many outfits that person has: black skirt and black blouse, black skirt and white blouse, and so on. If the two sets are not too big, this can be shown in a diagram.

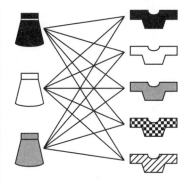

A Cartesian Product $3 \times 5 = 15$

2.2 Number Models and Number Sentences

A number sentence is something like $10 = 7 + 3$ or $12 / n = 6$ or $14 > 3$. Number sentences have a left-hand side, a relation symbol, and a right-hand side. Symbols for numbers, unknowns, and operations can appear on either side of the relation symbol. Number sentences can be true, false, or open, meaning neither true nor false. The sentence $5 + \_ = 8$ is open. The sentence $5 + 3 = 8$ is true; the sentence $5 + 4 = 8$ is false.

A number model is a number sentence that models some real or hypothetical situation. For example, $7 + 3 = 10$ is a number model for the situation, "Gupta had 7 pennies and got 3 more. Then he had 10 pennies." Number models can be based on stories made up by children, on situations invented by the teacher, or on information from everyday life.

In *Everyday Mathematics,* number models are used to represent situations and to summarize relationships between quantities in problems. In the primary grades, the program emphasizes concrete, verbal (usually oral), and pictorial representations. Number models, however, are also often present, usually written on the board or overhead projector by the teacher, often with blank response lines for unknown numbers. Symbols for operations ($+$, $-$, $\times$, and so on) and relations ($=$, $>$, $<$, and so on) are introduced informally. In second and third grades, the children take on more responsibility for writing the number models.

Number models in the primary grades are not a method for solving problems. Rather, number models in the lower grades are used to represent and clarify the quantitative relationships in the problem. The idea is not to translate a problem into a number model that is manipulated to find the answer; that comes later in the curriculum, when children begin to learn formal algebra. Writing number models can help children decide how to solve the problem, but, more importantly, it helps them learn the mathematical symbol system. Children in Grades 4–6 will begin to use the algebraic symbol system to solve actual problems.

When they are first introduced, number models usually appear after a problem has been solved. A typical instructional sequence might read like this:

1. The teacher poses a problem.

2. The children solve the problem.

3. The children share their solutions and the teacher makes a record of them on the board. During the discussion of solutions the teacher writes number models and draws operation diagrams on the board. There should be no blanks in the number models or operation diagrams.

Later, the sequence might be as follows:

1. The teacher poses a problem.

2. The teacher and children discuss the problem and write a number model or diagram that corresponds to the problem. The number model or diagram includes a blank or a question mark for the unknown quantity.

3. Children solve the problem. They may use the number model or operation diagram to help them, or they may use another method entirely.

4. Children share their solutions and the teacher records them on the board. During the discussion of the solutions, the teacher fills in the blanks in the number model or diagram.

Writing number models is in some ways similar to writing English sentences. Both written English and written mathematics have rules and conventions about grammar, syntax, punctuation, and usage. These rules clarify thinking and make communication easier. The following sections address first the arithmetic symbols themselves and how they are used in number sentences.

2.2.1 Arithmetic Symbols

To anyone other than mathematicians, it may seem that mathematics has far too many symbols. However, symbols are not just an annoying nuisance, they are vitally important to mathematics. They make the language of mathematics concise, and ultimately, easier to understand. The philosopher and mathematician Alfred North Whitehead (1861–1947) put it well when he wrote, "By relieving the brain of all unnecessary work, a good notation sets it free to concentrate on more advanced problems, and, in effect, increases the mental power of the race."

The mathematics curriculum must introduce both the symbols needed for classroom activities and the symbols required for real-world general knowledge. Symbols for classroom activities can be introduced on an ad hoc basis, and could be restricted to a small and efficient set. But the need for children to understand the vocabulary of mathematics within a broader social context means the curriculum must include a far more expansive list of symbols. Each group in society—grocers, scientists, engineers, advertisers, journalists, and so on—has a different set of symbols it considers necessary. Even the way we write numbers can spark debate: Should it be .1, or 0.1? Is 1/2 better than $\frac{1}{2}$, or is $\frac{1}{2}$ the best? Should we write -3, -3, or ⁻3?

Calculators and computers, which might have been expected to standardize notation a bit, have actually increased the need for understanding that different symbols can mean the same thing. There are different symbols for multiplication, division, powers, and opposites (negatives), to name just a few. *Everyday Mathematics* provides many activities to help make children aware of alternative notations so they can adapt to different situations as necessary. The program employs different notations for the same operation so children will become familiar with all common symbols. The symbols for addition, subtraction, multiplication, and division are discussed below.

Addition and Subtraction Symbols

Two symbols for which there exists no real alternative today are $+$ for addition and $-$ for subtraction. Although the ideas behind them are thousands of years old, the symbols $+$ and $-$ first appeared in print in 1498 in a book by the German mathematician Johann Widman. The symbols gradually caught on and are now universally accepted. The words we use for these symbols, however, do vary: *plus, add,* and *positive* all refer to $+$; *minus, take away,* and *negative* are all interpretations of $-$.

Students of *Everyday Mathematics* see these symbols only after they have informal experiences with the underlying operations. Kindergarten children, for example, hear the words "add" and "subtract" as they put lumps of modeling dough on or remove them from a pan balance, yet they do not need symbols to describe the activity. One of the first encounters that kindergarten children have with the addition symbol occurs when they use the [$+$] key on their calculators in a counting-on activity. Establishing this informal connection between the $+$ symbol and counting supports later use of the $+$ symbol for paper-and-pencil representations of addition and the understanding of a rule such as "$+$ 3" in "What's My Rule?" and Frames-and-Arrows activities. Similar counting-back activities use the [$-$] key.

Multiplication and Division Symbols

Multiplication and division are each represented by several symbols. All of the symbols are discussed in the *Everyday Mathematics Teacher's Lesson Guide.* To standardize symbolic representation in the materials, some choices have been made that need to be clarified here.

Mathematics textbooks traditionally use the symbol $\times$ ("times" or "multiplied by") to indicate multiplication. The Englishman William Oughtred introduced this symbol in 1631. When multiplication models are introduced in *Second* and *Third Grade Everyday Mathematics,* the $\times$ symbol is used. A disadvantage of $\times$ is that it can be confused with the addition symbol ($+$). Another disadvantage is that it does not appear on a standard computer or typewriter keyboard, though it is standard on most calculator keypads. Finally, $\times$ can easily be mistaken for the letter x, which becomes a problem in fourth grade, when letter variables begin to be used more frequently. One solution to this problem is to use a

NOTE: On some calculators, keying in 10 [/] 7 enters the fraction 10/7, rather than dividing to give 1.428571. Some calculators also have "integer division," which means division with remainder.

raised dot for multiplication (5 · 6 rather than 5 × 6). Gottfried Leibniz, one of the inventors of calculus, introduced the dot notation in 1698. But an obvious difficulty with the raised dot is confusion with the decimal point. In fact, in some countries a raised dot is used as the decimal point.

Eventually, children must learn to indicate multiplication by juxtaposition, that is, by writing symbols next to each other: writing (15)(23) to mean 15 × 23, $2a$ to mean $2 × a$, and ab to mean $a × b$. Juxtaposition to indicate multiplication is common in formulas, which are among the earliest uses of letter variables that *Everyday Mathematics* students encounter. For example, the area A of a rectangle with width w and length l is written as $A = lw$. In fact, the only place where this formula would be written as $A = l × w$ is an elementary school mathematics textbook.

Historically, symbols for division have included $÷$, $\overline{)}$, /, :, and the fraction bar. Their inventors were respectively, Johann Rahn in 1659; Michael Stifel in 1544; Manuel A. Valdes in 1784; Gottfried Leibniz in 1684; and al-Ḥaṣṣâr in the 12th century.

In second and third grades, *Everyday Mathematics* uses $÷$. Unfortunately, $÷$ shares two disadvantages with the multiplication symbol ×: it can easily be misread as +, and it does not appear on standard computer or typewriter keyboards. Still, it is the symbol for division on almost all calculators.

Division with a remainder can be a bit of a problem in written form. Consider what can happen if equal signs are used:

$$12 ÷ 5 = 2 \text{ R2}$$
$$102 ÷ 50 = 2 \text{ R2}$$

Since 2 R2 = 2 R2, it seems that

$$12 ÷ 5 = 102 ÷ 50.$$

If you do the divisions, the problem becomes apparent:

$$12 ÷ 5 = 2.4$$

which does not equal

$$102 ÷ 50 = 2.04$$

The real difficulty is that 2 R2 is not really a number, so using it in equations is problematic. Since $102 ÷ 50$ is a number, but 2 R2 is not, they cannot possibly be equal. To eliminate this problem, *Everyday Mathematics* uses arrows in number models for divisions with remainders:

$$102 ÷ 50 → 2 \text{ R2}$$

This notation, though nonstandard, will not mislead children as using = may. Later, when children learn to show remainders as fractions, the problem disappears altogether:

$$12 ÷ 5 = 2 \tfrac{2}{5}$$
$$102 ÷ 50 = 2 \tfrac{2}{50}$$

The symbol $\overline{)}$ is closely linked to the traditional long-division algorithm. Actually, it is really more like a template for carrying out a procedure than a mathematical symbol. Using it, therefore, may suggest the use of the long-division algorithm when another method is warranted. It can be useful, however, for recording answers to division problems with remainders.

---

in perspective Beginning in fourth grade, *Everyday Mathematics* uses the slash and fraction bar symbols for division, as in *a/b* and $\frac{a}{b}$. These symbols have been used for centuries to indicate division, especially in higher mathematics. The slash appears on some calculators, is easy to write, and is on almost all computer and typewriter keyboards. There is another, more important advantage: The forms *a/b* and $\frac{a}{b}$ reinforce the relation between division and fractions. Grasping this concept is a goal for students in later grades of *Everyday Mathematics*.

Other Arithmetic Symbols

Many other symbols in addition to those discussed above are used in arithmetic. Several are discussed elsewhere in this manual: symbols for relations ($=$, $<$, and $>$) are discussed in Section 1.5; symbols for numbers are discussed in Section 1.7; symbols for variables are discussed in Section 2.2.3.

In addition to all the conventional symbols that children should learn to use, they should also be encouraged to create their own notations. While these invented notations will not be much good for formal mathematical communication, they can be useful for clarifying complicated situations. We must remember that every standard notation we use today began as someone's creation.

---

in perspective Although exponents are not used in K–3 *Everyday Mathematics,* children in Grade 3 receive an informal introduction to square numbers (1, 4, 9, 16, 25, . . .) by observing how such numbers can be displayed in square arrays. Beginning in Grade 4, students use exponents to read and write large numbers using powers of 10. They are also introduced to scientific notation, which is used by both scientists and by calculating machines. Next they see how the exponential notation can be used for doubling (powers of 2: $2^0 = 1$, $2^1 = 2$, $2^2 = 4$, $2^3 = 8$, $2^4 = 16$, $2^5 = 32$, . . .) and for squaring (2 as a power: $0^2 = 0$, $1^2 = 1$, $2^2 = 4$, $3^2 = 9$, $4^2 = 16$, $5^2 = 25$, . . .). Finally, they generalize the use of exponential notation to represent the product of b factors of the base a as a^b where a is any number and b is a whole number.

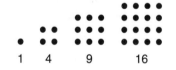

$$a^b = a \times a \times \ldots \times a$$

b factors

2.2.2 Number Sentences

Just as English words become meaningful when they are arranged into sentences, the mathematical symbols discussed above become meaningful when they are arranged into sentences. And just as proper punctuation and grammar are needed to make written English easy to read, rules and conventions are needed in number sentences to ease communication.

A number sentence has three parts: a left-hand side, a relation, and a right-hand side. In the sentence $4 + 3 = 7$, for example, "$4 + 3$" is the left-hand side, "$=$" is the relation, and "7" is the right-hand side. Number sentences in which the relation is represented by $=$ are called *equations*. Sentences in which the relation is represented by $<, \leq, >$, or $\geq$ are called *inequalities*. A phrase without a relation, such as $3 + y$, is called an *expression*.

Grouping Symbols

An established order of operations eliminates ambiguity about the order in which additions, subtractions, and other operations are to be done in number sentences. Learning this order is a formality reserved for students late in the *Everyday Mathematics* program. In *K–3 Everyday Mathematics,* grouping symbols, such as parentheses and brackets, are used to avoid confusion.

The ordinary operations of arithmetic—addition, subtraction, multiplication, and division—are called "binary operations" because they are carried out on two numbers at a time. (Addition and multiplication can certainly involve more than two numbers, but the final product or sum is obtained by repeatedly adding or multiplying pairs of numbers.) When only two numbers and one operation are involved, there is no need for grouping symbols. Similarly, no grouping symbols are needed in adding several numbers, or in multiplying several numbers, because these operations may be performed in any order. However, in situations involving several numbers with subtraction, division, or a combination of operations, one may obtain different results depending on the order in which the operations are performed. The value of $4 + 3 \times 5$, for example, is 35 if the addition is done first and 19 if the multiplication is done first. To avoid such ambiguity, one can insert parentheses to indicate the order in which operations are to be carried out. If the addition is to be done first in the expression above, it should be written $(4 + 3) \times 5$; if the multiplication is to be done first, write the expression as $4 + (3 \times 5)$.

Brief exercises with parentheses are worth repeating throughout each year of the program. Most children find such exercises to have an appealing, game-like quality. Such exercises also provide children with practice with basic number facts and their extensions, reminders of the effect of multiplying by or adding zero, and practice with expressing solutions in games such as *Name That Number.*

Order of Operations

In order to reduce the need for grouping symbols, mathematicians have agreed on an order for carrying out arithmetic operations. Grouping symbols are used only for greater clarity or to specify an order different from the conventional order. The conventional order is called the *algebraic order of operations* or simply the *order of operations.* The order of operations is not covered in *K–3 Everyday Mathematics,* but once children begin to use variables they do need to understand it. An understanding of the order of operations is assumed in most of the mathematics students will encounter in middle school and beyond.

The order of operations is as follows:

1. Do all the operations inside grouping symbols. Work from the innermost grouping symbols outward. Within grouping symbols, or if there aren't any, follow Rules 2–4.

2. Find all powers.

3. Do all multiplications and divisions in order from left to right.

4. Do all additions and subtractions in order from left to right.

A mnemonic for the order of operations is <u>P</u>lease <u>E</u>xcuse <u>M</u>y <u>D</u>ear <u>A</u>unt <u>S</u>ally: Do work inside the <u>P</u>arentheses first, and then <u>E</u>xponentiation, and then <u>M</u>ultiplication and <u>D</u>ivision, and finally <u>A</u>ddition and <u>S</u>ubtraction.

Open Number Sentences

The number sentence $5 + x = 8$ is neither true nor false. When x is replaced by 3, $5 + x = 8$ is true. When x is replaced by any number other than 3, then $5 + x = 8$ is false. As written, however, the sentence $5 + x = 8$ is neither true or false. It is an *open sentence.*

Open number sentences include unknowns or variables like x in the example above. In *First Grade Everyday Mathematics,* children encounter unknowns in situation diagrams. These diagrams display the numbers in number stories so that the quantitative relationships are easier to understand. The empty part of a diagram represents the unknown—the variable.

Also beginning in first grade, open sentences are written by the teacher to model number stories. At first, a blank or question mark is used for the unknown ($4 + \_\_ = 12$ *or* $4 + ? = 12$); by fourth grade, letter variables are used ($4 + N = 12$). Beginning in second grade, the responsibility for writing simple sentences using the four basic operations and grouping symbols is put increasingly in the children's hands.

Solving Equations

In *K–3 Everyday Mathematics,* number models are used primarily to represent and understand quantities and relationships in number stories. For example, before solving a number story like "Marie has $5. She wants to go to a movie that costs $8. How much more does

NOTE: Some calculators follow the algebraic order of operations and some do not. Be sure to test your calculators before discussing this issue.

Total	
8	
Part	**Part**
5	

Total	
8	
Part	**Part**
5	

parts-and-total diagrams
for $5 + \_\_ = 8$

she need?" a child might write the number model "$5 + N = 8$." The model shows the relationships between the quantities in the story and suggests finding the answer by counting up or thinking of an addition fact. After solving the story, the child might write "$5 + 3 = 8$" to summarize her work. Learning to use number models to represent number stories helps children learn the mathematical symbol system that is the foundation of algebra.

In third and fourth grades, more complicated equations are treated informally through such puzzles as, "I am the number x in $6 + 5 \times x = 16$. What number am I?" Solving this puzzle requires knowing the order of operations dictates that x be multiplied by 5 before 6 is added. Children are encouraged to clarify this by rewriting the left-hand side of the number sentence as $6 + (5 \times x) = 16$. Children solve such puzzles by trial and error or by working backward. Solving equations by formal algebraic manipulations is not part of *K–3 Everyday Mathematics.*

2.2.3 Variables

As children write number sentences to represent problem situations, they often find that they need to represent numbers that are unknown. For example: "There are 24 children in our class, but today only 18 are here. How many are not here?" This problem might be modeled as $24 - ? = 18$, or as $18 + ? = 24$, or as $24 - 18 = ?$ Alternatively, a letter, a response line, or a box can be used to indicate the unknown number: $24 - n = 18$, or $18 + \_\_\_ = 24$, or $24 - 18 = \square$. All four symbols ($?$, n, $\_\_\_$, and $\square$) are variables. Representing an unknown quantity is just one of several uses of variables that are important in mathematics.

Any symbol that stands for a number is called a *variable*. A number sentence that includes a variable, such as $10 + ? = 15$ or $14 = t - 9$, is called an *open sentence*. Any number can replace the variable and, depending on the replacement, the resulting sentence will be either true or false. Any number that makes the sentence true is called a *solution*. For example, 5 is a solution for $10 + ? = 15$.

In K-3 *Everyday Mathematics,* variables are used primarily as *unknowns* in open sentences, so introducing the term "variable" is unnecessary. Also, in sentences like $5 + N = 13$, the unknown is a single number that doesn't vary, so explaining the root of "variable" (vary) is not helpful.

In contrast, using variables for unknowns in inequalities usually results in more than one possible solution. For example, "I'm thinking of a number less than 10" can be modeled as $x < 10$, which has whole-number solutions 0, 1, 2, . . . , 9, as well as many other solutions if fractions, decimals, or negative numbers are allowed.

There can also be more than one unknown in situations modeled by an equation. For example, the problem "Which pairs of whole numbers have 8 as their sum?" can be modeled as $m + n = 8$; solutions include pairs 0 and 8, 1 and 7, 2 and 6, and so on.

Variables in *formulas* are used to abbreviate a relationship that could be expressed at greater length in words. For example, "The area of a rectangle can be found by multiplying the length of the rectangle times the width" may be written as the formula $A = l \times w$, or simply $A = lw$. Area relationships for triangles, parallelograms, and other figures can be expressed similarly, as can volume and many other relationships.

It is important to keep track of the units (inches, dollars, people, hours, and so on) that correspond to the variables and to ensure those units are consistent with the relationships expressed by the formula. For example, an area formula will not yield a correct result if one length is measured in feet and another in meters. In *K–3 Everyday Mathematics,* unit boxes emphasize the importance of units.

Variables are also used to express basic mathematical *properties.* For example, the "turn-around rule" for addition says that two numbers can be added in either order and the sum will be the same. With variables, the turn-around rule becomes, "$m + n = n + m$" or, more formally, "For any two numbers m and n, $m + n = n + m$." Similarly, properties of 0 and 1 can be expressed as follows: "For any number n, $1 \times n = n$, $0 + n = n$, and $0 \times n = 0$."

This use of variables differs from variables in formulas. The level of generality is much higher. The variables m and n in the properties above can be any numbers whatsoever. There is no specific physical or mathematical situation underlying the property as there is for an area or volume formula.

Another important use of variables, at least in higher mathematics, is their use in *functions.* In its simplest form, a function is a rule that gives a certain output for a given input. For example, "add 2" is a simple function. Using variables, this function could be written OUTPUT = INPUT + 2 or $y = x + 2$. In *K–3 Everyday Mathematics,* children explore functions through function machines and by playing "What's My Rule?" (Functions are discussed in Section 9.4.)

2.3 Basic Facts

"Knowing" the basic number facts is essential for success in mathematics. Many cognitive scientists have noted the importance of automaticity in complex tasks, and many mathematics educators emphasize the importance of number-fact reflexes. Students are often told that habits—good and bad—come from doing something over and over until they do it by rote. The key to developing number-fact reflexes is a matter of developing good fact habits.

In *Everyday Mathematics,* good fact habits are called *fact power.* Children in Grades 1–3 keep Fact Power tables of the facts they know. By the end of second grade, most children using *Everyday Mathematics* will have mastered the basic addition and subtraction facts. In third grade, the emphasis shifts to learning the multiplication and division facts. While not every student will be

in perspective

Describing a pattern with variable and algebraic notation often makes the pattern much more understandable than descriptions of the same pattern in words do. The paradigm shift four hundred years ago from "rhetorical algebra" (algebra written out in words) to symbolic algebra was a major advance for mathematics. Students of *Fifth* and *Sixth Grade Everyday Mathematics* practice describing patterns with variables.

in perspective

In *Everyday Mathematics* Grades 4–6, students find and graph values of such functions as $y = 2 + x$.

able to demonstrate mastery of all the basic facts by the end of third or even fourth grade, those that have not reached that level should be well on their way to mastery. Our expectations for the basic number facts are shown in the table below.

Everyday Mathematics Expectations for Basic Facts					
grade level					
	K	**1**	**2**	**3**	**4**
addition					
easy facts	B	D/S	S		
hard facts		B/D	D/S		
subtraction					
easy facts	B	D/S	S		
hard facts		B	D/S		
multiplication					
easy facts			B	D/S	S
hard facts			B	D/S	S
division					
easy facts			B	D/S	S
hard facts			B/D	D/S	

B Beginning. Most children are learning the meaning of the operation and are developing strategies for solving facts. Basic-fact work occurs most often in problem contexts. There is no emphasis on speed.
D Developing. Most children are learning efficient ways to answer fact problems, including recall from long-term memory and other strategies. Speed practice might be appropriate for many children.
S Secure. Although a few children may be slower on some facts, most children have achieved automatic recall.

Practicing the facts traditionally involves pages upon pages of drills. This can be tedious and can make children learn to dislike mathematics. Teachers of *Everyday Mathematics* have had great success with the following alternative approaches:

• *Games* Your *Teacher's Lesson Guide* suggests games in which numbers are generated by dice, dominoes, number cards, spinners, egg-carton shakers, or other manipulatives. Games can be played repeatedly, though many teachers supplement these games with others of their own design. Since much of the basic-fact practice in *Everyday Mathematics* is formatted as games, skipping them would seriously weaken the program.

• *Choral Drills* Beginning in first grade, children participate in many short drills that review small groups of facts written on the board. To hold everyone's interest, you can vary the drill over a period of several days by playing with the numbers, formats, and speed. You might, for example, work with doubles (3 + 3, 5 + 5, and so on) for several days and then advance to near doubles (3 + 4, 5 + 6). A good time to work on the drills is just after a break, such as lunch or recess.

- **Fact Triangles** Fact Triangles are the *Everyday Mathematics* version of flash cards. Fact Triangles are more effective than traditional flash cards because they emphasize fact families. An addition/subtraction Fact Triangle has two addends and a sum; a multiplication/division Fact Triangle has two factors and a product. A Fact Triangle for one of the fact families is shown in the margin.

- **Double-nine Dominoes** Double-nine dominoes are wonderful concrete models of the addition/subtraction facts through 9 + 9 and 18 − 9. Dominoes help children visualize the facts as well as develop an understanding of the meanings of addition and subtraction and the relationship between the two operations. Many suggestions for using dominoes for basic-facts work are included in the *Teacher's Lesson Guide.*

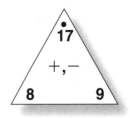

8 + 9 = 17   9 + 8 = 17
17 − 9 = 8   17 − 8 = 9

Everyday Mathematics believes that young children can understand the inverse relationships between arithmetic operations (addition "undoes" subtraction, and vice versa; multiplication "undoes" division, and vice versa), that, in many cases, they even "discover" them on their own. *First Grade Everyday Mathematics* uses Fact Triangles to establish and emphasize addition/subtraction fact families through 9 + 9. In second grade, the addition/subtraction fact families are reviewed and multiplication/division Fact Triangles are introduced. In third grade, children get both addition/subtraction and multiplication/division Fact Triangles. In all grades, a useful long-term project is to have students write the four number models in the fact family on the back of each Fact Triangle.

Fact Triangles are best employed in a cooperative learning situation. One player covers a corner with a finger and the other player gives a fact that has the hidden number as an answer. For example, one player might cover up the 4 in a (4, 5, 20) multiplication/division Fact Triangle. The other player would respond by saying, "20 divided by 5 equals 4." Fact Triangles can also be sorted into known/unknown facts or by strategy—doubles, near doubles, +1, +2, and so on—to make for efficient practice. Because these activities are easy to do at home, Fact Triangles are strongly recommended as Home Links.

You may recognize that the two addition facts in a fact family are related by the "turn-around rule" or *commutative property of addition.* (Although *Everyday Mathematics* does not require that children learn mathematical names for properties, it can be helpful to have a name to use occasionally, so *Everyday Mathematics* calls the commutative property of addition the turn-around rule for addition.) From a practical viewpoint, the turn-around rule means that any time you learn a new addition fact, you learn a second one

2

for free. Of course there is no turn-around rule for subtraction: $7 - 4$ is not equal to $4 - 7$.

Everyday Mathematics calls properties of arithmetic *shortcuts,* and the four facts in a fact family are all related by shortcuts. A major reason for teaching fact families is to give children different options when solving problems that are new or difficult. By recalling a shortcut, the student can then work backwards, rewording or rewriting the problem. For example, faced with $7 - 3 = ?$, a first grader may think, "Hmm, I don't know. What plus 3 is 7? Ah, that's easy, it's 4."

Basic facts should be extended to multiples of 10 and 100. If children know $3 + 4 = 7$, they should also know $30 + 40 = 70$ and $300 + 400 = 700$. If children know $6 \times 5 = 30$, they should also know $60 \times 5 = 300$, $600 \times 5 = 3000$, $3000 \div 600 = 5$, and so on. Attention to such "fact extensions" begins in first grade and continues throughout the program.

Since numbers in real life nearly always occur in some context, *Everyday Mathematics* recommends that you and your children select labels for the day to use with fact practice. The kinds and numbers of labels you need depend on the operations being used. In addition and subtraction, only one label is needed. Choose, for example, the label "pencils." Then the problem $7 + 9 = ?$ becomes 7 pencils + 9 pencils = 16 pencils for that day. In multiplication and division, two or three related labels are needed. You might use "cartons," "pounds per carton," and "pounds." Then the problem $5 \times 8 = \_\_$ becomes 5 cartons × 8 pounds per carton = __ pounds. Sometimes it makes sense for the factors in multiplication to have the same label; when finding an area, 5 feet × 8 feet = 40 square feet.

Post the labels and refer to them occasionally as children practice the facts. The labels of the day reinforce the idea that numbers refer to something real and useful. Keep the labels simple. They can be true-to-life or fanciful, serious or silly. They can be units of measure (centimeters, minutes, pounds) or countable objects (cats, hats, ribbons). Although the main purpose for using labels is to keep numbers from becoming too abstract, labels are also important in other curriculum areas, especially reading, the sciences, and language arts.

2.4 Games for Practice

Frequent practice is necessary for children to build and maintain strong mental-arithmetic skills and reflexes. Although drills have their place, most of the practice in *Everyday Mathematics* is in games. Games are not an merely attractive add-on: they are an essential component of the complete *Everyday Mathematics* program and curriculum.

Games should not be viewed as competitive drills, nor should games be thought of as time-fillers or rewards. In fact, games satisfy most standard drill objectives—and may even surpass them in many respects. Drill tends toward tedium and monotony, and therefore gradually loses its effectiveness. Games alleviate boredom because the children enjoy them. Indeed, children often want to continue to play games during their free time and, in the process, practice far more than they ordinarily would with the traditional approach to mathematics.

The ultimate goal of drill is to build fact and operations skills. Learning through games shares these objectives. At the same time, games often reinforce other skills, including calculator skills, money-exchange and shopping skills, logic, geometry and spatial sense, and, because many games involve numbers that are generated randomly, intuition about probability and chance. Using games to practice number skills also greatly reduces the need for worksheets. As mentioned before, because the numbers in most games are generated randomly, the games can be played over and over without repeating the same problems. Many of the *Everyday Mathematics* games come with variations that allow players to progress from easy to more challenging versions. Games, therefore, offer a virtually unlimited source of problem material.

ESSAY

3

Algorithms and Mental Arithmetic

outline

3.1 Algorithms and Procedures 95
   3.1.1 Computational Algorithms 96
   3.1.2 Inventing Algorithms 98
   3.1.3 Focus Algorithms 99
3.2 Standard and Alternative Algorithms 100
   3.2.1 Addition Algorithms 101

3.2.2 Subtraction Algorithms 103
3.2.3 Multiplication Algorithms 106
3.2.4 Division Algorithms 109
3.3 Mental Arithmetic 111

An algorithm is a well-defined procedure or set of rules used to solve a problem. Algorithms are often used in everyday life. A recipe, for example, is an algorithm. Having students become comfortable with algorithmic and procedural thinking is essential to their growth and development as everyday problem solvers.

Skillful use of algorithms can:

- enable students to use a single method to solve an entire class of related problems
- facilitate their use of mental arithmetic
- help students develop sound number sense, including a good understanding of place value
- strengthen students' mathematical power

Section 3.1 of this essay explains the *Everyday Mathematics* authors' approach to teaching computational algorithms, including the role of invented algorithms in developing understanding of operations, place value, and computational procedures.

Section 3.2 describes a number of algorithms for the basic arithmetic operations discussed in Essay 2, Operations and Facts. For each operation, one algorithm has been designated as a "focus" algorithm. The focus algorithms are not identical to the computational algorithms that are traditionally taught, but they are similar. In addition to being easier to learn and use than the traditional algorithms, the focus algorithms reveal more about underlying concepts (such as place value) and are less likely to lead to wrong answers.

Section 3.3 discusses the importance of mental arithmetic and describes some mental arithmetic strategies. As more and more computations are carried out by machines, mental arithmetic is becoming increasingly important, both because of its utility in double-checking machine results and because it builds understanding of the operations and flexibility in thinking that is essential to problem-solving skills.

3.1 Algorithms and Procedures

As a teacher, you establish many *procedures* to help your classroom run efficiently. For example, in the beginning of the year, you explain to the children the proper procedures for hanging up coats, sitting, lining up, and so on. *Everyday Mathematics* encourages you to establish procedures or routines for mathematics such as a weather record or the growing number line.

An *algorithm* is simply a well-defined, step-by-step procedure guaranteed to achieve a certain objective, often with a set of steps that "loop" as many times as necessary. For example, an algorithm for multiplication is a specific series of steps that will produce a correct answer no matter what the factors are. A good algorithm is efficient, unambiguous, and reliable. Though the most familiar algorithms are the traditional elementary school procedures for adding, subtracting, multiplying, and dividing, there are many other algorithms to be learned in both mathematics and real life.

Everyday Mathematics includes a variety of standard computational algorithms and children's invented procedures. Inventing procedures is a valuable exercise because it promotes conceptual understanding and flexibility, both of which are essential for effective problem solving. Inventing computational procedures also helps children learn about our base-ten place-value system of numeration. Invented procedures are discussed further in Section 3.1.2.

Using standard algorithms has its advantages, too. Standard algorithms are generally efficient and can also help children understand both our number system and the underlying operations. They also provide a common language that serves as a basis for the development of mathematical ideas. Standard computational procedures are discussed in Section 3.2.

In addition to studying specific algorithms, *Everyday Mathematics* students engage in activities to help them understand algorithms in a more general sense. Mathematics advances in part through the development of efficient procedures that reduce difficult tasks to routine exercises. An effective algorithm will solve an entire class of problems, thus increasing the user's mathematical power.

NOTE: The term *algorithm* or *algorism* comes from the name al-Khwarizmi. Muhammad ibn Musa al-Khwarizmi (c. 780–c. 850) was one of the greatest mathematicians of the Arab-Islamic world. We also have al-Khwarizmi to thank for the word *"algebra,"* which comes from *Hisab Al-jabr w'al-muqabalah,* the title of one of his books.

NOTE: Algorithmic and procedural thinking includes

- understanding specific algorithms or procedures provided by other people
- applying known algorithms to everyday problems
- developing algorithms and procedures when necessary
- realizing the limitations of algorithms and their procedures so they are not used inappropriately
- the ability to adapt known algorithms to fit new situations

The authors of *Everyday Mathematics* have found that paper-and-pencil computational algorithms are valuable means for developing algorithmic thinking in general.

3.1.1 Computational Algorithms

Several teachers have asked the *Everyday Mathematics* authors about the role of computational algorithms in elementary school mathematics. Should standard paper-and-pencil algorithms be taught? Should children be expected to use these algorithms to solve complex computational problems? Should calculators be used in the classroom, and if so, in which circumstances and under what conditions?

Before we attempt to answer these questions, consider the following story told by Professor Zalman Usiskin of the University of Chicago:

> **Scene 1:** An Office. Hal is preparing an end-of-the-month sales report. This involves doing many calculations, which he does, churning out each computation on paper. In walks the boss, horrified: "Hal, why aren't you using a calculator? You're wasting valuable time!"

> **Scene 2:** A Fourth Grade Classroom. The class is working on a page of difficult computational problems. Susie gets out her calculator and starts completing the assignment. The teacher walks over to Susie, horrified: "Susie, put that calculator away or you'll get done too quickly!"

These two scenarios highlight the need to rethink school mathematics in light of the widespread availability of calculators and computers. Children no longer need to spend the better part of six school years learning highly efficient paper-and-pencil methods of adding, subtracting, multiplying, and dividing. If efficiency is the goal, such computations should be carried out either mentally or with a calculator.

Some advocates of change even assert that standard paper-and-pencil algorithms have no place in the school curriculum. Several strongly argued articles make this case. "It's Time to Abandon Computational Algorithms" by Steven Leinwand (*Education Week,* February 9, 1994) and "Let's Abolish Paper-and-Pencil Arithmetic" by Tony Ralston (*Mathematics Education Dialogues,* May/June 1999) argue for eliminating the teaching of algorithms altogether. "Arithmetic: The Last Holdout" by Marilyn Burns (*Phi Delta Kappan,* February 1994) argues in favor of children sharing their own invented algorithms rather than for teachers continuing to teach standard paper-and-pencil algorithms.

Research shows that teaching the standard algorithms in the standard ways does fail with a large number of children. In one study, only 60 percent of U.S. ten-year-olds achieved mastery of subtraction using the standard regrouping ("borrowing") algorithm.

A Japanese study found that only 56 percent of third graders and 74 percent of fifth graders achieved mastery using this algorithm. The standard subtraction algorithm can be unreliable because students are plagued by "bugs," such as taking the smaller digit from the larger, that result from trying to carry out imperfectly understood and remembered procedures.

In spite of the failure of teaching paper-and-pencil algorithms, regardless of the fact that calculators make paper-and-pencil computation largely irrelevant in the practical world, and in light of the arguments of such people as Leinwand and Burns, the authors of *Everyday Mathematics* nevertheless believe that children should be exposed to paper-and-pencil algorithms. If taught properly, with understanding yet without demands for "mastery" by all children by some fixed time, paper-and-pencil algorithms can help reinforce children's understanding of our number system and of the operations themselves. Exploring different algorithms also helps build estimation skills and "number sense." Finally, situations do exist in which the most efficient or convenient way to carry out a computation is with paper and pencil. In the debate about algorithms, *Everyday Mathematics* takes a moderate position.

In *Everyday Mathematics,* children are encouraged to invent their own procedures during the early phases of learning an operation. They are asked to solve problems involving the operations "from first principles," before they have developed or learned systematic procedures for solving such problems. This helps them understand the operations better, and also gives them valuable experience solving non-routine problems.

Later, when children fully understand the concept of the operation, standard algorithms are introduced. Some of these algorithms are based on the approaches that many children devise on their own. Others are less likely to be discovered by children but have desirable characteristics. Children are urged to experiment with various algorithms in order to become proficient at using at least one alternative.

Finally, *Everyday Mathematics* introduces a focus algorithm for each operation. These algorithms are efficient and usually easy to understand and learn. All children are expected to master the focus algorithms, though they are not required to use them if they have alternatives they prefer. Focus algorithms provide a common ground for further work and offer reliable alternatives for children who have not developed effective procedures of their own.

The things children can learn from working with properly taught computational algorithms will carry over to other areas of their lives. More and more, we need to think algorithmically in order to operate technologically advanced devices. Algorithms are increasingly important in theoretical mathematics, the application of mathematics, computer science, and many areas outside mathematics.

NOTE: Kurt Van Lehn had this to say about using the standard subtraction algorithm in some of his research:

> [O]rdinary multidigit subtraction . . . is a virtually meaningless procedure [for] most elementary school children . . . . When compared to procedures they use to operate vending machines or play games, subtraction is as dry, formal, and as disconnected from everyday interests as the nonsense syllables used in early psychological investigations were different from real words. This isolation is the bane of teachers . . .

3.1.2 Inventing Algorithms

Because the authors of *Everyday Mathematics* view computational algorithms as more than rote procedures, the program aims to make children active participants in the development of algorithms. Such participation requires a good background in the following three areas:

- *Our system for number writing.* In particular, children need to understand place value.
- *The meanings of the operations and the relationships among operations.* To subtract 25 from 37, for example, a child might reason, "What number must I add to 25 to get 37?"
- *Basic facts.* Carrying out multistep computational procedures without automatic recall of the basic facts can result in cognitive overload and errors.

Everyday Mathematics believes children should be encouraged to invent and share their own procedures. As children devise their own methods, they use prior mathematical knowledge and common sense, along with new skills and knowledge. They must also learn to manage their resources—How long will this take? Is there a better way?—which helps them develop useful mental habits. Children who invent their own methods also learn that their intuitive methods are valid and that mathematics makes sense. *Everyday Mathematics* wants all children to develop a broad repertoire of computational methods and the flexibility to choose whichever procedure is the most appropriate in any particular situation.

Learning standard algorithms too early, however, may actually inhibit the development of children's mathematical understanding, and will certainly cause them to miss out on the rich experiences that come from developing their own methods. Although prematurely teaching standard paper-and-pencil algorithms fosters many persistent errors and "buggy" algorithms, the main problem with teaching standard algorithms too early is that children then use the algorithms as substitutes for thinking and common sense.

For example, the authors of *Everyday Mathematics* presented the problem in the margin to a large number of children. Most second and third graders immediately resorted to the standard algorithm, often failing to get the correct answer. Only a handful of children interpreted the problem as asking, "What number plus 1 gives 300?" or "What is 1 less than 300?" or "What is the number just before 300?" and answered "299" without performing any computations.

In the modern world, most adults reach for calculators when faced with any moderately complex arithmetic computation. This behavior is sensible and should be an option for children, too. Nevertheless, children do benefit in the following ways from developing their own noncalculator procedures:

$$\begin{array}{r} 300 \\ -1 \\ \hline \end{array}$$

Many children resort to the algorithm to solve this subtraction problem.

- Children are more motivated when they don't have to learn standard paper-and-pencil algorithms by rote. People are more interested in what they can understand, and children generally understand their own methods (as obscure as they may be at times to others).

- Children become adept at changing the representations of ideas and problems, translating readily among manipulatives, oral and written words, pictures, and symbols. The ability to represent a problem in more than one way is important in problem solving.

- Children develop the ability to transform any given problem into an equivalent, easier problem. For example, $32 - 17$ can be transformed to the easier $35 - 20$ (adding 3 to both numbers in a subtraction problem does not change the answer).

- In trying out creative problem-solving strategies, and in refining those strategies for use on a more permanent basis, children gain experience in decision making.

This approach to teaching computation also provides you with valuable clues about children's progress in numerical thinking.

Algorithm invention develops best when:

- it is allowed to flourish in an accepting and supportive classroom environment
- time for experimentation is allotted
- computational tasks are embedded in real-life contexts
- children share their solution strategies with you and with one another

3.1.3 Focus Algorithms

After children have had plenty of opportunities to experiment with computational strategies of their own, *Everyday Mathematics* introduces several algorithms for each operation. Some of these algorithms closely resemble methods that children are likely to have devised on their own. Others are traditional algorithms, including both standard algorithms customarily taught in U.S. classrooms and other algorithms that have been standard in other times and places. Still others are simplifications of traditional algorithms or wholly new algorithms that have significant advantages in today's technological world. Many of the algorithms presented are highly efficient, and most are easier to understand and learn than traditional algorithms.

Everyday Mathematics also includes a "focus" algorithm for each operation. These algorithms have been selected because they provide the greatest mathematical payoff for the least cost in instructional time. Focus algorithms are powerful, relatively efficient, and easy to understand and learn. All children are expected to master the focus algorithm for each operation. Once they can reliably execute the focus algorithm, children are

NOTE: Working on a grid of small squares—a piece of graph paper, for example—can help many children in organizing the placement of digits as they use paper-and-pencil algorithms. The grid lines help children keep digits with the same place value in a vertical orientation. Often such a grid is provided in *Everyday Mathematics* when children are expected to calculate using paper and pencil.

in perspective

In Grades 4–6 of *Everyday Mathematics,* the focus algorithms are adapted for computations with decimals.

encouraged to use it or any other method to solve problems. The aim of this approach is to promote flexibility while ensuring that all children know at least one reliable method for each operation.

The authors of *Everyday Mathematics* believe the focus algorithms are superior alternatives to the traditional U.S. standard paper-and-pencil algorithms. Nevertheless, parents and others often pressure children to master specific computational algorithms. This may also be your own preference. Indeed, many children learn the traditional U.S. standard paper-and-pencil algorithms from siblings or from adults at home. Given a choice, however, many children prefer their own procedures, procedures they "own"—or the *Everyday Mathematics* focus algorithms. In any case, *Everyday Mathematics* hopes you will do what is best suited to your situation. The program's aim is to *help* teachers, not to impose ideas or demands on them.

Finally, *Everyday Mathematics* encourages you to observe your children's algorithmic and procedural thinking when they are engaged in activities dealing with topics other than computation. For example, one child may have an algorithmic approach to drawing geometric figures or patterns, and another may invent ways to convert metric measures by "moving" decimal points. If a procedure warrants it, have a child share an algorithm with the class and point out the use of the "idea of an algorithm." A really good procedure might even be named after the child and entered into a class database of algorithms.

3.2 Standard and Alternative Algorithms

Base-ten place-value numeration spread from India to the Middle East and eventually all over the world in part because it makes calculation much easier. In the thousand years or so that Hindu-Arabic numeration has been in use, many algorithms have been devised for each of the fundamental arithmetic operations. All of these algorithms are "standard" in some sense—at some time and in some place a group of people used each of these algorithms. The traditional addition algorithm that many of us learned in school is only one of many alternatives. The same can be said for each of the other arithmetic operations.

In the following sections, the authors present some of the dozens of possible algorithms for adding, subtracting, multiplying, and dividing numbers. Some of these algorithms are easier to understand than the traditional U.S. algorithms, though they may seem at first to be more complicated since they are unfamiliar. Several of the algorithms presented are better suited for mental arithmetic or for very large numbers. Some are easier to learn, if perhaps a bit less efficient. (If efficiency is the goal, any paper-and-pencil algorithm will be inferior to a calculator or mental arithmetic in most situations.) Finally, a few algorithms on the next page are based on children's mental arithmetic efforts and search for procedures.

All of these algorithms are merely examples that you may suggest to children who need some help getting started.

Many different algorithms are described in the following sections. For each operation, the *Everyday Mathematics* focus algorithms are first described in some detail, then alternative algorithms are provided.

3.2.1 Addition Algorithms

Here we discuss several algorithms for whole-number addition: Partial Sums, Column Addition, and the Opposite-Change Rule, and the U. S. Traditional Algorithm.

Focus Algorithm: Partial-Sums

As the name suggests, the partial-sums algorithm calculates partial sums, working one place-value column at a time, and then adds all the partial sums to find the total.

$$\begin{array}{r} 6{,}802 \\ +\ \ 453 \end{array}$$

Add the thousands.	→	(6,000 + 0)	→ 6,000
Add the hundreds.	→	(800 + 400)	→ 1,200
Add the tens.	→	(0 + 50)	→ 50
Add the ones.	→	(2 + 3)	→ + 5
Add the partial sums.	→	(6,000 + 1,200 + 50 + 5)	→ **7,255**

The partial sums can be found in any order, but working from left to right is the usual procedure. This order seems more natural since we read from left to right, and it also focuses on the most important digits in the addends first (thousands before hundreds, hundreds before tens, and so on). A variation on this algorithm can be used to estimate sums quickly: The sum is estimated from only the partial sum(s) for the addends' leftmost digits. This is known as leading-digit estimation. The partial-sums algorithm can be readily adapted for mental arithmetic.

Partial-sums addition is the algorithm most similar to addition with base-10 blocks. Finding each partial sum corresponds to combining all of one kind of base-10 block. Adding the partial sums corresponds to exchanging blocks as necessary and then combining like blocks.

Column Addition

In column addition, vertical lines are drawn to separate ones, tens, hundreds, and so on. Once columns have been created, the usual place-value convention that each place must have only one digit can be broken without confusion. (If you wish, the columns can be labeled "ones," "tens," and so on.) The digits in each column are then added, beginning in any column. Finally, any necessary trades are made, again starting in any column.

	9	6	7
+	4	9	5
Add each column separately, working in any order. →	13	15	12
If necessary, adjust, working in any order. →	14	5	12
If necessary, adjust, working in any order. →	1,4	6	2

268
+ 483
751

Column addition with adjusting done mentally

Many students find this algorithm natural and instructive. For some, the process becomes so natural they start at the left and write the answer column by column, adjusting as they go without writing any of the intermediate steps. If asked to explain, they might say something like this:

> "200 plus 400 is 600, but (looking at the next column) I need to adjust that, so I write 7. 60 and 80 is 140, but that needs adjusting, so I write 5. 8 and 3 is 11. With no more to do, I can just write 1."

The column addition algorithm was shown and explained to the *Everyday Mathematics* authors by a first grader. It has become a personal favorite. The algorithm occurs naturally to many children, and it also has the advantage of producing a rough estimate of the sum quickly. It is also better suited to mental arithmetic than the traditional U.S. algorithm.

The Opposite-Change Rule

In the Opposite-Change Rule, a number is added to one addend and the same number is subtracted from the other addend; the sum, thus, remains the same. Consider, for example:

$$8 + 7 = 15$$

If 2 is added to the 8 and 2 is also subtracted from the 7, we have

$$(8 + 2) + (7 - 2) = 10 + 5 = 15$$

The idea behind this method is to rename the addends so that one ends in zeros. This may take several steps, but eventually the addition becomes trivial.

Example: Rename the first addend and then the second:

	268	→	270	→	300
	+ 483	→	+ 481	→	+ 451
				Add:	751

Explanation: Adjust by 2, and then adjust by 30.

Example: Rename the second addend and then the first:

	268	→	261	→	251
	+ 483	→	+ 490	→	+ 500
				Add:	751

Explanation: Adjust by 7, and then adjust by 10.

This approach is also well suited to mental arithmetic. With a little practice, children can become quite proficient.

U.S. Traditional Algorithm

The traditional addition algorithm used in the United States has much to recommend it. It is widely known, efficient (although obviously less efficient than a calculator or computer for adding lots of numbers), and fairly easy to learn. Many children learn how to use this algorithm from their parents or siblings: it is as much a cultural tradition as a mathematical procedure. It is, therefore, likely to be mentioned when you ask children to explain their solutions to multidigit addition problems.

The U.S. traditional addition algorithm is similar to column addition (see above), but it requires the user to proceed column-by-column from right to left and to observe place values at all times. These requirements make the algorithm more efficient but harder to learn.

The user begins with the rightmost column, mentally finds the sum of all the digits in that column, writes the ones digit of the sum below the line, and "carries" the tens digit of the sum to the top of the next column to the left. The process is repeated for each column to the left. The "carry" digits can be mysterious to children, so be sure to explain them in terms of place value and renaming when you discuss this algorithm.

In whole-number addition, the starting column is the ones place. In decimal addition, the starting column it can be the tenths, hundredths, or any other place.

	588
	+ 143
Add the ones. *(8 ones + 3 ones = 11 ones)* → Regroup. *(11 ones = 1 ten and 1 one)*	¹ 588 + 143 ____ 1
Add the tens. *(1 ten + 8 tens + 4 tens = 13 tens)* → Regroup. *(13 tens = 1 hundred and 3 tens)*	¹¹ 588 + 143 ____ 31
Add the hundreds. *(1 hundred + 5 hundreds + 1 hundred = 7 hundreds)* → **731** is the total.	¹ 588 + 143 ____ 731

U.S. traditional addition algorithm

The addition algorithm is probably the best of the traditional U.S. computation algorithms. While *Everyday Mathematics* does not focus on it, it is a viable alternative. If you do decide to teach the addition algorithm, be sure to treat it as one of several possibilities and, as with any algorithm, be sure that children understand why it works.

3.2.2 Subtraction Algorithms

There are even more algorithms for subtraction than for addition, probably because subtraction is more difficult. In this section, we discuss five algorithms for whole-number subtraction: Trade-First, Counting-Up, Left-to-Right, "European," and Partial Differences.

Focus Algorithm: Trades-First Subtraction

This algorithm resembles the U.S. traditional algorithm, except that all the trading is done before all the subtraction, allowing the user to concentrate on one thing at a time. The following steps are involved:

$$\begin{array}{r} \scriptstyle{8\ \ 10\,5\,12} \\ 9{,}0\cancel{6}\cancel{2} \\ -4{,}738 \\ \hline \end{array}$$

1. Examine all columns and trade as necessary so that the top number in each place is as large or larger than the bottom number. The trades can be done in any order. Working left-to-right is perhaps more natural, as with partial sums addition, but working right-to-left is a bit more efficient.

2. Check that the top number in each place is at least as large as the bottom number. If necessary, make more trades.

$$\begin{array}{r} \scriptstyle{8\ \ 10\,5\,12} \\ 9{,}0\cancel{6}\cancel{2} \\ -4{,}738 \\ \hline \end{array}$$

3. Subtract column by column in any order.

Trade-First subtraction is highly efficient, similar to the traditional algorithm, and relatively easy to learn. It is an effective algorithm for paper-and-pencil calculation.

Many teachers find that drawing vertical lines between the places is helpful for children first learning this algorithm. The vertical lines allow children to focus on one column at a time. They also help children avoid mistakes if unnecessary trades have been made.

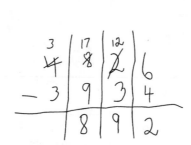

trade-first with columns   trade-first with
                                  an unnecessary trade

Counting-Up

This algorithm is similar to what cashiers do when they give change. In both procedures, the user begins at the smaller number and counts up to the larger number. In giving change, the cashier tenders bills or coins to the purchaser. In the Counting-Up algorithm, the user keeps a running total of the amounts counted up and then totals all of the count-up amounts to find the difference.

The counting-up technique that is the basis for this algorithm is useful in mental computation, although mentally keeping a correct running total requires practice. When the procedure is carried out mentally, it helps to start with the larger places.

Solve 932 − 356 by counting up

$$\begin{array}{r} 356 \\ \boxed{+\ \ 4} \quad \text{Count to the nearest 10.} \\ 360 \\ \boxed{+\ 40} \quad \text{Count to the nearest} \\ 400 \quad\quad\ \ 100. \\ \boxed{+500} \quad \text{Count to the largest} \\ 900 \quad\quad\ \ \text{possible 100.} \\ \boxed{+\ 32} \quad \text{Count to the larger} \\ 932 \quad\quad\ \ \text{number.} \end{array}$$

Then add the numbers you circled

$$\begin{array}{r} 4 \\ 40 \\ 500 \\ +\ \ 32 \\ \hline 576 \end{array}$$

So, 932 − 356 = 576

Left-to-Right Subtraction

With the left-to-right algorithm, the user starts at the left and subtracts column by column. For the problem $932 - 356$:

$$932$$

1. Subtract the 100s
$$
\begin{array}{r}
932 \\
-300 \\
\hline
632
\end{array}
$$

2. Subtract the 10s.
$$
\begin{array}{r}
-50 \\
\hline
582
\end{array}
$$

3. Subtract the 1s.
$$
\begin{array}{r}
-6 \\
\hline
576
\end{array}
$$

Like left-to-right addition, this algorithm can be used to find a rough estimate of the final answer.

"European" Subtraction

The traditional U.S. subtraction algorithm involves "borrowing" from the next place to the left. That is, in a problem like $623 - 345$, one of the 2 tens in 623 is traded for 10 ones. This is written as:

$$
\begin{array}{r}
{}^{1}6\overset{13}{\cancel{2}}\cancel{3} \\
-\ 345
\end{array}
$$

A variation on this procedure involves increasing the bottom number in the next column to the left:

$$
\begin{array}{r}
62\overset{13}{\cancel{3}} \\
-\ 3{}_{1}45
\end{array}
$$

The small mark next to the 4 in 345 is a ten that compensates for adding 10 to the 3 on top. The next step involves subtracting 50 instead of 40. Since the 2 in 623 is too small to take away 5, we use the same trick again, this time increasing the hundreds digit in the bottom number.

$$
\begin{array}{r}
6\overset{12}{\cancel{2}}\overset{13}{\cancel{3}} \\
-\ {}_{1}3{}_{1}45
\end{array}
$$

The mark next to the 3 on the bottom is a hundred that compensates for adding 10 tens to the top. The final step is subtract $(1 + 3)$ hundreds from 6 hundreds.

$$
\begin{array}{r}
6\overset{12}{\cancel{2}}\overset{13}{\cancel{3}} \\
-\ {}_{1}3{}_{1}45
\end{array}
$$

You may find this algorithm confusing, but it is the standard algorithm used in many other countries in the world today. You might want to spend a few minutes thinking about how increasing the number on the bottom has the same effect as decreasing the number on the top. If you want to experience what it might be like for a child to learn the traditional U.S. subtraction algorithm, you might try learning this "European" algorithm.

Partial Differences

There are many other subtraction algorithms that your children may reinvent. Partial-differences subtraction is a fairly unusual method, but one that appeals to some children.

The procedure is fairly simple: Write partial differences for each place, record them, and then add them to find the total difference. The complication is that some of the partial differences may be negative.

$$
\begin{array}{r}
932 \\
- 356 \\
\hline
\end{array}
$$

1. Subtract 100s: 900 − 300   600

2. Subtract 10s: 30 − 50   − 20

3. Subtract 1s: 2 − 6   − 4

4. Add the partial differences   576

Partial-Differences Subtraction

3.2.3 Multiplication Algorithms

Adults usually reach for calculators when they have to multiply "difficult" numbers. Calculators should be made available to children when they deal with problems that they understand, but involve calculations beyond their current skills. As always, *Everyday Mathematics* suggests that children share strategies for finding products of whole numbers and discuss how they created their own computational procedures. Inventing procedures for multiplication and division is more difficult than for addition and subtraction, but children who have experience with the latter will be well prepared to attempt the former. When doing mental arithmetic, for example, many children begin to compute partial products: "Ten of these would be . . . , so 30 of them would be . . . , and then we need 5 more, so. . . ." Beginning in *Third Grade Everyday Mathematics*, this approach is formalized as the *partial-products multiplication algorithm*. This algorithm and several others are discussed below.

Focus Algorithm: Partial-Products

In partial-products multiplication, each factor is thought of as a sum of ones, tens, hundreds, and so on. For example, in 67 × 53, 67 can be thought of as 60 + 7 and 53 as 50 + 3. Each part of one factor is then multiplied by each part of the other factor, and, finally, all of the resulting partial products are added together.

You don't have to work from left to right; any order will do, as long as all possible partial products are found. Working from left to right, however, does help keep the procedure orderly and also, as with left-to-right procedures for addition and subtraction, produces a

$$
\begin{array}{r}
67 \\
\times \quad 53 \\
\hline
50 \times 60 \rightarrow \quad 3000 \\
50 \times 7 \rightarrow \quad 350 \\
3 \times 60 \rightarrow \quad 180 \\
3 \times 7 \rightarrow \quad + \quad 21 \\
\hline
3551
\end{array}
$$

Partial-Products Multiplication

quick estimate of the product. In order to use the partial-products algorithm efficiently, children must be adept at multiplying multiples of 10, 100, and 1000—such as, 60×50 as in the example on the previous page. These skills also help children to make ballpark estimates of products and quotients. The partial-products algorithm can be demonstrated visually using arrays. The diagram below shows how a 23-by-14 array represents all of the partial products in 23×14.

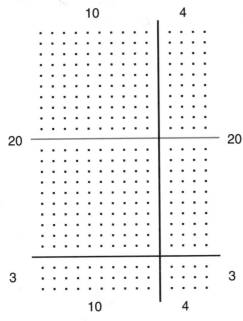

$$23 \times 14 \quad = (20 + 3) \times (10 + 4)$$
$$= (20 \times 10) + (20 \times 4) + (3 \times 10) + (3 \times 4)$$
$$= 200 + 80 + 30 + 12$$
$$= 322$$

Lattice Multiplication

Everyday Mathematics initially included lattice multiplication for its recreational value and historical interest, and because it provided practice with multiplication facts and adding single-digit numbers. To our surprise, lattice multiplication has become a favorite of many children in *Everyday Mathematics*.

It is not easy to understand exactly why lattice multiplication works, but it is a very efficient and powerful algorithm. For problems involving more than two digits in each factor, it is a more efficient method than standard long multiplication. And problems that are too large for long multiplication or even for most calculators can be solved using lattice multiplication. The principal disadvantages of the algorithm are that it is unfamiliar to many adults and making the lattice takes time.

To multiply 67 by 53:

1. Draw a 2-by-2 lattice. (Multiplying larger numbers requires only a larger lattice.)

NOTE: The partial-products algorithm uses the distributive property twice. First,
$20 \times (10 + 4) =$
$20 \times 10 + 20 \times 4$,
and,
$3 \times (10 + 4) = 3 \times 10 + 3 \times 4$.

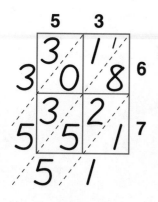

2. Write one factor along the top of the lattice and the other along the right, one digit for each row or column.

3. Multiply each digit in one factor by each digit in the other factor. Write the products in the cells where the corresponding rows and columns meet. Write the tens digit of these products above the diagonal and the ones digit below the diagonal.

4. Add the numbers inside the lattice along each diagonal. Write these sums along the bottom and left of the lattice. If the sum on a diagonal exceeds 9, carry the tens digit to the next diagonal.

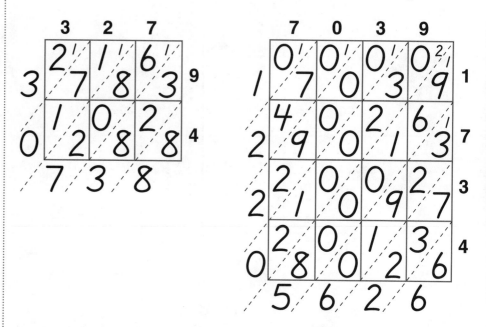

NOTE: In Treviso, Italy, in 1478 lattice multiplication first appeared in print, in what is said to be the first printed arithmetic book. Amazingly, it was in use long before that, with historians tracing it to Hindu origins in India before 1100.

The key to understanding why lattice multiplication works is to note that the diagonals in the lattice correspond to place-value columns. The far right-hand diagonal is the ones place, the next diagonal to the left is the tens place, and so on.

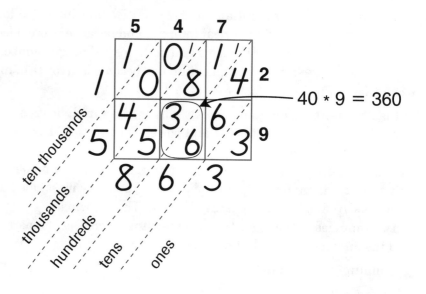

40 * 9 = 360

Modified Repeated Addition

Contrary to what is often taught, multiplication is not merely repeated addition, even for whole numbers and certainly not for decimals and fractions. Moreover, as a computational method for multiplying, repeated addition is inefficient for anything but small numbers. For example, it would be unbearably tedious to add together fifty-three 67s in order to compute 67×53.

If you think of ten 67s as 670, however, you can first add the 670s (there are five of them) and then add the three 67s, as shown in the margin. This algorithm is a good *Broken Calculator* exercise (find a product without using the [×] key).

Modified Standard U.S. Algorithms

Example A in the margin shows the standard U.S. paper-and-pencil multiplication algorithm for finding 67×53. Though the algorithm does work, there are probably few people who can explain why one shifts over a place in successive partial products. Even harder to explain is why the 3 in the 35 from 5×7 is written above the 6 in 67. When asked why the 3 is written in the tens place, many adults say that the 3 stands for 3 tens, which is, of course, incorrect. The 3 actually stands for 300 because it comes from $50 \times 7 = 350$. And these are adults who believe they "understand" long multiplication!

Example B solves the shift-over-a-place mystery by inserting a zero in the blank. This makes clear that for the second partial product, we are multiplying by 50 (five 10s) and not by 5. The reason for putting the 3 above the 6 is still unresolved—it's actually there for convenience in mentally adding to the product of 5 times 6 (which is really 50 times 60). This version is easier to understand than the traditional form.

Example C uses a left-to-right approach. Though it has its advantages, it is otherwise no different from the standard algorithm with 0s in place of the blanks.

3.2.4 Division Algorithms

One type of division situation involves making as many groups of equal size as possible from a collection of objects: How many dozens can you make with 746 eggs? How many 5-passenger cars are needed for 37 people? Such problems ask, "How many of these are in that?" More generally, $a \div b$ can be interpreted as, "How many bs are in a?" (See Section 2.1.2 of the Operations and Facts Essay for a discussion of other division situations.)

Equal-size grouping is the basis for many division algorithms. One approach is simply to subtract b from a as many times as possible and then to count the number of subtractions. To solve $37 \div 5$ using this repeated subtraction method is feasible (see margin), but for larger numbers this straightforward approach becomes impractical.

$$
\begin{array}{r}
67 \\
\times\ 53 \\
\hline
670 \\
670 \\
670 \\
670 \\
670 \\
67 \\
67 \\
+\ 67 \\
\hline
3551
\end{array}
$$

50 [67s] *or* 5 [670s]

3 [67s]

Modified Repeated Addition

$$
\begin{array}{ccc}
\textbf{A.} & \textbf{B.} & \textbf{C.} \\
\overset{3}{\underset{2}{}} & \overset{3}{\underset{2}{}} & \overset{2}{\underset{3}{}} \\
67 & 67 & 67 \\
\times\ 53 & \times\ 53 & \times\ 53 \\
\hline
201 & 201 & 3350 \\
335 & 3350 & 201 \\
\hline
3551 & 3551 & 3551
\end{array}
$$

Modified Standard U.S.
Algorithms

$37 \div 5$

$$
\begin{array}{r}
37 \\
-\ 5 \\
\hline
32 \\
-\ 5 \\
\hline
27 \\
-\ 5 \\
\hline
22 \\
-\ 5 \\
\hline
17 \\
-\ 5 \\
\hline
12 \\
-\ 5 \\
\hline
7 \\
-\ 5 \\
\hline
2
\end{array}
$$

7[5s] in 37.

A formal introduction to division algorithms is not included in K–3 *Everyday Mathematics.* Children do solve many division problems using conceptual methods like repeated subtraction, "dealing" out items to be shared, or looking for missing factors, but computational efficiency is not the goal. Instead, during these grades, the goal is to develop children's conceptual understanding of division and to build proficiency in the many skills that are required in multidigit division.

Note One often hears that dividing by zero is not defined or allowed. The reason for this is that dividing by zero does not produce a proper answer. Here are several ways to see why this is so:

1. Any division problem can be rewritten as a missing-factor multiplication problem. For example, the problem $56 \div 7 = N$ can be rewritten as $7 * N = 56$. The task then becomes to find the missing factor. In $7 * N = 56$, the missing factor is 8, which is the answer to the original division problem.

   When a division by zero is rewritten as a missing-factor multiplication problem, it becomes apparent that no answer will work. Consider, for example, $24 \div 0 = N$. When the problem is rewritten as $0 * N = 24$, it is clear that no number can be multiplied by zero to get an answer of 24.

2. When a series of division problems using the same dividend but smaller and smaller divisors is graphed, it becomes apparent that the closer the divisor is to zero, the larger the quotient becomes. For example, consider dividing 12 by a series of divisors:
   $12 \div 6 = \mathbf{2}$, $12 \div 4 = \mathbf{3}$, $12 \div 3 = \mathbf{4}$, $12 \div 2 = \mathbf{6}$, $12 \div 1 = \mathbf{12}$.
   The answer is clearly larger each time the divisor gets closer to zero. The effect becomes even more striking with divisors less than one: $12 \div \frac{3}{4} = \mathbf{16}$, $12 \div \frac{1}{2} = \mathbf{24}$, $12 \div \frac{1}{4} = \mathbf{48}$, $12 \div \frac{1}{8} = \mathbf{84}$, $12 \div \frac{1}{16} = \mathbf{168}$. See the graph of this example below. As the divisor approaches zero, the quotient "approaches infinity" (becomes large without limit). Since infinitely large quotients are not acceptable, division by 0 is not allowed.

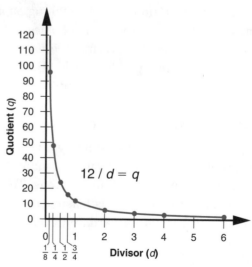

As the divisor approaches zero, the quotient approaches infinity.

3. Just as simple multiplication can be seen as repeated addition, division can be seen as repeated subtraction of equal groups. For example, $15 \div 5 = N$ can be solved by finding out how many times 5 can be subtracted from 15. However, if the divisor is zero, the question becomes how many times zero can be subtracted from a given number. Clearly, there is no sensible answer.

$$
\left.\begin{array}{r} 15 \\ -5 \\ \hline 10 \\ -5 \\ \hline 5 \\ -5 \\ \hline 0 \end{array}\right\} 15 \div 5 = 3
$$

4. Division problems can also be written as fractions. For example, $8 \div 4 = 2$ can also be written as $\frac{8}{4} = 2$, and $3 \div 4 = 0.75$ can also be written $\frac{3}{4} = 0.75$. Just as division by zero is not allowed, having zero as the denominator of a fraction is not allowed. The denominator of a fraction represents the number of parts into which a whole has been divided, but a whole cannot be divided into zero parts. For example, a pizza can be cut into fourths, or four equal parts; it can also be cut into halves, or two equal parts; or it could be left uncut, which means it has one part. But, there is no way to cut it so that it has zero parts. One whole pizza is one part before you start cutting it.

$$
\left.\begin{array}{r} 15 \\ -0 \\ \hline 15 \\ -0 \\ \hline 15 \\ -0 \\ \hline 15 \\ \cdot \\ \cdot \\ \cdot \end{array}\right\} 15 \div 0 = ???
$$

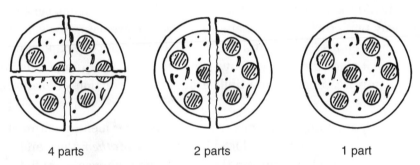

4 parts   2 parts   1 part

There is no way to cut a pizza so that it has 0 parts.

3.3 Mental Arithmetic

Children practice mental arithmetic to learn useful techniques, to develop flexible thinking, and to gain fact power. These skills contribute to children's number sense, which includes a flexible understanding both of numbers and of operations on those numbers. *Everyday Mathematics* emphasizes number sense in Grades K–3 because calculators and computers have actually increased the importance of estimation and mental arithmetic. Complicated paper-and-pencil computation has become relatively less important, while mental arithmetic and skillful calculator use have become relatively more important. *Everyday Mathematics* reflects this shift.

An important part of being a flexible problem solver is to continually add to a personal tool kit of mental-arithmetic skills that are "automatized"—skills that are so well-practiced they can be used reflexively, intuitively, almost without thinking, analogous to knowing scales in music. In *Everyday Mathematics,* good mental-arithmetic reflexes include fact power. The primary means for developing fact power are choral drills, games, and puzzles. (See Section 2.3 for a discussion of basic facts in *Everyday Mathematics.*)

Mental-arithmetic skills are developed throughout the Everyday Mathematics curriculum. The *Minute Math+* books outline many mental-arithmetic and problem-solving activities, and each lesson in first through sixth grades begins with a brief set of oral or slate exercises called Mental Math and Reflexes.

An important part of the Mental Math and Reflexes routine is having children share solution strategies after they complete the exercises. When they share strategies, children ought to verbalize their thinking, which, in turn, helps them build both understanding and automaticity. Children also gain insight from their classmates into alternative approaches, and flexible thinking is encouraged. Most importantly, children learn that common sense applies to mathematics and that they can solve difficult problems by thinking things through for themselves. Strategy sharing is vitally important throughout the *Everyday Mathematics* curriculum.

Children are frequently asked to use mental arithmetic in situations calling for estimates. Even when children use calculators, they should monitor whether the calculator's answers make sense. One way to do this is to estimate an answer before using the calculator. Children also use mental arithmetic in carrying out paper-and-pencil algorithms. Paper-and-pencil division, for example, usually requires estimation, multiplication, and subtraction—much of which is done mentally.

There are many strategies and techniques for mental arithmetic. Some are formally introduced in *Everyday Mathematics,* and children develop others on their own. The main goals are for children to realize that many techniques exist, to learn how they work, to master a few, and to build one or two into reflexes. Among the most common and useful strategies are the following:

Round Techniques include rounding to the nearest ten, hundred, thousand, and so on, and computing with rounded numbers. For example, $647 + 284$ is approximately $600 + 300 = 900$, or $650 + 280 = 930$.

Adjust the Numbers A sum is unchanged if one addend is increased and another is decreased by the same amount. For example, $86 + 37$ is equal to $(86 + 4) + (37 - 4) = 90 + 33$, which is equal to $(90 + 10) + (33 - 10) = 100 + 23$. A difference is unchanged if the same number is added to or subtracted from the original numbers—the minuend and the subtrahend. For example, $54 - 37$ is equal to $(54 + 3) - (37 + 3) = 57 - 40$.

Look for Easy Combinations In $17 + 25 + 3 + 15 + 8$, add 3 to 17 and add 15 to 25.

Estimate, Then Adjust An approximate answer is obtained first and then adjusted to make it more accurate. For example, $647 + 284$ is approximately $640 + 280 = 920$; adding $7 + 4$ to that results in 931.

Use Easy Numbers Multiplying 517 by 22 is a job for a calculator. However, 517 is close to 500, and 22 is close to 20, so the answer must be close to 500 × 20, or 500 × 10 two times, or 10,000.

For Whole Numbers, Multiply Nonzero Digits and Count Zeros It is important to keep track of how many zeros there are in an estimated product of whole numbers. For example, 543 × 32 is approximately 500 × 30. Multiply 5 × 3 and append the three zeros in the rounded factors to get 15,000.

For Division of Whole Numbers, Cross Out Zeros If you divide a multiple of 10 (or 100 or 1,000, and so on) by a multiple of 10 (or 100 or 1,000, and so on), you can simplify the problem by crossing out the same number of zeros in the divisor as in the dividend: 5,600 ÷ 800 = 56 ÷ 8.

Estimate Magnitude A useful check for answers found another way: Is a reasonable answer in the tens? Hundreds? Thousands? And so on.

Miscellaneous Strategies There are many other useful strategies, some of which are simpler than others, including the following:

- To multiply a whole number by 10, add one zero to the right of the number; to multiply by 100, add two zeros; and so on: 37 × 10 = 370; 100 × 98 = 9,800; and so on.

- To multiply a decimal by 10, move the decimal point one place to the right: 45.89 × 10 = 458.9.

- To change a decimal into the equivalent percent, move the decimal point two places to the right and add the percent notation; to change a percent into a decimal, move the decimal point two places to the left and delete the percent notation.

- To multiply a whole number by 5, multiply by 10 and then find $\frac{1}{2}$ of the result. For example, 383 × 5 = 383 × 10 ÷ 2 = 3,830 ÷ 2 = 1,915.

- The sum of the digits of a multiple of 3 must be a multiple of 3. For example, 59 × 3 = 177; 1 + 7 + 7 = 15; 15 is a multiple of 3.

- To multiply a two-digit number by 11, add the two digits and use the sum as shown in the examples that follow: For 34 × 11, think: "The first digit is 3; the second digit is 3 + 4; the third digit is 4, so the product is 374." For 69 × 11, think: "6 + 9 = 15, so the first digit is 1 more than 6; the second digit is the 5 from 6 + 9 = 15; the third digit is 9. The product is 759."

ESSAY

4

Data and Chance

outline

4.1 Data Collection, Organization, and Analysis 114

    4.1.1 Formulating a Question 114

    4.1.2 Collecting, Organizing, and Recording Data 115

    4.1.3 Organizing and Displaying Data 116

    4.1.4 Data Analysis 119

4.2 Probability 120

    4.2.1 Why Study Probability? 121

    4.2.2 The Language of Chance 121

    4.2.3 Making Predictions 122

4.3 Using Data and Probability 122

In a world inundated with numbers, understanding statistics and probability is more important now than ever before. Citizens and consumers need to understand claims about data and probabilities in journalism and advertising. Workers need to know how to gather, display, and analyze data in order to work efficiently and effectively. Even many recreational activities are increasingly becoming involved with data and chance. Statistics and probability have become prominent in the elementary school curriculum both because of their current importance and as a source of contexts for practicing arithmetic and other skills.

4.1 Data Collection, Organization, and Analysis

Children's initial data-exploration experiences should be informal, allowing them to collaborate with you and with one another to decide on methods of collecting, representing, and explaining their data. As children gain experience, they can be introduced to standard methods, such as using bar and line graphs and appropriate statistical landmarks (such as median and mean) to help them answer questions and communicate their findings to others.

4.1.1 Formulating a Question

Ordinarily, data are collected and analyzed to describe a situation and/or to make predictions. The process almost always begins with a question. When we want to know something, one way to approach finding an answer is to gather information. Then we look at the information—the data—in various ways in order to determine what we need to know. There are two important reasons to take time formulating a question for data exploration. The first is motivational. Data-collection activities are usually more meaningful to children if they are connected to a real problem in the class or to the gathering of information children really want to have. *Everyday Mathematics* presents many problem situations that require data collection and analysis, and you are encouraged to add your own and to personalize those suggested.

One such example of personalization comes from a Kindergarten class. A number of children didn't know how to tie their shoes, always relying on the teacher to do this for them. The children decided it would be much more efficient if they knew which children were able to tie shoes so they could help those that could not. This led to a survey, a tally and display of the collated data, and a solution to a problem meaningful to the children in the class.

A second reason to take time to formulate a question for data exploration is to clarify the essential information that can lead to an answer. In the shoe-tying survey, for example, is it important to know what color the shoes are or how long the laces are? If you want to know who runs the fastest, does hair color matter? Does distance matter? What about footwear or clothing? Even if the questions sometimes seem silly, it is important to ask them to help children develop habits of thinking about the possible effects various factors may have on the data they collect.

4.1.2 Collecting, Organizing, and Recording Data

Everyday Mathematics uses many sources of data and a variety of collection procedures, such as the following:

- Counting and measuring in the classroom
- Observing and measuring at home
- Taking surveys at school (including surveys of other classes)
- Collecting data from such sources as TV, newspapers, magazines, or encyclopedias

In *K–3 Everyday Mathematics,* the most common data are counts, and the usual goal is to examine the frequency of various occurrences. "How many . . . ?" is the classic beginning to the questions that are formulated by children: How many of each kind of Halloween candy did you get? How many brothers and sisters do you have? How many pets does your family keep? Investigations of this sort genuinely interest children, and can be used to build a foundation for later more sophisticated work in statistics and probability.

Data activities include games such as *Dice Roll and Tally,* in which results are kept with tally marks. Other investigations are formatted as Projects and Explorations, such as the second grade's "How Far Can I Run in 10 Seconds?" activity. Many opportunities arise naturally in the course of classroom life.

Data analysis begins as the data are collected. If the information is not recorded in an organized table or chart, students will end up with an indecipherable heap of numbers instead of useful data. *Everyday Mathematics* provides various tools to help with the initial collection and organization of data, including journal pages, masters, and suggestions for the Class Data Pad and bulletin-board displays.

4.1.3 Organizing and Displaying Data

The tools in *Everyday Mathematics* provide some organization during data collection, but it is also important for children to design their own ways of recording and displaying data. Organizing data can help you "see the data *better*"; reorganizing it can help you "see the data *differently*," in a way that may better suit your needs. Children are encouraged to make and observe a wide variety of data displays.

- *Data Tables* Tables are one of the most basic formats for the display of data. Newspapers, reference books, scientific articles, and some publications are filled with data tables. Tables have specific uses, such as tally tables, lists, and the input/output tables used in "What's My Rule?" Tables of numbers and arithmetic facts are also used extensively to help children improve their mental-arithmetic skills.

Largest Cities by Population (urban agglomerations)	
City, Country	**Population**
Tokyo, Japan	26,959,000
Mexico City, Mexico	16,562,000
Sao Paulo, Brazil	16,533,000
New York City, U.S.	16,332,000
Bombay (Mumbai), India	15,138,000
Shanghai, China	13,584,000
Los Angeles, U.S.	12,410,000
(above is from *World Almanac*, 2000)	

National League Standings, 6-9-00

CENTRAL	W	L	Pct	GB
St. Louis	33	26	.559	–
Cincinnati	31	27	.534	1 1/2
Pittsburgh	26	31	.456	6
CUBS	25	35	.416	8 1/2
Milwaukee	23	36	.390	10
Houston	21	38	.356	12
EAST	**W**	**L**	**Pct**	**GB**
Atlanta	37	21	.638	–
New York	33	26	.559	4 1/2
Montreal	31	25	.554	5
Florida	27	33	.450	11
Philadelphia	22	35	.386	14 1/2
WEST	**W**	**L**	**Pct**	**GB**
Arizona	35	24	.593	–
Los Angeles	32	25	.561	2
Colorado	31	25	.553	2 1/2
San Francisco	27	29	.482	6 1/2
San Diego	25	33	.431	9 1/2

(The above was excerpted from the *Chicago Tribune* for Friday, June 9, 2000)

- *Line Plots* Line plots or sketch graphs are used extensively to organize and display data. A line plot shows the data by using checks, Xs, or stick-on notes to indicate the different data values along a number line. A line plot can be thought of as a rough sketch of a bar graph.

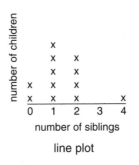

line plot

- *Bar Graphs* Bar graphs are introduced in second grade and are used throughout the rest of the program. Bar graphs are excellent for displaying "how much" or "how many," and can be drawn vertically or horizontally. Children need to be aware of the important parts of a graph, including the title, labels for axes, and the scales for numbering the axes. If the scale used for numbering an axis is too small or too large, the "look" of the data can be distorted. (Computer software programs for graphing allow for the scale to be set by entering a maximum and minimum for the range and an interval. This is a wonderful way to demonstrate how the change in scale affects the look of a graph.)

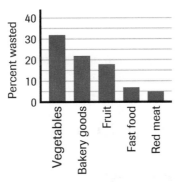

Source: The Garbage Product

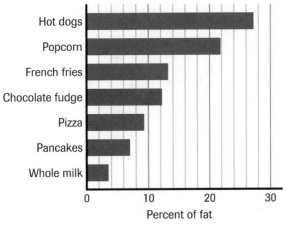

Source: The New York Public Library Desk Reference

Several other graphs are used in Grades 4–6 of *Everyday Mathematics*. Students are likely to see these common graphs in magazines, newspapers, or on television:

- **Line Graphs** Line graphs are useful for spotting trends and making predictions. They are most commonly used in science and business. *Everyday Mathematics* introduces them in Grade 3 and uses them with increasing frequency thereafter.

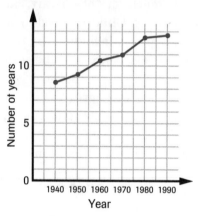

Median Number of Years of School Completed by People, Age 25 or Over, in the United States

Source: 1995 Digest of Education

- **Circle Graphs** Circle graphs, also known as pie charts, are often used to compare parts of a whole. Making them requires a good understanding of fractions, percents, and angular measurement.

Areas of the Continents
(in square miles)

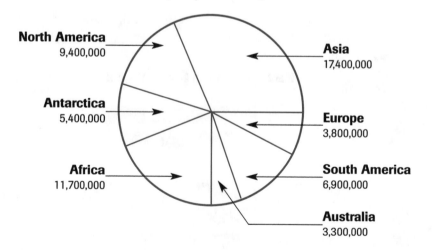

- **Stem-and-Leaf Plots** Stem-and-leaf plots can be used for the initial collection of data and produce a display similar to a line plot. As each new measurement or count is collected, a new "leaf" is added to the corresponding "stem." For example, in the stem-and-leaf plot below, a value of 86 would be entered as a 6 (the leaf) on the stem 8.

Pulse Rates of 6th Grade Students

Stems (100's and 10's)	Leaves (1's)
6	5
7	5 5 8 0 8 5 2 8 5 2 0 8
8	6 8 6 6 6 8 2 5 8 6
9	4 9 0 4 4 0 4 2 0 4
10	8 2 2 5
11	2

Do not insist that tally charts or line plots be neat and nicely labeled. Children should make these quickly, so that they can "see the data" and try to understand what's going on. Once children have analyzed the data they may be asked to report on it in some way. For reports, you should insist that any accompanying graphs be neat and properly labeled.

Two simple methods for organizing data are to arrange the data in order from the smallest value to the largest and to sort the data by one or more characteristics. Both can be done without using a tally table or a line plot. One example of this would be organizing children's ages by having the children line up by age. Or you could organize children by gender and then handedness. Direct all boys to move to the north wall of the room and all girls to the south wall; then have all right-handers move to the east wall and all left-handers to the west wall.

4.1.4 Data Analysis

To many people, data analysis is synonymous with statistics. In *Everyday Mathematics,* however, this is not the case. For our purposes, data analysis means the examination and explanation of data. A good data analysis for a first grader can be summed up in a single well-phrased comment, such as "More than half the class are girls." Statistics may be completely irrelevant in such an analysis. A statistic is simply a number used to describe some characteristic of one or more data sets and may not necessarily shed any particular light on the situation being examined.

One of the most common statistics is the average or mean of a set of data. Finding the mean requires adding a set of numbers and then dividing—tasks too difficult for most young children. Yet a lack of arithmetic skills should not bar students from data analysis of a more general nature. Several other statistics, or landmarks of data sets, are accessible to young children. Once data have been organized in some way, take every opportunity to have children discuss things they notice about their data. The following statistics are commonly used to describe features of data sets.

- **Maximum** The *largest* data value observed
- **Minimum** The *smallest* data value observed
- **Range** The *difference* between the maximum and minimum values
- **Mode** The "most popular" data value(s); the value(s) observed *most often*
- **Median** The middle value observed or, if there is an even number of values, the number halfway between the two middle values

These statistics are called "landmarks" in the data set because they show important features of the data. Children can use landmarks as reference points when discussing other features of the data.

Note that finding a median may require averaging the two values nearest the middle. This is probably the first use of *average* children encounter other than as a descriptive term for data found in newspapers, TV, and so on. Children often develop the idea of an average in the context of finding a median. The question, "What do we do if there is no middle value?" leads to an important discussion about what is a fair value between two others. One approach to finding that fair value can be to point to a spot on a number line. Another can be to guess and check. Sometimes children may develop the mathematical algorithm of averaging on their own.

In *Everyday Mathematics* Grades K–3, children discuss landmarks in "raw" data (data as they are recorded) and in ordered data (data numerically ordered, or grouped by categories). Children also discuss their data qualitatively (without using landmarks like median or range), noting where the data bunch together or spread out. Exploring reasons for the "shape of the data" can lead to a better understanding of the data set in question and the data analysis process. Formal treatment of averages and other statistics is reserved for the later years of the curriculum.

Remember that the usual reason for analyzing data is to solve a problem, make a prediction, or arrive at a decision. Never finish a data lesson before children have had an opportunity to summarize, discuss, report, or reach some sort of conclusion. Think of data analysis as a process with several stages: gathering the data, displaying the data, analyzing the data, and looking back. In some ways this last step, achieving closure, is the most important one.

4.2 Probability

Everyday Mathematics believes that most children must be exposed to concepts and skills many times in many different ways, often only briefly, before they are able to master them. The treatment of probability in the curriculum is a good example of this approach. In

Everyday Mathematics Grades K–3, children play informal games, and engage in activities involving the idea of fairness and the use of random-number generators such as cards, dot or number cubes, and spinners. The formal treatment of probability begins in *Third Grade Everyday Mathematics.*

4.2.1 Why Study Probability?

All of us are aware that our world is filled with uncertainties. Of course, there are some things that we can be sure of: The sun will rise tomorrow, for example, or the Chicago Cubs will not win the World Series this year (or any year, for that matter). We also know that there are degrees of uncertainty; some things are more likely to happen than others. There are also occurrences which, although uncertain, can be predicted with some accuracy. These qualitative ideas of probability—impossible, possible, likely, certain, and so on—are the basis for the mathematical treatment of probability in *Everyday Mathematics* and beyond.

Few people understand how to calculate the chances of something taking place. Yet many decisions in our personal lives, from the trivial (Should I take an umbrella with me?) to the vitally important (Should I undergo surgery?), are based on probabilities. Probability is more useful in daily life than most other branches of mathematics, and fully deserves the greater prominence given to it in most contemporary elementary mathematics curricula.

4.2.2 The Language of Chance

Because children should become comfortable talking about chance events as early on as possible, *Everyday Mathematics* begins by focusing on vocabulary development. Many terms are introduced: *sure, certain, probably, 50-50, unlikely, impossible,* and so on. These terms should not be taught formally. Through repeated use, children will gradually make them part of their vocabularies. Many children are familiar with terms like *forecast* and *predict,* but not *probability. Probability* is a difficult word and need not be used at first.

All children have had experience comparing the chances of various outcomes of a random process. They understand everyday statements like, "Rain is more likely than snow today." They may also understand that a seven is more likely than a three when two dice are rolled. Such informal comparisons are a good place to begin, since they provide a context in which the language of chance can be intuitively introduced. Discuss the fact that some things are certain to happen and other things are certain not to happen. The most interesting things are in between, neither certain nor impossible. Point out that if we think hard enough, we can often say which of these uncertain things are more likely to occur than others.

NOTE: For more information on random number generators see the Management Guide section on Tools for Exploring Data and Chance, page 34.

4.2.3 Making Predictions

Most of the probability activities in *Everyday Mathematics* follow a similar pattern: Children make a prediction about the likelihood of a particular outcome of some random process such as rolling a die or flipping a coin. They then check their predictions by performing an experiment that involves collecting, organizing, and interpreting data. Some activities call for children to compare the likelihood of several possible outcomes. Other activities ask children to estimate the chance that something will happen by assigning it a numerical value. For example, when a coin is tossed, the chance of its landing heads-up is 1 out of 2 or $\frac{1}{2}$ because there are two ways the coin could land, one of which is heads-up. When a single die is rolled, the chance of an even number is 3 out of 6 or $\frac{3}{6}$, since out of the six ways the die can land (1, 2, 3, 4, 5, 6), three are even (2, 4, 6).

For some events, all outcomes are equally likely: tossing a fair coin, rolling a fair die, spinning a spinner that is divided into equal parts, and so on. In other situations, the outcomes are not equally likely. For example, when a twelve-sided die is rolled, a 1-digit number is more likely than a 2-digit number.

Many random processes lend themselves to intuitive predictions because their outcomes obey very definite laws of chance. Coin tosses and spinner experiments are good examples of these. Other processes do not lend themselves to such precise analysis. Predicting the weather is much harder than predicting the outcome of a coin toss.

In the long run, *Everyday Mathematics* aims to help children understand that the more often they repeat an experiment, the more reliable their predictions will be. For example, if a coin is tossed 10 times, it is possible, but not certain, that it will land heads-up about half the time. (Try it—you may be surprised at how often you obtain a 7-3 or 8-2 split.) But if the coin is tossed 100 times, it is more likely to land heads-up about half the time—heads and tails tend to "even out" with more tosses. If the coin is tossed 1,000 times, it is even more likely that heads will show about half the time. This important idea, known to mathematicians as the *Law of Large Numbers,* is illustrated by a block-drawing experiment in *Third Grade Everyday Mathematics*. Children are asked to figure out how many blocks of different colors are hidden in a bag by examining the results of repeatedly drawing a block from the bag. The more times they draw a block, the more likely it is that they will make the correct guess.

4.3 Using Data and Probability

Everyday Mathematics is committed to developing mathematics through applications, and virtually any number drawn from an application is a piece of data. Each year of the program has routines centered around uses of data and/or probability: the Weather Chart in Kindergarten; Explorations (Group Tally of Penny Dates in Grade 1); Projects (the Collections Project in Grade 2); and games (the *Block-Drawing Game* in Grade 3).

In *Everyday Mathematics* Grades 1–3, children also have special Data Days: days on which they collect data and work with data sets. They put data in order; observe the spread or range from most to least; make graphs; estimate representative, typical, or middle measurements; and count to the middle to find the middle value (or median) of each data set.

You probably do not need specific suggestions for data sets as much as you may need suggestions for applications in other topic areas. Children are naturally interested in surveying favorite colors, favorite foods, pets, handedness, and so on. You know what interests your children better than anyone else, so use your best ideas and theirs. The goal is to have children understand data exploration as a sensible process. Can they ask sensible questions? Can they make sensible graphs? Can they make sense of graphs? If so, then they are intelligent users of data and probability.

in perspective

In *Everyday Mathematics* Grades 4–6, students continue to collect, organize, and analyze data, and explore probability. In Grades 4 and 5, most of the data analysis occurs within the context of the World Tour and American Tour, respectively. In Grade 6, data analysis and probability are explored in individual lessons.

4

outline

5.1	**Dimension** 125
5.2	**Points** 126
5.3	**Lines, Segments, and Rays** 127
5.4	**Plane Figures** 127
	5.4.1 Angles and Rotations 128
	5.4.2 Polygons 129
	5.4.3 Circles and Pi (π) 133
5.5	**Solid Figures** 135
	5.5.1 Solid vs. 3-D 135
	5.5.2 Spheres 136
	5.5.3 Prisms and Cylinders 136
	5.5.4 Pyramids 137
	5.5.5 Polyhedrons 137

5.6	**Transformations** 138
5.7	**Relations** 139
	5.7.1 Parallel and Perpendicular 139
	5.7.2 Congruence and Similarity 140
5.8	**Symmetry** 141
	5.8.1 Line Symmetry 141
	5.8.2 Other Symmetries 142
5.9	**Coordinate Geometry** 142
5.10	**Teaching Geometry** 143
	5.10.1 The van Hiele Levels 144
	5.10.2 Solid vs. Plane Geometry 144
	5.10.3 Geometric Tools 145

Geometry is the study of spatial objects, their properties and relationships. It should be a natural and deeply intuitive part of mathematics for young children. From birth, they try to make sense of forms and shapes—a mother's face, their own bodies, shapes that move, shapes that don't, curved things, sharp things. So it is that young children come to school with a wealth of informal knowledge about spatial objects. Our role is first to acknowledge this, to recognize the value in what children already know and to help them "notice" what they see, and then to help them organize these perceptions and understandings into a coherent system that has meaning for them.

The word *geometry* derives from the Greek words for "earth" and "measure," which gives us a major clue about the first geometric activity of humans. The earliest records of geometric thinking, from the Egyptians, Babylonians, and Chinese confirm that geometry revolved around the solutions to very practical problems—laying out fields; finding areas and

volumes; constructing of houses, temples, pyramids; and so on. It is the Greeks, however, who are credited with formalizing the study of geometry.

Most of us encountered the geometry of Euclid and its axioms and theorems in high school. And, for many, this was a mystifying experience. One reason is the inappropriate structure and content of many of these geometry courses—a situation that is slowly changing as new approaches to secondary school geometry instruction are being developed. But, an equally compelling reason is that many students have little or no experience with geometry prior to their high school courses. The *Everyday Mathematics* curriculum places significant emphasis on this part of mathematics beginning in Kindergarten.

–Adapted from *Everyday Teaching for Everyday Mathematics*™ by Sheila Sconiers

In this essay, we first discuss common 1-, 2-, and 3-dimensional objects. Then we describe some operations on these objects and some relations these objects have with one another. Finally, we discuss the tools and approaches used in *Everyday Mathematics* for teaching geometry.

5.1 Dimension

Dimension is a tricky word: one meaning refers to the size of an object, as in the dimensions of a room or of a piece of paper; another meaning, the one implicit in terms like *3-dimensional,* refers to how much information is required to specify an exact location. For example, a checkerboard would be considered 2-dimensional because two pieces of information are needed to specify a particular square: its row and its column. A line is 1-dimensional because to specify a location on a line requires only one number. An opera house is 3-dimensional because to specify a seat requires knowing not only the row and the seat number, but also the level (main floor, mezzanine, first balcony, and so on).

We live in 3-dimensional space, in 3-D. The objects that constitute our physical experience are all 3-dimensional. Objects in other dimensions—lines, triangles, circles—are abstractions that do not physically exist in the way that dogs, cellular telephones, and pencils exist. Even the checkerboard which we said was 2-dimensional a moment ago is really 3-dimensional; it has length, width, and depth. The 2-dimensional surface of the checkerboard is an abstraction that exists in our minds.

Many 1- and 2-dimensional abstractions are so useful to us in the 3-dimensional world that we name them and study their properties. We model them with wood or plastic, with drawings, and with special manipulatives. But the models are always 3-dimensional, not the "real" thing. Even a drawing made with ink has thickness, length, and width.

Below we discuss objects in dimensions zero through three, and describe how *Everyday Mathematics* engages children in examining them.

5.2 Points

Point is an undefined term in geometry. Since *point* has no mathematical definition, we cannot say what a point is. Nevertheless, we all have some idea what a point is. A point has neither extension, height, width, nor depth. A point cannot be broken into pieces: it is one indivisible thing. This indivisibility means a point has no (zero) dimension: since a point has no parts, no information is needed to specify which part of a point is being referred to.

We can model a point by drawing a dot on a piece of paper. If we get a finer pen and draw a smaller dot, then we have a better model of a point. But no matter how small we make our dot, no matter how fine our pen's tip, we still cannot draw a true point. Even the smallest dot of ink has height, width, and depth; therefore, it is not a point.

● ● • ·

Models of points

Another way to think about points is as locations: A point is an exact position. On a map, a point marks where something is. There is, for example, a point on a number line that is exactly 3 units from the origin. In fact, there are two such points, one at $+3$ and one at -3, and they are there even if you can't really capture them. In *Kindergarten Everyday Mathematics,* children use points on maps when they follow maps and count steps to get from one room in the school to another. Children also locate points on numberlines and timelines beginning in Kindergarten. Children must imagine points on objects every time they measure a height, width, or depth: Length is the distance between two points. Points on maps are used to estimate distances and learn about map scale in Grade 3.

Sometimes a location is a point, but in a more abstract way. The vertices (corners) of a polygon, for example, are the points where the sides meet. Unless the polygon is on a coordinate system, the position of a vertex is of little interest. But the fact that it is a vertex is important—often the vertex receives a name and that contributes to a name for the whole polygon. Points are usually named with capital letters: point A, point B, and so on. Naming geometric figures using the names of points begins in Grade 2.

Sometimes, ordered pairs of numbers correspond to points. Graphing ordered pairs begins in third grade. There are other uses and models of points, but they are not discussed here. Our aim is to give you some ways to think about and discuss points and to help you realize how commonly we use them in our 3-dimensional world.

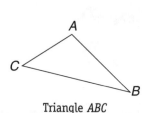

Triangle *ABC*

5.3 Lines, Segments, and Rays

Line is another undefined term, but, again, one for which we have good intuition. Lines have length, but not width or depth. We can model a line with pen and ink, by folding a piece of paper, or pulling a piece of string taught. Since one number is enough to specify a position on a line, lines are 1-dimensional.

A line is made up of infinitely many points. Think about "infinite" in two ways here. First of all, "infinite" means the line extends forever in two directions; it never ends. Although it has length, it cannot be measured. If you started marking off unit intervals on a line, you would never finish, no matter how long you kept it up. Models of lines have arrowheads on the "ends" to indicate that the line does not stop.

Now think about any two points on a line. No matter how close together they are, there are infinitely many points on the line between them. Mathematicians say lines are *dense,* meaning that between any two points on a line there is always another point. The fact that each point on a line can be associated with a number is a key to why our real-number system does not run dry. Just as there is always a point between any two points on a line, there is always a number between any two numbers.

Line segments and rays can be defined in terms of a line. A line segment is a part of a line with a beginning point and an ending point. (Mathematicians call both the beginning and ending points *endpoints.*) A segment has a finite length and a measure that you can approximate. A ray is a part of a line with a beginning point but no ending point. Rays are sometimes called *half-lines.* A ray, like a line, has no measure. A model for a ray usually has an arrowhead at the "end" opposite the beginning point.

Everyday Mathematics is consistent about using models with arrowheads for lines and rays. Encourage children to use them as well. One place that the arrowheads are not used, however, is in computer geometry packages such as the Geometer's Sketchpad and Cabri Geometry. It is not practical to draw arrowheads in these packages because you can "grab" lines and rays with a cursor and move them around. What you see, then, are models for rays and lines that extend to the edge of the screen and beyond.

5.4 Plane Figures

Plane is yet another undefined geometric term, but, again, one for which we have some intuition. A plane is a flat 2-dimensional object having length and width but no depth. Like a line, a plane does not end; it extends forever in every direction. And like a line, a plane cannot be measured. A tabletop, a smooth floor, or the surface of a calm body of water all suggest planes.

Just as 0-dimensional points make up 1-dimensional objects like lines, both 0-dimensional and 1-dimensional objects make up objects

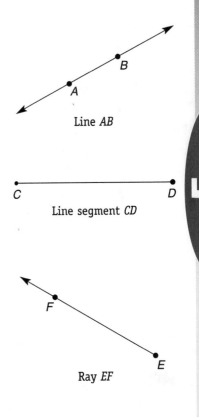

Line *AB*

Line segment *CD*

Ray *EF*

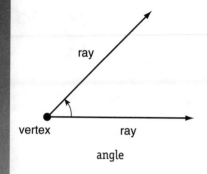

ray

vertex   ray

angle

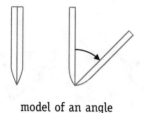

model of an angle

in a plane. There are infinitely many points and infinitely many lines in a plane. Objects that are entirely contained in a plane are called plane figures or planar figures.

5.4.1 Angles and Rotations

In mathematics, an angle consists of two rays or segments that have the same endpoint, called the vertex of the angle.[1] The rays or segments are called the sides of the angle. In *Everyday Mathematics* angles are most often modeled by segments because angles are introduced in Grade 1 as features of solids and in Grades 2 and 3 as parts of polygons.

It is often useful to think of an angle as being formed by starting with both rays or segments pointing in the same direction, and then rotating one ray or segment around the common endpoint. From first grade on, children model angles in this manner by bending a straw in half and rotating one of the halves around the bend.

Angles are measured in degrees. One complete rotation, a full circle, is 360 degrees (360°). If a child begins with both parts of the straw together and then rotates one of the parts one-quarter of the way around the bend, the resulting figure will model an angle of 90 degrees (90°). If the rotation continues another one-quarter of the way around the bend, the straw is straight and models an angle of 180 degrees (180°). A further one-quarter rotation models an angle of 270 degrees (270°). A final one-quarter rotation returns the straw to its starting position—an angle of 360 degrees (360°) (which looks like an angle of 0 degrees).

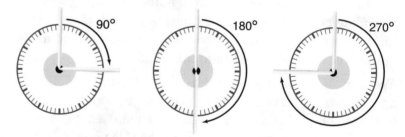

An analog clock also demonstrates angles. At 12 o'clock, the overlapping hands model an angle of 0° (or 360°); at 3 o'clock, the hands model an angle of 90° (or 270°). At 6 o'clock, they model an angle of 180°; at 9 o'clock, 270° (or 90°).

90°   180°   270°

---

[1] Sometimes angles are defined as consisting only of two rays with the same endpoint. Under this definition, angles formed by the line segments must be thought of as actually being formed by rays that extend the segments. In *Everyday Mathematics* we prefer to avoid this complication by allowing line segments to form angles.

Angles can be categorized according to the orientation of the rays. An angle of exactly 90° is a right angle. (A rectangle has four right angles.) An angle of exactly 180° is a straight angle. An angle of more than 90° but less than 180° is an obtuse angle, an angle of less than 90° is an acute angle, and an angle greater than 180° is a reflex angle.

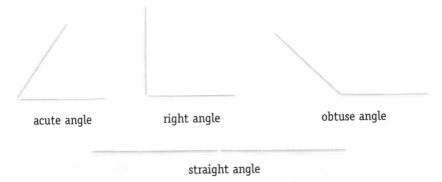

acute angle   right angle   obtuse angle

straight angle

Children in *Everyday Mathematics* are not expected to learn the names of various kinds of angles. They should, however, have significant experience manipulating angles of each category before the terms are introduced in later grades.

5.4.2 Polygons

A polygon is a closed, 2-dimensional figure, composed of line segments that do not cross each other. The points where the sides meet are called *vertices*. The sides form angles—one angle at each vertex.

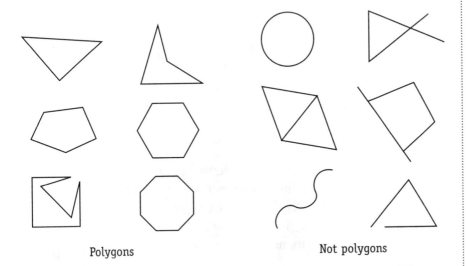

Polygons   Not polygons

Many polygons are named according to the number of sides they have:

Polygon	Number of Sides
triangle	3
quadrangle or quadrilateral	4
pentagon	5
hexagon	6

Polygon	Number of Sides
heptagon	7
octagon	8
nonagon	9
decagon	10

NOTE: The region inside a polygon is not properly part of the polygon. Strictly speaking, the polygon is just the line segments. The term *polygonal region* refers to both the line segments and the region inside. In informal discourse, however, this distinction is often ignored. We say, for example, that a cracker is a square or that a piece of paper is a rectangle. Therefore, do not try to force children to observe the distinction between polygons and polygonal regions.

A polygon can have any number of sides. For example, a polygon with 38 sides is called a 38-gon. More generally, a polygon with *n* sides is an *n*-gon.

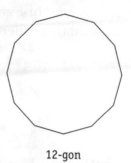

12-gon

Triangles

A three-sided polygon is called a *triangle*. (Unlike *quadrangles*, which are also called quadrilaterals, triangles are almost never called *trilaterals*.) Triangles may be classified according to side lengths: scalene (no two sides of equal length); isosceles (two sides of equal length); and equilateral (three sides of equal length). Triangles may also be classified by angles: acute (each angle less than 90 degrees); obtuse (one angle greater than 90 degrees); and right (one right angle).

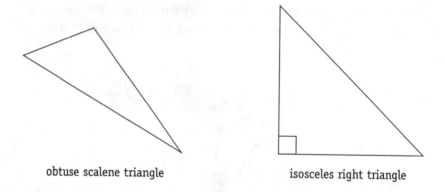

obtuse scalene triangle   isosceles right triangle

K–3 *Everyday Mathematics* students begin their explorations of triangles by finding them in shapes and pictures. They cut them out and make designs. Eventually they begin to learn some of the categories. Beginning in third grade, they label vertices, read and write names for them, and read and write names for their sides.

in perspective
In *Everyday Mathematics* Grades 4–6, students learn how to find areas of triangles, how triangles can be used in tessellations, and how to represent triangles analytically by graphing them in the coordinate plane.

Quadrilaterals

A four-sided polygon is called a *quadrangle* or *quadrilateral*. The segments connecting opposite corners of a quadrangle are called *diagonals*. Certain quadrangles have special features:

- *trapezoid* A quadrangle with exactly two parallel sides. If the other two sides are congruent, the trapezoid is called *isosceles*.

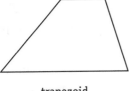

trapezoid

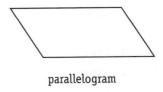

isosceles trapezoid

- *parallelogram* A quadrangle with parallel opposite sides. The opposite sides of a parallelogram are equal in length. Diagonals in a parallelogram bisect each other (intersect at their midpoint—that is, cut each other in half).

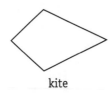

parallelogram

- *kite* A quadrangle in which two distinct pairs of adjacent sides are equal in length. Diagonals of a kite are perpendicular. *Note:* A kite is not a parallelogram.

kite

- *rhombus* A parallelogram in which all sides are equal in length. Diagonals of a rhombus bisect each other and are perpendicular.

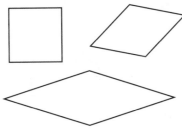

rhombuses

- *rectangle* A parallelogram in which all angles have the same measure (90°). Diagonals of a rectangle are equal in length and bisect each other.

- *square* A rectangle in which all sides are equal in length. Diagonals of a square are equal in length, bisect each other, and are perpendicular.

rectangles

squares

As you read through this list of quadrilaterals, note that some definitions depend on previously defined quadrangles. For example, a rectangle is first of all a parallelogram; it is also a parallelogram with equal angles. This means that a rectangle has all the properties of a parallelogram, along with some new properties that are rectangle-specific.

The diagram below shows the hierarchy of quadrangles. *Everyday Mathematics* doesn't expect you to use it with your children—most children in K–3 have neither the geometric experience nor the logical-thinking skills to understand hierarchical classification schemes like this one—but you may find it useful yourself. Pick any quadrangle in the hierarchy. It has all the properties of any quadrangle on a path leading to it. For example, a square is a rectangle, a rhombus, a parallelogram, and a quadrangle.

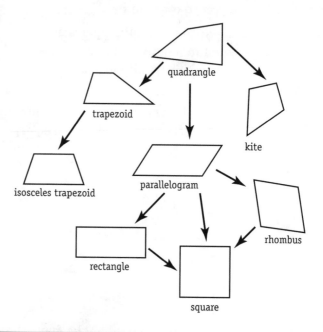

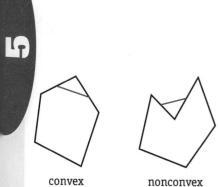

convex   nonconvex

Regular Polygons

A regular polygon has all sides the same length and all angles equal. If a polygon is regular, then it is possible to draw a circle that passes through each vertex, and the vertices will be equally spaced on the circumference. (Circles can also be drawn through every vertex of any triangle or rectangle, but the points will not be evenly spaced unless the triangle is equilateral or the rectangle is a square.)

regular
triangle

regular
quadrangle

regular
pentagon

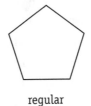

regular
hexagon

in perspective

In *Everyday Mathematics* Grades 4–6, student exploration of polygons is extended to include transformations of polygons. See Section 5.6 for a discussion of transformations.

5.4.3 Circles and Pi (π)

A circle consists of all the points in a plane that are the same distance from a given point in the plane. The given point is the center of the circle. Many things in the world have circular shapes, although nothing in the natural world is perfectly circular. Features and properties of a circle include:

- *radius* A line segment connecting the center of a circle and any point on the circle; also, the length of that segment.

- *chord* A line segment with endpoints on a circle.

- *diameter* A chord through the center of a circle; also, the length of that chord. The diameter of a circle is twice its radius.

- *circumference* The distance around, or perimeter of, a circle.

You may want to try to think of a circle as a regular *n*-gon where *n* is infinitely large. For example, start with a square. A square is not a very good approximation of a circle, but it's a beginning. Double the number of sides, to obtain a regular octagon. That's closer to a circle. Double the number of sides again to obtain a regular 16-gon. That's closer still. Doubling a few more times would give a figure that could be distinguished from a circle only with a magnifying glass. Double infinitely many times and the result would actually be a circle.

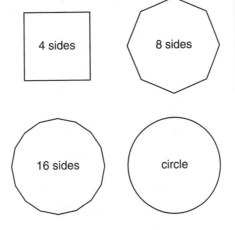

4 sides   8 sides

16 sides   circle

NOTE: A circle may be distinguished from a circular region, or disk, but this is not something to be emphasized with children.

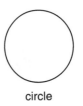

circle   circular region

An important characteristic of a circle is that the ratio of the circumference to the diameter is always the same number. This number is called *pi* and is denoted by the Greek letter π. Pi is an irrational number; its decimal equivalent does not repeat and never

NOTE: A list of some of the digits of pi appears on page 56.

ends. Two commonly used approximations for π are 3.14 and 22/7, but neither of these is exactly equal to π.

In third grade, children explore the relationship between the diameter and the circumference of a circle. They roll food cans to find circumferences, measure across the tops of the cans to find diameters, and display the results in a table. From these results, they discover that the circumference of a circle is consistently about 3 times its diameter. This is a first approximation of π, and a pretty good approximation at that.

Mountains of Pi

The earliest known reference to π occurs in an Egyptian papyrus scroll, written around 1650 B.C. by a scribe named Ahmes. He found the area of a circle using a rough approximation of π. Around 200 B.C., Archimedes of Syracuse (in Sicily, then a Greek colony) found that π is somewhere between 3 10/17 and 3 1/7, about 3.14. Little more was learned about π until the seventeenth century, when new formulas were discovered. Ludolph van Ceulen, a German mathematician, spent most of his life calculating π to thirty-five decimal places. Now most inexpensive calculators display π to 8 or 10 decimal places.

Today, most investigations of π involve powerful computers. Such calculations have been a standard task for each new generation of computers. In 1949, π was calculated to 37,000 places on ENIAC, one of the first computers. Later, π was computed to 100,000 digits on an IBM 7090 computer, and in 1981, to 2 million digits on a NEC supercomputer. In the next few years, these calculations were extended to 17.5 million digits, then 34 million, then past 200 million, and then in 1989 to more than 1 billion digits. As of September 1999, the world record, held by the laboratory of Dr. Yasumasa Kanada of the University of Tokyo, is 206.1 billion digits.

The article, "The Mountains of Pi," by Richard Preston (*The New Yorker,* March 2, 1992, pages 36–67), relates the fascinating history of pi and why it has attracted mathematicians for thousands of years. According to the article, "The decimal for pi goes on forever, so the number cannot be written with complete accuracy: 3.14159265358979323846264338327950288419 7 . . . is only an approximation . . . No apparent pattern emerges in the succession of digits . . . They do not repeat periodically, seeming to pop up by blind chance, lacking any perceivable order, rule, reason, or design . . ."

"The Mountains of Pi" tells the story of two mathematicians, David and Gregory Chudnovsky, who calculated π to more than two billion digits on a computer of their own design, which they built in Gregory's apartment using mail-order parts. Calculating π to so many digits not only tests the power of new supercomputers, it also continues the search for patterns in the digits—a search that, so far, has yielded no results. As the article puts it, "[The Chudnovskys] wonder whether the digits contain a hidden rule, as yet unseen architecture, close to the mind of God . . . . If we were to explore the digits of π far enough, they might resolve into a breathtaking numerical pattern . . . and it might mean something . . . On the other hand, the digits of π may ramble forever . . ."

5.5 Solid Figures

Space is the 3-dimensional world of our experience. Like points, lines, and planes, space cannot be defined geometrically. Spatial objects have length, width, and depth. Like lines and planes, space never ends and it cannot be measured. There are infinitely many points, infinitely many lines, and infinitely many planes in space. Spatial figures are objects in space, and they come in infinitely many shapes, sizes, and orientations.

Having good spatial sense means you can mentally manipulate 1-, 2-, and 3-dimensional objects in space and describe their orientations to one another. Spatial sense is also important in constructing 3-dimensional objects, in representing 3-dimensional objects in two dimensions by drawing on paper or on a computer screen, and in interpreting drawings of 3-dimensional objects. Video games often demand a well-developed spatial sense of the latter kind—at least if you want to win.

5.5.1 Solid vs. 3-D

The objects listed below are models for common 3-dimensional mathematical figures. Before reading on, compare the objects.

Empty shoe box	Brick
Basketball	Baseball
Empty soup can	Rolling pin

You probably noticed differences and similarities among these objects. The items in the left-hand column are hollow, and those in the right-hand column are filled.

All the objects listed above are solid in the sense that they can be felt when touched. Virtually all concrete models of 3-dimensional figures are solid in this sense. For example, a cube can be modeled by a construction made of drinking straws, by an empty box, or by a die. All three models are solid, but each highlights a different mathematical aspect of cubes. The drinking-straw model shows a cube's edges, the box models the surface of a cube, and the die models a cube and its interior.

In *Everyday Mathematics,* we define a geometric solid as all the points on the surface of a 3-dimensional figure. A "geometric solid" is actually just the "skin." Thus, despite its name, a geometric solid is "hollow" and does not properly include the points in its interior. Just the edges and vertices of the figure form is what is sometimes called a *wireframe,* the "skeleton" of the figure. Both the hollow figure and the figure with its interior—both a balloon and a baseball—are 3-dimensional.

NOTE: The advent of computer geometry packages is already beginning to improve the authors' hopes for more exploration of 2-dimensional and 3-dimensional orientation. These packages model the drawing and moving of objects on the surface of the computer monitor. It is hoped that as computers become less expensive and more powerful, these tools will make it into the hands of children, who will perhaps learn more geometry faster than their high-school counterparts today.

Three representations of a cube

Common 3-dimensional figures such as cones, pyramids, spheres, cubes, cylinders, and prisms do not include points in their interior. These common solids are only the skins of the figures. That's why the objects in the first column of items at the beginning of this section are better models for a prism, sphere, and cylinder, respectively, than the items in the second column.

However, having said this, do not try to keep children from using the names *cone* or *pyramid* when both the figure and its interior are meant. In informal discourse both the surface and its interior are often meant when terms like *pyramid* or *cone* are used. Since such language is so commonly used, we do children no favors preaching "right" names. When eventually the distinction becomes mathematically necessary, it can be made and understood easily enough.

5.5.2 Spheres

A sphere is the set of all points in space a given distance from a given point. The given point is the center of the sphere; the given distance is the radius of the sphere. A sphere is perhaps the simplest 3-dimensional figure, but note that the definition includes only the points on the surface, so a sphere is like a very thin balloon. The space inside the sphere, the interior, is not part of the sphere. A solid sphere (modeled by a baseball) is a sphere along with all its interior points.

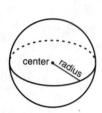

5.5.3 Prisms and Cylinders

A prism is a geometrical solid with two bases that are polygons. The bases must be the same size and shape and parallel to each other. All the other faces must be parallelograms.

Imagine making a prism in the following way. Begin with a closed figure (for example, a pentagon) and its interior region in a plane. This is the *pre-image*. Translate or "slide" it to a parallel plane to get an image. (Section 5.6 discusses translations and other geometric transformations.) The original figure and its translation image are the bases of the solid. The faces of the solid are formed as the sides of the pre-image slide to the image. The height, or altitude, of a prism is the perpendicular distance between its bases.

Solids of this type are named according to the shapes of their bases:

• **cylindrical solid** This solid has two bases of any shape. Most commonly, however, the bases are circles, in which case the skin of the solid is a cylinder.

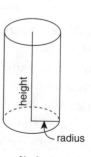

cylinder

cylindrical
solid

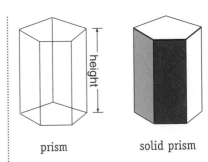

- **prism** This is a cylindrical solid that has two polygonal bases. The number of sides the bases have determine the number of other faces. Each other face has four edges. The skin of the solid is a prism.

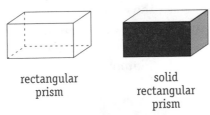

rectangular prism

solid rectangular prism

prism

solid prism

- **rectangular prism** This prism has two rectangular bases. There are four other faces, each with four edges. The skin of the solid is a rectangular prism.

5.5.4 Pyramids

Imagine making a pyramid in the following way. Start with a polygon and its interior; this will be the base of a pyramid. Also imagine a point called a *vertex* that is not in the same plane as the base. Use line segments to connect each point on the polygon to the vertex. All points on these segments and between the segments and the base form a solid. The "skin" of this solid is a pyramid. Other than the base, all the faces in pyramids are triangles.

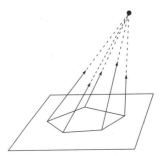

Unlike prisms and cylinders, which have two bases, most pyramids have only one base. Only one type of pyramid has more than one base. In a pyramid with four faces, all of them triangles, any of the faces is a base. This is a triangular pyramid or tetrahedron.

Names of pyramids depend on the shape of the base. If the base is a square, the pyramid is a square pyramid; if the base is a hexagon, the figure is a hexagonal pyramid; and so on.

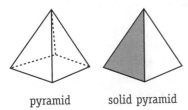

pyramid   solid pyramid

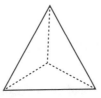

triangular pyramid or tetrahedron

5.5.5 Polyhedrons

A *polyhedron* is a closed 3-dimensional figure made up of polygonal regions.[2] The polygonal regions are called *faces*. The line segments where two faces come together are called *edges*. The points where three or more edges come together are called *vertices* or corners. The word *polyhedron* comes from Greek words meaning "many bases" or "many seats." Polyhedrons include cubes, pyramids, prisms, and many other shapes.

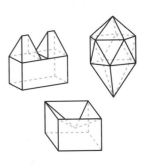

polyhedrons

---

[2] A polygonal region is a polygon and its interior. A rectangular piece of paper, for example, is a model of a polygonal region.

In a *regular polyhedron,* all the faces are congruent (the same size and shape) and the same number of faces come together at the same angle at every vertex. There are five regular polyhedrons, as illustrated below. From left to right they are the tetrahedron (4 equilateral triangles), the cube (6 squares), the octahedron (8 equilateral triangles), the dodecahedron (12 regular pentagons), and the icosahedron (20 equilateral triangles). The regular polyhedrons are also known as the Platonic solids.

  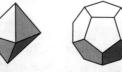

tetrahedron   cube   octahedron   dodecahedron   icosahedron

Students of K–3 *Everyday Mathematics* explore geometric solids by manipulating the standard blocks available in most classrooms, paper models constructed from blackline masters, and a wide variety of real-life materials, such as shoe boxes. In first and second grades, the class creates a Shapes Museum of objects brought from home.

One goal of the geometry strand at all grade levels is to help children see connections between 2-dimensional figures, such as polygons and curves, and the corresponding polyhedrons and curved surfaces in three dimensions. There are two main roads toward this goal in K–3 *Everyday Mathematics.* One is identifying 2-dimensional figures as parts of 3-dimensional ones using manipulatives. The other is building 3-dimensional models using various materials (e.g. straws and twist ties, paper, clay). These constructions, which begin in first grade, help children develop good connections between 1-dimensional line segments, 2-dimensional polygons, and 3-dimensional wireframes having polygonal regions as faces.

5.6 Transformations

A geometric transformation is an action that somehow changes a geometric object. Some transformations do not change the size or shape of the object; others do.

There are several kinds of transformations that do not change an object's size and shape. The simplest of these is a *slide.* In a slide, an object (called the pre-image) is simply moved to a new position. The object in the new position is called the image.

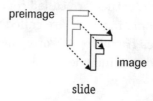

slide

in perspective

Formal definitions of many geometric terms are left to Grades 4–6.

For more on straws and twist ties, see pages 32–33 in the Management Guide.

Other size- and shape-preserving transformations include flips and turns. These are illustrated below. Slides, flips, and turns can be combined to obtain more complicated transformations.

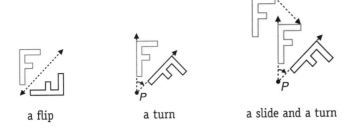

| a flip | a turn | a slide and a turn |

Geometric objects can also be transformed in ways that change size and shape. In a stretch, for example, a shape can be expanded in one or more directions.

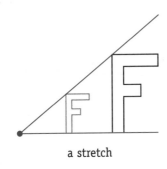

a stretch

The transformational approach to geometry can be very powerful. Below we will explain ideas like congruence and symmetry in terms of transformations. Although children's exposure to transformations in K–3 *Everyday Mathematics* is limited, you need not hesitate to begin talking about transformations in simple patterns if you think your children are ready.

in **perspective**

Translations, reflections, rotations, and scalings are topics covered in Grades 4–6.

5.7 Relations

Just as numbers can be related to one another in various ways ($5 > 3$, $6/2 = 3$, $5 \neq 3$, and so on), geometric objects can likewise be related to one another in various ways. If two figures are exactly the same size and shape, for example, we say they are *congruent*. In the following sections, we discuss several of the most important geometric relations.

5.7.1 Parallel and Perpendicular

Two lines in a plane either cross or do not cross. Lines in a plane that never cross are *parallel*. Parallel lines are always the same distance apart. Many objects in our everyday world suggest parallel lines: window gratings, highway lane markings, and lines on paper. The symbol $\parallel$ is used to indicate parallelism.

Two lines that cross each other are said to *intersect*. When two lines intersect, they form several angles. When the angles formed are right angles (90°), the lines are *perpendicular*. The symbol ⌐ is often included in a drawing of perpendicular lines to indicate the right angle. The symbol ⊥ is used to indicate perpendicularity.

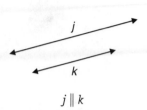

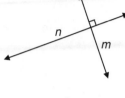

$$j \parallel k \qquad\qquad m \perp n$$

Planes can also be parallel or intersecting. If two planes intersect at right angles, they are perpendicular. The same is true of line segments, squares, and many other geometric objects. Opposite faces of a cube, for example, are parallel; adjacent faces are perpendicular.

parallel faces   adjacent faces

Beginning in first grade, children are introduced to the ideas of parallel and perpendicular through the exploration of solids, their faces and edges. Drawing and naming parallel and perpendicular line segments begins in second grade. You can also point out the vast array of perpendicular and parallel objects throughout your classroom and school.

5.7.2 Congruence and Similarity

Two figures that are exactly the same size and shape are *congruent*. The shapes can be as simple as two six-inch line segments or as complicated as two rocket motors. (Of course, no two rocket motors could ever be *exactly* the same size and shape, since each would have tiny nicks and other marks that the other would lack. Only abstract geometric objects can ever be perfectly congruent. Real objects always differ from one another.)

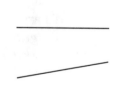

congruent line segments

congruent polygons

congruent polyhedrons

Two figures that are the same shape but not necessarily the same size are *similar*. Any two squares, for example, are similar, as are any two equilateral triangles, or any two copies of Michelangelo's statue of David.

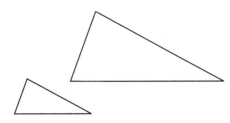

similar polygons

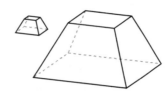

similar polyhedrons

5.8 Symmetry

A figure is symmetric if you can do something to it and it looks the same. For example, a heart is symmetric because you can flip it over and it looks the same. A starfish is symmetric because you can turn it and it also looks the same. A strip of wallpaper border is symmetric because you can slide it to a new position and it looks the same.

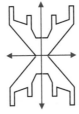

line symmetry

rotational symmetry

translation symmetry

5.8.1 Line Symmetry

The simplest kind of symmetry is *line symmetry*. If a figure has balance over a line, meaning it can be divided along a line into two halves that match exactly, then that figure has line symmetry. The line is called a "line of symmetry of the figure."

There are easy tests to check a figure for line symmetry. Fold or imagine folding the figure on the line. If the halves match,

the fold is a line of symmetry. Figures may also have more than one line of symmetry. An isosceles trapezoid has one line of symmetry. A square has four lines of symmetry. A circle has infinitely many lines of symmetry.

Solid figures can have a form of symmetry very much like line symmetry. Each half of the human face, for example, is the mirror image (more or less) of the other half. Many other living

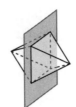
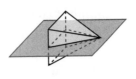

things have this sort of bilateral symmetry. The main difference between this sort of symmetry and line symmetry is that the reflection is in a plane instead of a line. (Also, it's not so easy to fold one's face in half to demonstrate that the two halves match.)

Children explore line symmetry as a topic beginning in *Kindergarten Everyday Mathematics.* However, the idea could easily come up in class discussion any time children are playing with pattern blocks or other geometric manipulatives. They may find line symmetry when they look for mathematics in newspapers or magazines. Many corporate logos, for example, have line symmetry.

5.8.2 Other Symmetries

Sometimes people think a figure has line symmetry when it actually doesn't. They may think, for example, that there is a way to fold a parallelogram so the two halves match.

Parallelograms do not have line symmetry, but they do have *rotational symmetry.* If a parallelogram is given a half-turn, it will look unchanged. The amount of turning required can vary; a starfish, for example, looks the same after a $\frac{1}{5}$ turn. Rotational symmetry, also known as *turn symmetry,* can be combined with line

 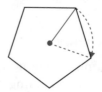

symmetry. A pentagon, for example, has five lines of symmetry, one through each vertex as well as $\frac{1}{5}$ turn symmetry.

Line symmetry and turn symmetry are not the only kinds of symmetry. Tessellations, or tilings of a plane, involve symmetry based on slides, just as line symmetry is based on flips and rotational symmetry is based on turns. In K–3 *Everyday Mathematics* the focus is on line symmetry; tessellations and rotations are introduced in Grades 4–6.

5.9 Coordinate Geometry

Coordinate geometry integrates numbers and geometry. The simplest coordinate geometry is a number line. A point on a number line is identified by a single number, the coordinate. For example, the point marked with an X on the number line below has coordinate -2.5.

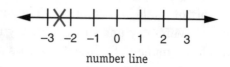

number line

Two perpendicular number lines that intersect at 0 form a rectangular coordinate system. The two number lines, called *axes*, make it possible to use pairs of numbers, called *coordinates,* to locate points. For example, point X on the coordinate plane below is at (3, 2).

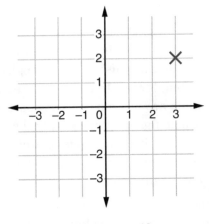

coordinate grid

Rectangular coordinates have been used for centuries; the ancient Egyptians and Romans used them to survey fields. They received a big boost in the early seventeenth century, though, when the French philosopher and mathematician René Descartes (1596–1650) made significant advances in coordinate geometry. Today, rectangular coordinates are often called Cartesian coordinates in honor of his work.

Since Descartes, coordinate geometry has been a powerful tool for advances in many areas of mathematics. In *Everyday Mathematics,* the serious study of coordinate geometry begins in fourth grade. Before that, work with coordinate geometry is restricted mostly to number lines and graphing data.

See Section 1.4.3 for a discussion of number lines, and Sections 4.1.3 and 7.3.1 for more information about graphing.

5.10 Teaching Geometry

Children in *Kindergarten Everyday Mathematics* play with models of shapes, manipulate pattern blocks, cut shapes out of paper, and look for shapes in their everyday environment. This informal approach is intended to let children's curiosity lead them toward recognizing features of polygons. Vocabulary is introduced as necessary in order to identify groups of shapes by name. Many common shapes that young children recognize are embedded in solids: A square is a face on a cube; a rectangle is a face on a box; a circle is the shape on the end of a can, and so on.

This approach—concrete manipulations leading to the recognition of key features and the naming of objects—continues throughout the grades. Children in Grade 3 will reach a point where they know most of the names of the polygons listed in Section 5.4.2 above. They will also be able to categorize triangles and quadrilaterals by important characteristics such as parallel sides, equal sides, right angles, and equal angles.

5.10.1 The van Hiele Levels

The *Everyday Mathematics* curriculum is based on research that has been carried out by the authors and others over several decades. In geometry, some of the most important research was done in the late 1950s by two Dutch researchers, Dina and Pierre van Hiele.

The van Hieles identified five stages in the development of geometric understanding. During the first stage, children approach shapes holistically. A triangle is a triangle because its overall shape is like other objects that are also called triangles. At this stage, shapes are not broken down into parts; line segments, vertices, and angles of the triangle are not considered separately. Instead, the child grasps the whole figure at once. At this stage, the visualization stage, children can benefit from hands-on work with pattern blocks, geometric solids, geoboards, straws, and connectors, and real objects from their everyday environment.

During the second stage, children begin to notice the individual elements that make up geometric figures. They see that a triangle has three sides and three corners; they see that a square has four sides all the same length and four right angles. At this stage, children should continue hands-on work and should begin to compare, measure, sort, and describe shapes. They can also begin to learn the names for the parts of geometric figures: *side, angle, face, edge,* and so on.

In the third stage, students begin to move beyond the analysis of single shapes and start thinking about relationships among different shapes. They can, for example, understand that squares are rectangles since they meet the minimal requirements: four sides and four right angles. Children also begin to understand hierarchical classification schemes like the one for quadrilaterals in Section 5.4.2. They should also be formulating simple chains of reasoning. If the context is not too abstract, children at this stage can work with formal definitions of geometric objects and properties. This is also the stage of informal proof, which is the highest level in elementary school geometry.

Beyond the informal proof stage, the van Hieles identified two further levels. One is the level of deductive reasoning, the level at which high school geometry is traditionally taught. The highest level is the formal axiomatic geometry of professional mathematicians, a level most of us would not even recognize as geometry.

5.10.2 Solid vs. Plane Geometry

Which is less abstract, a cube or a square? In a purely mathematical sense, both are equally abstract. But in a practical sense, a cube is less abstract than a square. Good, concrete models for cubes are commonplace: a sugar cube, a die, or a lump of clay pressed into shape are all excellent representations of a cube. A square, on the other hand, is not so easily modeled. The face of a cube is a model for a square region, not a square. We can use straws to build a model of the square, but everyday objects that are good models of squares (or circles, triangles, and other plane figures) are hard to find.

So, odd as it may sound, solid geometry is more concrete than plane geometry. For this reason, *Everyday Mathematics* includes work with spheres, prisms, cylinders, and other 3-dimensional figures much earlier than has been traditional.

5.10.3 Geometric Tools

The study of geometry in *Everyday Mathematics* involves many hands-on experiences, such as manipulating pattern blocks and attribute blocks, tracing shapes from templates, working with geoboards, cutting out shapes, folding shapes, drawing shapes with straightedges or compasses, constructing shapes out of straws, and constructing 3-dimensional figures from 2-dimensional nets (flat figures that can be folded to form closed, 3-dimensional solids). For more information on some of the tools used for geometry in *Everyday Mathematics,* see the section on Other Tools, pages 31–36 of the Management Guide.

Measurement

6

outline

6.1 Personal Measures 147

6.2 Measurement Systems 149

    6.2.1 U.S. Customary System 149

    6.2.2 Metric System 149

    6.2.3 Converting between Measures 150

6.3 Measurement Tools and Techniques 150

    6.3.1 Measurements as Estimates 150

    6.3.2 Measuring Sticks and Tapes 151

    6.3.3 Scales and Balances 151

6.4 Length 153

6.5 Area 153

    6.5.1 Discrete Conception of Area 153

    6.5.2 Continuous Conception of Area 154

6.6 Volume 154

    6.6.1 Discrete and Continuous Conceptions of Volume 154

    6.6.2 Capacity 155

    6.6.3 Linking Area and Volume 155

6.7 Weight and Mass 156

6.8 Angle Measure 156

6.9 Elapsed Time 157

6.10 Money 157

    6.10.1 Money Facts 158

    6.10.2 Money History 160

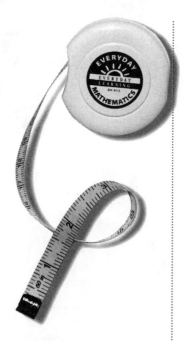

Measurement is one of the most widespread uses of mathematics in daily life. Even very young children show considerable interest in measure. How tall is my block building? How long can we make this block train? How much water until the sink overflows? and How long until lunch time? are common questions spontaneously pursued by preschool and primary grade children. Older children continue to be curious about how much, how long, how far, and the like. Many become fascinated with measures and ways of determining them, whether it is the height of a tall building or the amount of water in a swimming pool. *Everyday Mathematics* recognizes and capitalizes on children's natural curiosity about measure and measurement. Throughout the grades, children engage in interesting and purposeful tasks as they learn how to measure and how to interpret other people's measures.

Measurement is the source of many of the numbers that we use in everyday life. Measures, along with their units, tell "how much" of something there is. You can perform arithmetic operations with measure numbers and obtain results that make sense. For example, a 6-pound cabbage weighs twice as much as a 3-pound cabbage, and someone who spends 30 minutes on homework spends twice as much time as someone who spends 15 minutes on homework. Quantifying and comparing seem to be common quests of childhood (adulthood, too) and both are important when exploring measurement. Furthermore, because all measures are estimates, knowing how to measure means knowing how to approximate and deal with error. This topic is discussed later in this essay, in Section 6.3.1.

Sections 6.1 and 6.2 discuss measurement systems and units, including personal measures, the metric system, and U.S. customary measures. Section 6.3 highlights some measurement tools and their uses. Sections 6.4 through 6.6 address measurement in one, two, and three dimensions (length, area, and volume), while section 6.7 discusses weight and mass. Angle measures, elapsed time, and money are discussed in Sections 6.8 through 6.10.

6.1 Personal Measures

Units for measures of length appeared relatively early in human history and were based on things familiar to people—namely, their bodies. Just as many early number systems were based on ten—probably because humans have ten fingers—many early linear measures were based on the lengths of certain body parts. This is the origin of such measures as foot, digit, span, and hand—each of which was, or still is, a commonly used unit for measuring length.

The problem with a measurement system based on body parts is that all bodies differ. Who is to say *whose* cubit (a measure based on the distance between the elbow and fingertips) is the cubit to measure by? Without agreement, how do buyers know that they are getting their money's worth when someone sells them 56 cubits of cloth? In ancient Egypt, this problem led to the creation of a royal master cubit. The royal master cubit, which was made of black granite, became the standard against which every cubit stick in the land was periodically matched. The thousands of cubit sticks used to build the Great Pyramid of Cheops at Giza were made so precisely that the length of any one side of the pyramid differs only 0.05% from the mean length of all four sides. Eventually, nations established their measures by agreeing on standards against which all measurement implements were compared.

Another problem arose when members of two or more groups that had been isolated—because of distance, geography, or political barriers—came into contact with one another. In the medieval trade fairs of Europe, for example, merchants from many nations gathered to sell their wool cloth. Most agreed to measure their cloth in ells, but the length of an ell differed among the various nations' merchants. Therefore, an iron standard ell of two feet, six inches

NOTE: See Section 6.2 for a discussion of current measurement systems.

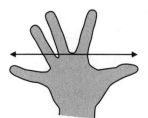

hand span

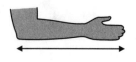

cubit

yard

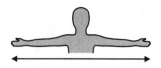

fathom

digit

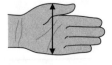

hand

was made and left with the Keeper of the Fair. Each participating merchant was required to use this ell in all business dealings at the fair.

In England, cheating and abuse of measures became so common that a few years after the Magna Carta of 1215, the "Assize of Weights and Measures" was drawn up. The Assize defined and standardized a broad list of units that lasted for almost 600 years. One of these units, "The Iron Yard of Our Lord the King," was prescribed and divided into 3 feet of 12 inches each. Eventually, all kinds of measures became standardized in some way, and many national systems of measures came into being. Nearly all of these systems were replaced in Europe by the metric system during the nineteenth century. Britain and its former colonies in America kept to their old ways until well into the twentieth century. The United States still uses the old system.

The origins of some of our common measures give us a good way to approximate various things. The list below describes some common measures based on dimensions of the adult human body. For children, these personal measurements are likely to be smaller than the standards.

hand span The distance from the end of the thumb to the end of the little finger in an outstretched hand; a useful way to measure smaller things. The span has been standardized at 9 inches.

cubit A very old unit of measure, based on the distance between the elbow and the extended fingertips. The Egyptians used the cubit as early as 3000 B.C. to build their pyramids. The cubit has been standardized at various times at values between 18 and 22 inches.

yard The distance from the tip of the nose to the tips of the fingers; often used to measure cloth. A yard has been standardized at 3 feet (36 inches).

fathom The distance from fingertip to fingertip of the outstretched arms; said to be derived from an Anglo-Saxon word meaning "embrace." Fathoms are often used to measure the depth of water. Perhaps this is because the "leadsman" on a boat or ship in the days before electronic depth finders would drop a lead weight on the end of a rope until it hit bottom and then count the number of fingertip-to-fingertip measures as he gathered in his line. A fathom has been standardized at 6 feet (2 yards).

digit The width of a finger. A division of the royal master cubit in ancient Egypt.

Some special situations employ special measures. For example, horses are said to be so many "hands" high. A hand is the width of the palm. The hand has been standardized at 4 inches. Units of length too long to be measured conveniently with the body tended to vary widely from country to country before the adoption of the metric system. For example, where we used a mile (5,280 feet), the Russians used a verst (about 3,500 feet or about 1 kilometer).

Beginning in Kindergarten, children measure various items or parts of their classrooms with parts of themselves and discuss which body parts are more appropriate for which objects—a predecessor to choosing measurement tools and units that "fit" the measuring task. These activities are expanded in first grade as children learn about measuring techniques with their body-part units, such as putting the measuring device end-to-end to measure larger objects. They are also asked to make a habit of labeling their measures appropriately. This habit is important not only for the act of measuring itself, but as an important part of learning to solve number stories. From second grade on, children continue to use personal reference measures, but the focus shifts to finding body parts that approximate customary or metric units. These parts can then be used to estimate measures without using a ruler, tape measure, or other standardized measuring device. For example, the width of a finger may be about one centimeter, or a child's foot may be about eight inches long.

in perspective

Body-part estimation activities continue in *Everyday Mathematics* Grades 4–6 in part because of practical needs: children grow and their personal reference measures may change.

6.2 Measurement Systems

The standardized measurement systems that we use today are the U.S. customary system and the metric system, both of which are discussed below. By "customary" measures we mean the ones commonly used in the United States. If you have children from other countries in your class, though, the metric system may be customary to them, so be sure to make the difference clear.

There are also several types of measures in common use that are neither metric nor U.S. customary: measures of angles, elapsed time, and monetary value to name a few. *Everyday Mathematics* includes many activities to engage children in understanding these types of measures, as discussed later in this essay.

6.2.1 U.S. Customary System

The U.S. customary system is adapted from the English system, which was developed around the 13th century. Although most people in the United States are relatively comfortable with the U.S. customary system, it has definite drawbacks compared to the metric system. For one thing, because they evolved gradually out of specific, often local, needs, customary units of length, weight, and capacity are largely independent of one another. Another drawback is that the relationships between units are cumbersome. For example, a foot is $\frac{1}{3}$ of a yard, but an inch (the next-smaller standard unit) is $\frac{1}{12}$ of a foot. A quart is $\frac{1}{4}$ of a gallon, but a pint (the next-smaller standard unit) is $\frac{1}{2}$ of a quart.

6.2.2 Metric System

The metric system, on the other hand, was deliberately developed by scientifically-minded people in France at the end of the 18th century. Metric units of length, area, volume, capacity, and weight are interrelated. For example, a liter is a measure of capacity equal to 1 cubic decimeter, and a cubic decimeter is equal to the volume of 1 kilogram of distilled water at 4 °C.

The basic unit of measure in this system is the meter. Originally, the meter was defined as one ten-millionth of the distance from the North Pole to the equator along the global meridian through Paris. These days, it is defined as the distance light will travel in a vacuum in $\frac{1}{299,792,458}$ seconds. In the metric system, many units are defined relative to the meter. Next-smaller or next-larger units differ by a power of 10 and, thus, are easily converted from one to another. For example, a decimeter is one-tenth (or 0.1) of a meter, and a centimeter is 0.1 of a decimeter.

6.2.3 Converting between Measures

Because the United States uses both metric and customary measures, being able to convert between these systems can sometimes be important. For example, Minnesota, a neighbor of metric-using Canada, has posted road signs proclaiming that 55 miles per hour is 88 kilometers per hour. It is also important to be able to convert from one unit to another within a system. Knowing how many inches are in a foot, feet in a yard, yards in a mile, and so on provides the power to convert numbers from one unit to another, which can be very handy in many situations.

In the early grades of *Everyday Mathematics,* children learn what U.S. customary and metric measures are, how to estimate them generally, and how to approximate them using measuring tools. Children in *Everyday Mathematics* Grades K-3 do not convert units from one system to the other; they convert only within a given system. As children gain more experience and the appropriate arithmetic skills in the later grades, they learn how to convert between the systems.

6.3 Measurement Tools and Techniques

No matter which system or unit is being used, measuring tools provide ways to attach numbers to many common and uncommon things in everyone's life. There are measuring tools to measure in any unit or system; some tools even provide help with conversions. The history of science is very much intertwined with the development of improved measuring instruments. New scientific discoveries often hinge on new and more precise measuring tools, and verification or rejection of theories often depends on increasingly precise measurements. Much of modern industry and technology depends on using very precise measures that are standardized throughout the world. Children will learn that the measuring tools that we all use are based on mutually agreed-upon standards, but that our own measurements are mere approximations, as the following paragraph explains.

6.3.1 Measurements as Estimates

Physical measurements are never exact. Even measures that seem exact are actually estimates that are "close enough" for practical

perspective

Converting between measurement systems is first addressed in *Fourth Grade Everyday Mathematics.*

considerations. We can never line up the precise edge of an object with a precise point on a measuring tool. For example, this page is not exactly 11 inches long. If you look at its edge under a microscope you will see that it is not exactly even and straight. Also, no matter how small the subdivisions on a ruler, there are always unmarked spaces between the marked lines. Thus, when children learn to measure—with inexact body measures in Kindergarten, or to the nearest half-inch, quarter-inch, or centimeter in second or third grade, for example—they also are learning to approximate and deal with error.

6.3.2 Measuring Sticks and Tapes

Along with weighing scales and balances, rulers and tape measures are among the first tools for practical everyday measurements, both in human history and in the lives of children. Children use such tools beginning in *Kindergarten Everyday Mathematics.* First, they learn to give "ballpark" estimates of heights and lengths; then, over the years, they get progressively more sophisticated in their use of measuring instruments to find approximate lengths. Carpenters' rules are important tools for applying the "half" fractions in later grades ($\frac{1}{2}$, $\frac{1}{4}$, $\frac{1}{8}$, and so on—each fraction being half the previous one); and metersticks and centimeter rulers are also instructive when teaching about decimals.

If your children are using the retractable tape measures, teach and enforce the "2-inch, 5-centimeter no-zap rule" (do not "zap" the tape measure until no more than 2 inches or 5 centimeters show). This will extend the life of these tools, as well as make your own life quieter and easier.

6.3.3 Scales and Balances

A scale is another "early" measuring tool. Scales are used to measure how heavy something is according to a standard weight. (See Section 6.7 below for a discussion of weight.) There are many different kinds of scales. Some of the ones that *Everyday Mathematics* students will become most familiar with are highlighted below.

The **balance** scale was the first device for weighing. It was used in Egypt about 3500 B.C. and made use of a simple lever. In ancient Egypt, gold dust was used as currency and needed to be weighed very precisely in order to determine its value.

balance scale

Balances with the fulcrum (the support on which a lever moves) at the center of a horizontal bar are called equal-arm balances. The material being weighed is placed in a pan at one end, and known weights are placed in a pan at the other end until a pointer at the

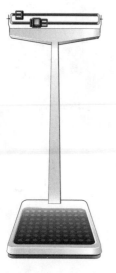

doctor's beam scale

spring scale

market scale

fulcrum indicates that the pans are balanced. Balances with unequal arms, known as steelyards, were developed by the ancient Romans. The object to be weighed is placed on the shorter arm, and a weight is moved along the longer arm until it balances the load.

Beam scales use a counterweight that is moved along the beam until the load is balanced. Calibrations on the beam give the weight. Doctors use this type of scale to weigh patients. Similarly, **platform** scales use a system of levers, so that a heavy object can be balanced by a relatively small counterweight on the beam. Truck and railroad scales are often of this type.

Spring scales, such as bathroom scales, use linkages to stretch or compress one or more springs. One spring causes the weight indicator to move and automatically give the weight. With simple spring scales, a pan or hook at the bottom of the spring holds the object to be weighed. This type is often seen hanging from ceilings in the produce sections of supermarkets.

Electronic scales were first commercially used in the 1950s and are now seen everywhere. They use a device called a strain-gauge load cell, which measures the stress an object puts on a mechanical element. The measurement is converted into an electrical signal and transferred to an electronic weight indicator, which gives the weight reading. Some high-precision scales determine weight by measuring the magnetic force needed to counter the downward pull of gravity and support the load on the scales.

Different scales are designed to measure different amounts of weight. There are scales with a variety of capacities and a variety of increments. High-precision scales can measure the weight of a piece of hair or a dose of medicine in increments as small as 0.001 gram or 0.000001 pound. Some platform scales can weigh trucks as large as 100 tons or railroad cars of 825 tons.

Scales have a variety of uses. In the kitchen, they are used to weigh food for cooking and for monitoring diets. Bathroom, nursery, and doctor's scales help monitor personal health. All kinds of scales are used by businesses that sell produce, meat, fish, and bakery items. The post office and other delivery services determine shipping prices based on package weight. Scales are used to weigh trucks to determine the amount of tax that drivers must pay for using the roads. Scales are also used to count pieces, such as the number of nails in a box or pennies in a bag. Scales may give the weight on a dial or digital display in U.S. customary units, metric units, or both.

Everyday Mathematics has designed activities for children to weigh objects and then order them by weight using pan balances, bathroom scales, and spring scales. Children use these tools primarily in Exploration lessons due to limited supply. Activities begin with informal play in Kindergarten, where children first compare weights with their own hands and then with pan balances.

6.4 Length

Distances along 1-dimensional objects, or along paths, are measured with linear measures. Like all measures, a linear measure consists of a value and a unit. For example, to say, "The edge of my desk is about 3.5 long" makes no sense. Saying, "The edge of my desk is about 3.5 feet long" provides both the approximate length and a unit of measure.

The two most common linear measures are length (the distance between two points on a line or arc) and perimeter (the distance around an object). The perimeter of a circle is called the circumference of the circle.

Some of the most common tools for measuring length—measuring sticks and tapes—were discussed in Section 6.3.2 and in the section on Toolkits in the Management Guide.

Just as 1-dimensional objects can be looked at as building blocks for 2- and 3-dimensional objects, so length is a building block for 2- and 3-dimensional measures. These are called area and volume, respectively. They are discussed in the following sections.

2 inches

6.5 Area

Just as length and perimeter are measures of a finite distance along a path, area is a measure of a finite amount of a 2-dimensional surface. This surface may lie in a single plane (for example, the interior of a rectangle), or it may exist in 3-dimensional space (for example, the curved surface of a cylinder or cone). The latter type of area is called surface area.

Like other numerical measures, a measure of area always includes both a number (a value) and a unit. Units of area are typically square units based on linear units (for example, square inches, square centimeters, square yards, and square meters). Some traditional units of area are not square units; for example, an acre of land is said to have been based, a long time ago, on the amount of land a farmer could plow in one day.

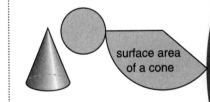

interior of a rectangle

surface area of a cone

6.5.1 Discrete Conception of Area

In most schoolbooks, the definition of area is based on the idea of "tiling," or covering a surface with identical unit squares, without gaps or overlaps, and then counting those units. This conception of area is 'discrete' because it involves separate, countable parts. If the surface is bounded by a rectangle, it is natural to arrange the tiles in an array and to multiply the number of tiles per row by the number of rows. The usual formulas, $A = l \times w$ and $A = b \times h$, are then easily linked to array multiplication: Area is the number of square-unit tiles in one row (equal to the length of the base in some linear unit) times the number of rows (equal to the width, or height, in that same linear unit). For other surfaces, defined by regular or

40 square units

about
21 square units

in perspective

In *Everyday Mathematics*
Grades 4–6, students will
estimate areas of land and
research the areas of
countries and continents.

irregular boundaries, the tiling with square units can be thought of as (or actually done by) laying a grid of appropriate square units on the region and counting, estimating, or calculating how many squares or partial squares it takes to cover the region.

6.5.2 Continuous Conception of Area

With young children, you will probably count or compute the number of square units required to cover a surface. In other words, the children will manipulate discrete conceptions of area through tiling activities. In later grades, though, students touch on the continuous conception of area. The area of the rectangle is obtained not by counting squares (a discrete conception), but by sweeping the width of the rectangle across the interior of the rectangle, parallel to its base. The area is simply the product of the length of the base and the width of the rectangle. In the classroom, this can be shown by rubbing the long part of a piece of chalk on the chalkboard to mark a rectangular surface—the further you sweep it along, the bigger the rectangle and the greater the area.

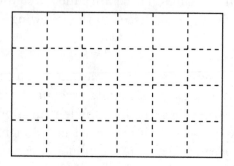

A discrete model of area

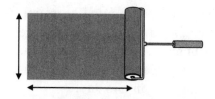

A continuous model of area

6.6 Volume

Volume is the measure of a finite amount of 3-dimensional space. As with measures in one and two dimensions, all measures of volume require a unit, and all are approximate. Volume units are typically cubic units based on linear measures, such as cubic inches, cubic centimeters, cubic yards, and cubic meters.

6.6.1 Discrete and Continuous Conceptions of Volume

The concept of volume can be given a discrete meaning by building three-dimensional shapes with identical cubes (or filling shapes completely with such cubes) and then counting the cubes. If the shape is a rectangular prism, a natural strategy is to build one layer of cubes, count the number of cubes in that layer, then multiply that number by the number of layers needed to fill the prism. Since the number of cubes in one layer corresponds to the area of the base (often represented by the formula $A = l \times w$), this process can be linked to either of the two standard formulas for the volume of rectangular prisms: $V = l \times w \times h$ (the product of the length and width of the rectangular base and the height perpendicular to that base) or $V = B \times h$ (the product of the area of the base and the height perpendicular to that base). The latter formula captures a continuous conception of volume similar to the "sweeping" out of area. Both conceptions of volume are used throughout K–6 *Everyday Mathematics*. A discrete approach dominates in Kindergarten through second grade, where children fill objects with cubes. In third and fourth grades, students experiment with a continuous conception of volume by filling objects with water or sand.

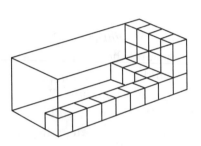

in perspective

In fifth and sixth grades, students use variables in formulas to model volume symbolically.

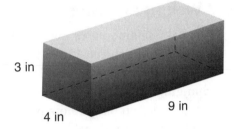

3 in

9 in

4 in

Filling a box with cubes is a discrete model of volume.

A continuous model of volume

6.6.2 Capacity

Sometimes we need to know amounts of things such as liquids or small grains of sand or sugar—things that take the shapes of their containers and can't be measured by their lengths, widths, and heights to get a volume. For these cases, we use measures of capacity. Capacity is a measure of how much a container can hold. Units of capacity are special types of volume units. For example, to determine how much milk or sugar is needed for a particular recipe or how much gasoline a car's tank will hold, we would use measures of capacity. (Dry ingredients, such as sugar, are sometimes measured by weight. This is common in recipes from other countries and when talking about bulk amounts.) In the U.S. customary system, containers are marked in cups, quarts, gallons, and so on; in the metric system, liters and milliliters are used to measure capacity.

6.6.3 Linking Area and Volume

The idea of dimension is at the heart of area and volume, and understanding dimension requires plenty of experience with 1-, 2-, and 3-dimensional figures—both individually and in relation to one another. This is one reason why measuring actual objects for their 1-dimensional attributes, such as length or perimeter; 2-dimensional attributes, such as area and surface area; and 3-

NOTE: See section 5.1 in the Geometry essay for a further discussion of dimension.

dimensional attributes, such as volume and capacity, is such an integral component of *Everyday Mathematics* beginning in Kindergarten.

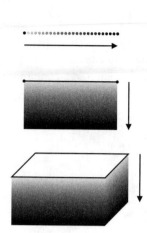

Moving between dimensions

NOTE: See Section 6.3.3 for more information about scales and balances.

in perspective

Students in *Fourth Grade Everyday Mathematics* begin using protractors to measure angles in degrees. They learn that a degree is $\frac{1}{360}$ of a full rotation.

in perspective
By fourth grade, students should be comfortable identifying attributes of 1-, 2-, and 3-dimensional figures and their measures. They will also have had many informal experiences relating objects in different dimensions. In *Everyday Mathematics* Grades 4–6, students explore relationships between the dimensions through the continuous conceptions of area and volume. The movement of a point to trace out a path shows the change from 0 to 1 dimension. The movement of a line segment shows the change from 1 to 2 dimensions. Moving a plane figure to generate a 3-dimensional object with volume shows movement from 2 to 3 dimensions.

6.7 Weight and Mass

Mass is the amount of matter in an object. *Weight* is the force of gravity on an object. If you took a trip around the solar system and weighed yourself on each planet, you would find your weight changing drastically depending on the size of the planet. You would weigh more on big planets because their gravitational pull is stronger. On small planets you would weigh less because they don't exert as much pull. Your mass, however, would remain the same regardless of the planet you were on because the amount of matter in your body is not affected by gravity.

This distinction between weight and mass is noted for you, but because most of us and the objects we weigh are firmly planted on Earth, it is not of everyday practical consequence. With young children, it is neither necessary nor appropriate to make any distinction between weight and mass.

Weight is measured using a variety of scales. A balance scale compares an object's mass to a standard mass set. The spring scale measures the pull of gravity as evidenced by an object's push or pull on a spring.

6.8 Angle Measure

Angular measures quantify turns or rotations. Kindergarten through third grade children measure angles as fractions of a circle: a right angle is a quarter-turn; a straight angle is a half-turn; and so on.

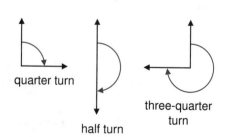

quarter turn

half turn

three-quarter turn

6.9 Elapsed Time

Numbers are used both to mark time and to measure it. We mark time by establishing reference frames, such as a calendar year and the number of days in a month. Events are then described by locations on one or more of these frames—for example, "She was born August 15, 1989 at 2:00 A.M." These numbers are not "measures" because, unlike measures, they cannot be added or subtracted with any meaning. For instance, 2:00 P.M. plus 3:00 P.M. is not 5:00 P.M.. Nor is April 12 plus April 15 equal to April 27. The reference labels "P.M." and "April" are not units of measure.

Once reference frames have been established, however, there are reference units that can be used as measures. For example, the play lasted 68 minutes; he finished the race in 3.9 seconds; the past 4 years have been warm. The use of time units to measure the duration of an event, or the time between events is called elapsed time.

Our units of time have the longest history of any measuring units. The 24-hour day comes from the ancient Egyptians, who divided the period from sunrise to sunset into 12 equal parts, and the period from sunset to sunrise into 12 equal parts as well. (Because the times of sunrise and sunset vary, the lengths of these two kinds of "hours" changed daily.) The seven-day week is credited to the Babylonians, who observed seven moving celestial bodies—the Sun, the Moon, and five planets. Also, the Babylonians used a numeration system based on 60 (probably because 60 can be divided evenly by many whole numbers), which led to the 60-second minute and the 60-minute hour.

Children use time measures frequently throughout *Everyday Mathematics,* most often in the context of number stories. As children learn new arithmetic skills, elapsed-time applications of these skills are developed. For example, in first and second grades, children use addition and subtraction to figure out elapsed times. (What time was it 2 hours ago? What time will it be in 3 hours?) Beginning in third grade, children answer ratio questions about time, such as, "What fraction of a year is 9 months?"

6.10 Money

Money may be viewed as a reference frame because it is an arbitrary scale used to establish the values of goods and services. Like the variations in the linear measure "foot" before standardization, however, different people place different values on the same goods or services. To make matters even more complicated, the differences are not just physical, but emotional, spiritual, and intellectual in nature. Even an individual's perceived value of something changes with time and experience.

In everyday life, though, money is more a measure of relative value than a reference frame. We measure the value of one thing versus

NOTE: See the essay on Reference Frames for a further discussion of this topic.

in perspective

In Grades 4–6, time measurements are important parts of rate problems in which students figure out gallons per minute of water flow, an animal's speed in feet per second, or calculations per millisecond by a computer, to name a few examples.

another, or of one thing now versus that thing yesterday or last year. Expressions like "This TV costs $50 more now than it did three months ago" or "Bananas are up 17 percent this season" indicate how we use arithmetic to compare monetary values. This is a sign that money behaves like a measure, so it is categorized as such in *Everyday Mathematics*.

Young children are exposed to money, prices, buying and selling on a daily basis, but few have experience with money details. That is, children see money transactions, are given an exact amount to spend, or hand over coins and accept change without checking. Although there are exceptions, many first grade children are unable to distinguish among coins (nickels and quarters are often confused), and relatively few beginning first graders know the exchanges among coins or their links to the basic dollar unit.

Experience with money is important because of its inherent usefulness and, like most measures, because of the context it provides for number stories. Additionally, our base-ten monetary system is an excellent vehicle for the study of place value, fractions, and decimal notation. In *Everyday Mathematics,* we provide students with early experiences to develop their knowledge about the details of money. We then make use of the familiar context of money to make it easier for children to become acquainted with fractions and decimals at earlier ages than they would in a traditional mathematics curriculum.

6.10.1 Money Facts

Talking about coins and bills also provides a unique opportunity to bridge various curriculum areas. Money lore contains interesting facts about the history of our country, about the science of metals, and about symbols in our heritage. Use these facts liberally in your teaching about coins and bills in the *Everyday Mathematics* money lessons and at other times during the year. Some selected definitions follow.

alloy A mixture of two or more chemical elements, at least one of which is a metal.

denomination The official value of a coin.

E Pluribus Unum The original motto of the United States; translated from Latin as "From many, one." This motto is required by an 1873 law to appear on any coin that contains an eagle. In fact, it appears on all U.S. coins.

In God We Trust A motto that was permitted, but not required, on coins by the 1873 law; a 1955 law required that the motto be placed on all coins and bills. In 1956, President Dwight D. Eisenhower signed a law making "In God We Trust" the official motto of the United States.

intrinsic value The actual worth of the metal in a coin.

obverse The face or "front" of a coin; "heads."

reverse The back or "rear" of a coin; "tails."

rim The edge of a coin, which is quite functional because it allows the coin to be stacked and protects the design from damage. U.S. coins with values of more than 5 cents each have always had rims that are ornate, lettered, or reeded (that is, with parallel grooves that are perpendicular to the face of the coin, as in our dime and quarter). This was intended to discourage the scraping of the coin edges to steal some of their metal; it also makes it easier to identify coins by touch, which is necessary for people with vision impairments and is useful for pulling a specific amount of change out of your pocket without looking.

New designs for coins and bills are adopted periodically, putting currency in the United States in a constant (albeit slow) state of flux. For example, at this writing, the U.S. Treasury Department was producing a new series of quarters and has put a new one-dollar coin into circulation. If desired, you can go into great detail about individual coins and their designs with your students, touching upon history, metallurgy, and architecture in the process. An example of the type of information you might want to share with your students is included below for the nickel.

Nickels

Until 1866, five-cent pieces were called half-dimes. The word *nickel* comes from the metal in the coin. Currently, nickels are made of an alloy of 75% copper and 25% nickel.

Obverse The Jefferson bust was designed by Felix O. Schlag, whose initials, FS, appear between the rim and the bottom of the bust on nickels produced after 1965.

Information about Thomas Jefferson	
Born	April 13, 1743; Shadwell (now Albemarle County), Virginia
Died	July 4, 1826; at Monticello in Albemarle County, Virginia. Jefferson died on the day of the 50th anniversary of the Declaration of Independence. (The second President of the United States, John Adams, died on the same day.)
Occupations	Lawyer; delegate to the Continental Congress; author of the Declaration of Independence; Governor of Virginia; ambassador to France; Vice President; President; founder of the University of Virginia; farmer; architect
Important Dates	1797 elected Vice President under President John Adams 1801 inaugurated as 3rd President 1803 Louisiana Purchase 1804 reelected President

Reverse Monticello, Jefferson's home in Virginia, appears on the reverse, along with its name. This coinage design was suggested by President Franklin D. Roosevelt in 1938.

Information about Monticello	
Location	Albemarle County, Virginia
Architect	Thomas Jefferson
Built	1st version 1769–1793 2nd version 1793–1809

6.10.2 Money History

The history of money in our country is also quite interesting. The first coin used extensively in the American colonies was the Spanish milled dollar, a silver coin referred to as a piece of eight because it was worth 8 *reales* (pronounced ray-al-ays). The coin was also called a peso. Even today, our $ symbol is the same as that for the Mexican *peso*. The milled dollar was often cut into eight pieces to allow for smaller denominations. Each of the eight pieces was called a *real* or a *bit*. Thus, for many years, a dollar was referred to as eight bits, a half-dollar as four bits, and a quarter as two bits.

When the United States began to produce its own coins, it used the Spanish milled dollar as its model. The first U.S. dollars, which weighed exactly as much as the Spanish coins, were made of an alloy composed of fifteen parts silver to one part gold. In 1792, Congress passed the first coinage act for the new country and authorized the production of coins in various denominations: an eagle ($10), a half-eagle ($5), coins with the modern values, and a half-cent. With the exception of the cent and the half-cent, these early coins did not show their denominations. This oversight was corrected by an 1837 Act of Congress. Until 1909, the head, or bust, of all people represented on U.S. coins were abstractions (for example, Liberty) or generic figures (for example, an Indian). In 1909, the first coin picturing a real person—Abraham Lincoln—appeared.

The American Eagle, which appears by law on all coins with a value of more than 10 cents, is the likeness of an actual eagle—"Peter the Mint Bird," the mascot of the Philadelphia Mint in the 1840s and 1850s. After his death, Peter was stuffed and is, to this day, preserved in a glass case in the Philadelphia Mint.

References

Information about U.S. coins and bills and the history of money can be found on the U.S. Treasury's Web site: http:/www.ustreas.gov and in books such as the following:

NOTE: Cheers like "Two bits, four bits, eight bits, a dollar! . . . All for U.C., stand up and holler!" continue to carry the early terms for coins into the present. "Shave and a hair cut, two bits" may be dying out, although the rhythm behind the saying lives on.

Barabas, Kathy. *Let's Find Out About Money*. New York: Scholastic. 1997.

Doty, Richard. *America's Money, America's Story*. Iola, WI: Krause. 1988.

Yeoman, R. S. *Guide Book of United States Coins*. New York: Golden Books Adult. Issued yearly.

Reference Frames

outline

7.1 Temperature 163

7.2 Time 165

   7.2.1 Clocks 166

   7.2.2 Calendars 167

   7.2.3 Timelines 170

7.3 Maps 170

   7.3.1 Map Cordinates 171

   7.3.2 Map Scales 173

Reference frames are something of an oddity in mathematics. Unlike measurements or counts, numbers in reference frames locate things only within definite systems or contexts. Examples of numbers in reference frames include dates, times, Celsius and Fahrenheit temperatures, and coordinates on maps. The numbers in reference frames are set arbitrarily. For example, the year 2000 in our calendar system is not the same as the year 2000 in the traditional Chinese calendar system, and the Celsius temperature scale is quite different from the Fahrenheit scale.

Almost all reference frames have a *zero point,* leading to the use of positive and negative numbers to describe locations on one side of zero or the other. Zero in a reference frame means something different from zero as a count or a measure. In counts and measures, zero indicates nothingness: a measure or count of zero means that there is none of whatever is being measured or counted. In contrast, the zero point within a reference frame is an arbitrary starting point; it does not necessarily correspond with nothingness or the lowest possible value. As a result, numbers in reference frames are not governed by the same mathematical rules that other numbers are.

Arithmetic operations cannot always be performed on numbers in reference frames to obtain results that make sense. For example, no meaningful result is obtained by adding the year 1930 to the year 1990; 30°C is not 3 times as warm as 10°C; and 3:00 P.M. plus 2:00

P.M. does not equal 5:00 P.M. On the other hand, the numbers in reference frames can be used to find the distance from one point to another in the same reference frame. For example: 1930 was 60 years earlier than 1990; 30°C is 20 degrees warmer than 10°C; and 5:00 P.M. is 2 hours later than 3:00 P.M.

FRANK & ERNEST® by Bob Thaves

With permission of Bob Thaves.

See Section 1.4 of the Number and Counting essay for information on number lines and Section 5.9 of the Geometry essay for information on coordinate grids.

In *Everyday Mathematics,* children learn about a variety of contemporary and historical reference frames. This essay will discuss reference frames used to establish temperature (Section 7.1), time (Section 7.2), and location on maps (Section 7.3). Of these, time and temperature reference frames are the major focus in *Everyday Mathematics* Grades K-3. Number lines and coordinate grids can also be considered reference frames, but are not discussed in detail here.

7.1 Temperature

The temperature systems that we are most familiar with— Fahrenheit and Celsius—are reference frames that help us quantify hotness or coldness. Both establish an arbitrary zero point and an interval scale, with each interval being equal to a degree in that system. As you know, the Fahrenheit and Celsius scales have different zero points and different-size intervals from one another: 0° Fahrenheit does not feel the same as 0° Celsius, and a change of one degree Fahrenheit is not equal to a change of one degree Celsius.

Fahrenheit This scale was invented in the early 1700s by the German physicist D. G. Fahrenheit. The zero point of this scale (0°F) is the freezing point of a saturated salt and water solution at sea level. Pure water freezes at 32°F and boils at 212°F. The normal temperature for the human body is 98.6°F. The Fahrenheit scale is used primarily in the United States.

Celsius This scale was developed in 1742 by the Swedish astronomer Anders Celsius. The zero point for this scale (0°C) is the freezing point of pure water. Pure water boils at 100°C. The Celsius scale divides the span between these two points into 100 equal parts, each equal to one Celsius degree. For this reason it is also called the centigrade scale. The normal temperature for the human body is 37°C. The Celsius scale is standard for most people living

in perspective

Exploration of coordinate systems and maps begin in fourth grade.

in perspective

Beginning in fourth grade, students use formulas to convert between Celsius and Fahrenheit degrees.

mercury thermometer

thermometer with circular scale

bimetallic thermometer

outside of the United States and for most scientists everywhere.

Thermometers have been evolving since the late 16th century. The first known thermometer, an inaccurate device called a thermoscope, was built by Galileo in about 1592. In 1709, D. G. Fahrenheit made an accurate thermometer using alcohol. In 1714, he built a mercury thermometer like those we use today. In 1954, U.S. Army Colonel George T. Perkins invented an electronic thermometer.

Because thermometers are used to measure[1] in reference frames, the zero point and the size of the intervals on a thermometer vary according to the temperature system(s) being used. The designs of thermometers also vary, depending on the temperature scale(s) they intend to display and the range of temperatures of interest. Common thermometers include those used for cooking (candy, deep-frying, oven); health (body parts); machines (automobile engine and climate control); and air temperature. Many thermometers have circular scales, but the straight-line scale is still popular. You can also buy thermometers with digital readouts. The zero point and scale intervals are often not evident on the latter, making them less desirable as learning tools than the circular and straight-line designs.

Three common types of thermometers are described below:

Mercury or colored alcohol When the temperature rises, the volume of a liquid increases. So if a liquid is contained in a little bulb attached to a thin, straight tube with a sealed end, the liquid will rise in the tube as the temperature increases. Both alcohol and mercury are commonly used liquids. Mercury freezes at a little above −40°F or −40°C (the Celsius and Fahrenheit scales are equal at −40°). To display temperatures lower than that, alcohol is used. These liquid-in-glass type thermometers are the least expensive and most popular. They are the kind we often use to determine whether we have a fever or to measure how warm or cold it is outside.

Bimetallic When the temperature rises, most solids expand, but different solids expand by different amounts. For example, brass expands about twice as much as iron when heated. If a bar is made by fastening a strip of brass next to a strip of iron, the bar will bend as the temperature rises. The bend will be toward the iron side, which expands less. If one end of the bar is fixed in place, the other end can act as a pointer on a scale. Most home thermostats contain such bimetallic thermometers.

---

[1] Technically, one should probably not use the term "measure" to determine a number in a reference frame, since these numbers differ from actual measures. ("Locating," "establishing," or "reading" a number in a reference frame would be more proper.) Once a reference frame has been established, however, many locations are commonly treated as measures. In *Everyday Mathematics,* we follow this convention and will often refer to measuring time or a temperature and to time and temperature measurements. You and your students should do the same.

Thermocouple A thermocouple contains a loop made by joining two wires of different materials, such as copper and iron, at their ends. If the temperatures at the two joints are different, a voltage is created that is proportional to the difference. One joint is placed where the temperature is to be taken, while the other is kept at a constant lower temperature. The voltage is read by a measuring device and translated into a temperature reading.

Each of the above types of thermometers can be calibrated to quantify temperature in degrees Celsius or Fahrenheit.

In *Kindergarten* and *First Grade Everyday Mathematics,* children keep daily temperature charts that are color-coded by temperature range for easier reading. Most air-temperature thermometers use mercury or colored alcohol and are based on number-line scales, either straight-line, vertical, or circular. In first grade, the Fahrenheit temperature scale is emphasized. In second and third grade, both Fahrenheit and Celsius scales should be available.

One must be careful about doing arithmetic with temperatures. 30°F plus 20°C does not add up to anything. Temperature changes can be calculated within one scale, but not across different scales. For example, knowing that it was 58°F this morning and the temperature rose 30° to the high for the day allows you to conclude that the high was 58 + 30 = 88 degrees Fahrenheit.

The limitations of doing arithmetic with reference frame numbers can be a difficult concept. Although some children will grasp it intuitively, others will need to work with numerous examples over time before they understand when reference frame numbers cannot be manipulated like other numbers and when they can be meaningfully added and substituted.

7.2 Time

As with all reference frames, locating an event or point in time requires a zero point and a unit interval. Both of these depend on the context in which time is being examined. Calendars and timelines (discussed in Sections 7.2.2 and 7.2.3) help us keep track of broad expanses of time, from days to millennia. Clocks (see Section 7.2.1) help us track short-term time passage. And just like units in other reference frames, it does not make sense to use arithmetic with the numbers we use to locate time. For example, June 8 plus June 13 is not June 21; and 8:30 P.M. minus 1:20 P.M. is not 7:10 P.M. Within one reference frame, however, you can calculate elapsed time as a difference (or distance) between two time locations.

The concepts of telling time, the passage of time, and elapsed time within the frameworks of calendars and clocks are not easy for young children to grasp. However, children can engage in many everyday activities that help them develop a "time sense." They can begin to use calendars and clocks to anticipate and record their activities. Using such ordering vocabulary as *before, after, early, late,* and *morning,* and including such clock and calendar references as, "We have only 5 minutes left" or "We will have a special surprise tomorrow" will help familiarize young children with the language of time without burdening them prematurely with formality.

7.2.1 Clocks

Clock time is a reference frame with second, minute, and hour intervals that may seem logical and almost second nature to us as adults, but that often seem quite arbitrary and confusing to children. One of the primary tools for locating time in this reference frame—the analog clock (see page 167)—makes the task doubly confusing because the numerals on the clock can simultaneously correspond with different numbers in the reference frame (for example, depending on which hand is pointing to it, the numeral 1 can mean the 1 o'clock hour, 5 minutes after any hour, or 5 seconds after any minute). The development of time-telling concepts and skills in most young children takes repeated experiences over an extended period of time; it requires an understanding of how the reference frame for clock time is organized and how the tools for telling time (clocks) reflect this system. Though initially confusing, learning to tell time with an analog clock actually aids children's understanding of the intervals within intervals of this reference frame.

In Kindergarten and first grade, lessons focus on the hour hand of analog clocks as the most important aspect of "locating" or telling time on the clock. Telling time is always an estimate, and children learn to do surprisingly well using just the hour hand. When the hour hand is pointing exactly to "3," for example, then the time is very near "3 o'clock." When the hour hand is just before a number, just after, or between two numbers, people often say that the time, for example, is "just before 3 o'clock," "just after 3 o'clock," or "between 3 and 4 o'clock." More hands, minute and second, or more places on a digital display only improve the estimates.

Starting in first grade, children learn about 24 hours in a day, A.M. and P.M., and the improved estimates possible when minute and second hands (or minute and second digital displays) are added to a clock. By second grade, children are expected to be able to tell time reliably to within 5 minutes. Second grade is also when children practice writing time. In third grade, activities extend to the use of fractions to describe time. For example, 9:45 is "a quarter to 10 o'clock." From third grade on, elapsed time, or the distance between two times, is a common context for number and variable stories. Also in third grade, children carry on a yearlong project collecting weekly data to investigate patterns in sunrise and sunset times. This and many other uses of elapsed time are common in number and variable stories from third grade onward.

Clocks have been important in the development of many human enterprises, such as navigation, business, and science. Three important types of clocks are analog, digital, and atomic. Students of *Everyday Mathematics* Grades K–3 practice telling time using both digital and analog clocks.

Analog Clocks Analog clocks are clocks with hands, what used to simply be called *clocks* before the invention of digital clocks. In general, *analog* refers to any system that measures a continuously changing quantity—in this case, time—with continuously varying markers of some kind. The first analog clocks may have been trees with markers showing where their shadows fell at different times during the day. These were precursors to sundials, which worked on the same principle. For thousands of years, water clocks were the standard for telling time (they worked even when the sun was down or behind a cloud). In a water clock, the position of water between two vessels was the analog for the time. In the late Middle Ages, the first successful mechanical clocks were constructed, a development that has thoroughly transformed our culture. Nowadays, most people use the term *analog clock* to refer to the type with hands on a round face. The first of these, with only an hour hand on it, is credited to the German inventor Henry de Vick in the 1300s. More advanced features came along in the 1700s, including minute and second hands and a pendulum. Electric analog clocks use an alternating current that vibrates sixty times per second to keep the clock on time.

analog clock

Digital Clocks Digital clocks are not analog because time is not displayed in a continuous manner. Instead, every digital clock has a smallest increment of time that it displays without changing until the next increment is reached. Commonly, the increment is minutes. The clock display 10:10, for example, does not change for one minute. On some digital clocks, the colon in the time display blinks on and off once per second to indicate that time is still passing (or perhaps just to let you know the clock is still working). Most digital clocks work on alternating current.

digital clock

Atomic Clocks Atomic clocks keep time according to the vibrations of atoms or molecules. The vibrations are so reliable that an atomic clock may lose or gain only a few seconds in 100,000 years. There are both analog and digital versions of atomic clocks.

7.2.2 Calendars

There are many different calendrical systems, each one its own reference frame for marking the passage of time. The word *calendar* has roots in the Latin word *kalendae,* meaning "first of the month." *Kalendae,* in turn, was rooted in the word *calare,* which means "to call out solemnly." This etymology points to the importance that people have always placed on keeping track of months and marking their beginnings and passings.

In the earliest times, the lunar month of 29.5 days was an important measure because of its close association with seasonal planting and harvesting schedules. Unfortunately, no whole number of lunar months coincides with a solar year of 365 days, 5 hours, 48 minutes, and 46 seconds (about 365 and one-fourth days). Twelve lunar months are 354 days; thirteen lunar months are 383.5 days. The fact that these important, naturally occurring cycles can't easily be reconciled has led to the peculiar natures of the calendar systems used throughout history. According to the *World Book Encyclopedia*, some noteworthy calendars include the following:

Babylonian This ancient middle-eastern calendar was based on a now-unknown zero point and a lunar month interval. The calendar had alternating 29- and 30-day months, with an extra month added 3 times every 8 years to make up for error.

Egyptian This ancient calendar had a zero point at the annual flooding of the Nile when the Dog Star, *Sirius,* first appeared. The year was broken into twelve 30-day months, with 5 days added at the end of the year. The extra one-fourth of a day per year wasn't accounted for, so the calendar slowly got out of whack over the years. It has been calculated that the earliest recorded date on this calendar corresponds to 4236 B.C. on our current Gregorian calendar.

Roman According to legend, Romulus, the founder of Rome, introduced the earliest Roman calendar in the eighth century B.C. It came from the Greeks and was made up of 10 months and a 304-day year. The zero point was March 1 (by our current calendar). It is not clear how the other 61-odd days were accounted for. The names of eight of our current months came from the names for the ten Roman months: *Martius, Aprilis, Maius, Junius, Quintilis, Sextilis, September, October, November,* and *December. Quintilis* through *December* came from the numbers 5 through 10. The name *Martius* came from Mars, the Roman god of war; *Junius* from Juno, a Roman goddess; and *Maius* from Maia, a Greek goddess. It is thought that *Aprilis* may derive from the Latin word *aperire,* meaning "to open," referring to the unfolding of buds and blossoms during this month; though another possibility is from Aphrodite, the Greek goddess of love and beauty. Every 2 years a 22- or 23-day month was added to account for error with the solar year. Later, two more months, *Januarius* and *Februarius,* were added to the end of the year. *Januarius* was likely named from Janus, the Roman god of gates and doorways, and *Februarius* took its name from Februa, a Roman festival of purification held on the 15th day of this month.

Julian In 46 B.C. (known as the "year of confusion" because of calendar reform), Julius Caesar acted on suggestions from his astronomer Sosigenes to upgrade the Roman calendar. A system close to our own was implemented, including what we now know as the leap day in February every fourth year. To accommodate the fact that the Roman calendar was three months out of line with the seasons, Caesar made 46 B.C. 445 days long. Later, *Quintilis* was renamed July for Julius Caesar and *Sextilis* was named August to honor Emperor Augustus Caesar.

The Christian version of the Julian calendar was invented in A.D. 532 by an abbot named Dionysius Exiguus—Dennis the Short. In his plan, the Christian era was to begin January 1st of the year after Christ was born. He called the beginning year the Year of Our Lord, or Anno Domini (A.D.) 1. The Christian version of the calendar was not taken up immediately by church authorities, but became widely used in Western Europe beginning in the 11th century. The abbreviation B.C. for Before Christ was introduced later. As is well known, Dennis got the year of Christ's birth wrong. It now seems likely that Christ was born in 4 B.C., if not earlier. The abbreviations C.E. (Common Era) and B.C.E. (Before the Common Era) are sometimes used instead of A.D. and B.C.

Gregorian By 1582, the Julian calendar was off by about 10 days (because of the slight difference between $365\frac{1}{4}$ days and 365 days, 5 hours, 48 minutes, and 46 seconds), so Pope Gregory XIII dropped 10 days from October. He then decreed that February should continue to get an extra day every 4 years, as in the Julian calendar, except in century years that were not divisible by 400. This calendar is so accurate that, over 400 years later, we are only about 26 seconds off. Most of the western world uses the Gregorian calendar.

Hebrew The zero point for the Hebrew calendar is Creation, which has been calculated at 3,760 years and 3 months before the Christian era began. To find a year on the Hebrew calendar, add 3,760 or 3,761 to the year in the Gregorian calendar. (This conversion is presented as a formula in *Fifth Grade Everyday Mathematics*.) The Hebrew year is based on the moon and usually has 12 months, each 29 or 30 days long. Seven times every 19 years, an extra 29-day month is added.

Islamic The zero point for the Islamic calendar is Muhammad's flight from Mecca to Medina in 622 A.D. on the Gregorian calendar. This calendar is also lunar, with 12 months alternating between 29 and 30 days long. The months do not keep to the same seasons relative to the sun each year, so the Islamic New Year moves backward through the seasons. Nineteen of every 30 years have 354 days each, and the other 11 years have an extra day each.

There are groups that advocate standardizing all calendars around the world. Three such calendars have been proposed: The **Thirteen-Month** calendar, with 13 months each 4 weeks long; the **World** calendar; and the **Perpetual** calendar. The latter two propose variations on a 12-month, 30- or 31-day-per-month design. And according to *Star Trek,* by the 24th century, the calendar will be metric.

This historical background is included for your information. You may want to share some of it with your students, who would benefit from knowing that other calendar systems exist. They also might enjoy hearing how calendars originated and have evolved. Most importantly, though, students of K–3 *Everyday Mathematics* learn about the practical aspects of using our own confusing and rather irregular calendar through daily and monthly routines.

7.2.3 Timelines

Timelines are also reference frames. They are simply number lines labeled with time units. Their zero points and unit intervals vary according to their purposes. A time line designed to track the development of the Earth may have "The Big Bang" as its zero point and use a large interval (millions or perhaps billions of years) to allow for a display over billions of years. A family history timeline might use generational intervals and mark its zero point with the most distant known relative. A timeline of someone's life might use the person's birthdate as its zero point and track in one-year intervals corresponding to the person's age. For example, a timeline of a young child's landmarks might include such events as rolling over at about $\frac{1}{2}$ year, learning to walk at age 1, having a sibling when she was 3, and going to Kindergarten shortly after her 5th birthday. (A timeline such as this could also include numbers that refer to the Gregorian dates for the above events, for example, birth (1999), walking (2000), sibling (2002), and Kindergarten (2004), but would not need to include these dates if birth was established as the zero point and age intervals were the specified unit.) Keep in mind that in each instance above, times "before" the chosen zero point exist. This is true with most reference frames, which have numbers on both sides of the zero point.

You may have timelines associated with social studies or science units, or your colleagues teaching different grades may have them. If they are available and appropriate, it would be instructive to review them with your children from a reference-frame point of view. Ask, "What is the zero point? What is the unit interval? Why did they choose this zero point and these intervals for this timeline?"

In *First Grade Everyday Mathematics,* children make a class timeline as a daily routine. In second grade, children have a lesson about the use of timelines and track the invention of common household appliances. You will probably find other occasions to incorporate timelines into your curriculum as well. Timelines are useful for reinforcing sequencing concepts and, because they are concrete and visual, can be helpful for young children as they begin to develop a sense of history.

7.3 Maps

Maps are a common use of reference frames in *Everyday Mathematics*. In *Everyday Mathematics* Grades K-3, map activities range from using maps to track steps going from room to room in the school, to estimating distances between cities and towns on a map, to interpreting temperature maps. Maps also provide a rich supply of ideas that children can use to invent number stories.

7.3.1 Map Coordinates

Maps make use of reference frames to locate geographic points within a given region. Often, the reference frame for a map is a coordinate grid system, where a given landmark can be found at a location called F5 or B3 or 300W/500N or something similar. In order for these location referents to make sense, one must understand how the map is set up—in these cases, according to a reference frame that we call a coordinate grid.

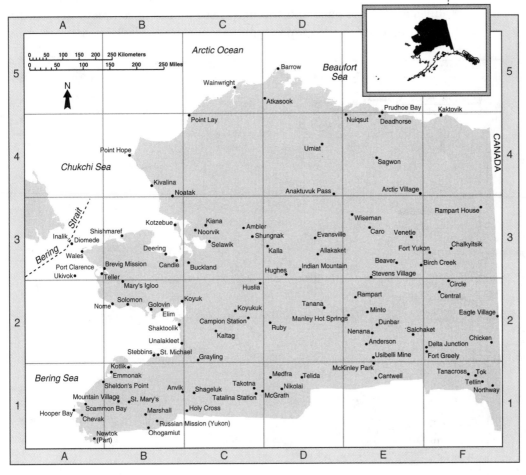

map with coordinate grid

Coordinate grids are reference frames that extend infinitely in two or more directions from zero. Each is defined by two or more lines called *axes*. On rectangular coordinate grids (used in many maps), the axes are perpendicular to each other and intersect at a common point called the origin—the zero point of the reference frame. In such a 2-dimensional coordinate grid, the axes are called *ordinates* and points along each axis are called *coordinates*. One can use ordered pairs to locate points anywhere in the coordinate system that is defined by the axes. By convention, the first coordinate in an ordered pair gives position along the horizontal axis and the second coordinate gives position along the vertical axis.

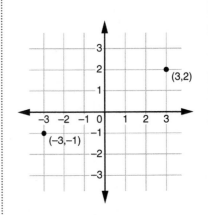

Coordinate grids and graphing are also discussed in Section 5.9 of the Geometry essay, but the above should provide sufficient information to help you understand how coordinate grids are linked to reading and understanding many maps.

As mentioned above, a 2-dimensional map is often based on a rectangular coordinate grid. One axis is usually horizontal, the other vertical; they usually have the same scale. Often, the full grid is not drawn on the map. Rather, points along each axis are labeled at the outer edges of the map. You can envision drawing horizontal and vertical lines across the page and through these points to complete the coordinate grid upon which the map is built.

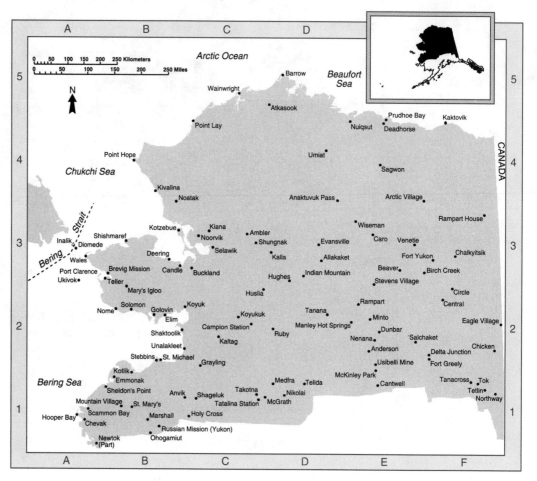

map without coordinate grid

Now that one knows how the markings on the sides correspond to coordinates along each axis, finding the location F5 or B3, as in the example at the beginning of this section, makes perfect sense. Simply find the point that is marked by the ordered pair (F, 5) on the invisible grid and you have located that landmark (or a small region in which the landmark will be found) on the map. Different maps label their coordinates differently—some with all numbers, some with letters and numbers, some with other markings. In each case, though, labels refer to points or regions within the coordinate grid.

Many cities and towns use a 2-dimensional coordinate grid to determine the address of each building in town. For example, 200 Third Avenue NE may locate a house two blocks north and three blocks east of the intersection (point zero) of two central roads in that town. Assuming that north is "up" on the vertical axis, east will be to the right of the zero point, and the position of the house could be given by the ordered pair (3,2).

7.3.2 Map Scales

Maps not only make use of reference frames, they make use of scales. A scale is an application of a size-change factor, usually where one of the figures is from real life and the other is a model. For example, a toy train is a scaled-down model of a real train; a map is a scaled-down model of a real landscape. More precisely, a scale is a *ratio comparison*. It is used to quantify the relative sizes of two things being compared.

Scales are often given graphically on a map where the overall length of a line segment represents a map unit and real units are marked along the segment. You can simply mark a string (or the edge of a piece of paper) with the length of the segment and then place the string on the map and read distances in real units. The string even allows you to follow winding roads with greater accuracy than a ruler allows.

Other scale drawings follow conventions similar to those used in maps. For example, in architectural drawings, $\frac{1}{4}$ inch often represents 1 foot (so the scale is 1:48). Or a drawing of an insect might have the notation "$2 \times$ actual size," meaning every linear measure in the drawing is twice the actual measure of the insect.

Map scales are introduced in *Third Grade Everyday Mathematics* where students use them to estimate mileage between cities on a U.S. map.

in perspective Fourth grade students review map and scale-drawing skills and then draw their classroom. This exercise requires identifying key features in the classroom (for example, positions of furniture, doors, and so on), and then choosing an appropriate scale to fit a drawing on a paper grid. In fifth grade students continue to practice reading maps and work with a scale to construct 3-dimensional models.

in perspective
The global grid system, a reference frame that divides the Earth into lines of latitude and longitude, shares many similarities with the rectangular coordinate systems used in 2-dimensional maps. But it is also different in several important respects. This reference frame is explored by fourth, fifth, and sixth graders in *Everyday Mathematics*.

ESSAY

8

Estimation and Number Sense

outline

8.1 Why Estimate?   175
    8.1.1 Estimates Are Sometimes Necessary   175
    8.1.2 Estimates Are Easy to Understand   176
    **8.1.3 Estimates Can Help in Problem
        Solving**   177

8.2 Extreme Numbers   177
8.3 Estimates in Calculations   178
8.4 Rounding   179
    8.4.1 Rounding Algorithms   179
**8.5 Number Sense and Mathematical
    Connections**   180

NOTE: Many ideas and examples in this essay are from "Reasons for Estimating and Approximating," in *Applying Arithmetic* by Max Bell and Zalman Usiskin. *Applying Arithmetic* was published in 1983 by the University of Chicago and is currently available in three parts from ERIC (ED 264087, ED 264088, and ED 264089).

Estimation is a common theme in *Everyday Mathematics* because of its importance both in mathematics and in everyday life. We estimate counts, measurements—all measurements are actually estimates—and results of calculations. In practical matters, "ballpark" estimates are often as important as exact answers. Sometimes we use estimates because we have no choice; other times because they are easier to understand than exact quantities; and other times to help in solving problems or to check answers given by machines.

Despite the utility of estimation, many children (and some adults) sometimes feel that approximating an answer is somehow wrong, like cheating or lying. In reality, estimation is not a shoddy alternative to doing things right. Estimation requires good intuition about numbers, good understanding of practical situations, and a flexible repertoire of techniques. The best estimators in a particular area are the experts in that area. Estimation skills take years to develop, but are worth striving for. Focusing on estimation can help children build a broad, flexible view of mathematics, good number sense, and confidence that mathematics does make sense.

The first section of this essay outlines the principal reasons for estimating. Later sections address estimates in calculations, rounding, and "extreme" numbers. The last section discusses number sense and mathematical connections.

8.1 Why Estimate?

Usually people estimate out of necessity, or as an aid to understanding, or as a step in solving problems.

8.1.1 Estimates Are Sometimes Necessary

Estimates are necessary in many situations because exact values are not obtainable.

- **A number may simply be unknown,** therefore an estimate is necessary. Predictions about the future, guesses about the past, judgments of economic conditions of countries or companies, and even educated guesses about what groceries will cost are all examples of estimates required by a lack of precise knowledge.

- **A quantity may be different each time it is measured.** Temperatures, populations, air pressures, and keyboarding speeds are common examples. Situations involving random processes, such as the number of heads in 100 tosses of a coin, are also examples of this type.

- **Physical measurements are not exact.** For example, no sheet of paper is exactly 11 inches long. (Under a microscope the edge of this page will appear quite rough—so the length to be measured is not really well defined.) Thus measures that may seem exact are actually only close enough for practical considerations.

- **Getting an exact value may be too expensive,** so an estimate is substituted. In many situations the numbers are so large that exact counts cannot be obtained. More often than not, large counts are estimated by taking samples and using statistics to generate results. Pollsters sample the viewing public to estimate how many people saw a particular TV program; they don't poll the entire television-watching public.
  In *Everyday Mathematics,* children explore many ways of estimating large counts and measurements using surveys, polls, and experiments. Class discussions encourage children to cultivate a healthy skepticism about absolute claims based on such estimates.

- **Sometimes decimal or fractional results just don't make sense,** so the numbers are adjusted. For example, if candy is 3 for a dollar, you pay 34 cents for one piece and 33 cents for each of the other two pieces because there are no fractional parts of pennies.

- **Some situations require a built-in margin of error,** so quantities are overestimated. For example, you overestimate the costs of items in the store to make sure you have enough money to pay the cashier. Safety factors in new buildings are overestimated to more than meet the minimal requirements.

- **A number is not in a form that lends itself to computation,** so it is approximated. For example, to add irrational numbers like $\sqrt{2}$ or π to rational numbers, you need to approximate them first.

In the situations above, there is no choice about whether to estimate. People who believe that estimates are inferior to exact answers are thus ignoring many situations in which it is *necessary* to estimate.

8.1.2 Estimates Are Easy to Understand

Estimates are handy for helping us communicate by making numbers easier to understand. Many such estimates are obtained by rounding, a topic discussed in Section 8.4.

Estimates for Clarity A school budget of $148,309,563 for a school population of 62,772 students might be reported as "about $150 million for 63,000 students." A house on a lot whose width was surveyed as 40.13 feet would almost certainly be said to be on a "40-foot" lot. In such cases, the estimate is easier to understand than the more precise actual figure. Sometimes we estimate other estimates to make them clearer. For example, the 3,849,674 square miles given in an almanac as the area of Canada is necessarily an estimate. Rounding this estimate to 4 million or 3.8 million square miles makes the measure easier to understand and communicate. Children in *Everyday Mathematics* encounter many examples of estimates made for the sake of clarity.

Estimates for Consistency Government reports on the percent of unemployed workers always give a percent to the nearest tenth. For instance, if 8 million of 99 million potential workers are unemployed, the government would report 8.1% unemployed rather than 8.08% or any closer approximation to 8.0808 . . . %. Here an estimate is necessary because the original data are inexact, but the particular choice to report in tenths is done to be consistent from month to month and in line with the precision of the original data.

Similarly, results of calculations from physical measurements should be consistent with input measurements. For example, if you measure two pieces of lumber to the nearest quarter-inch, then the sum of the two measures should be given to the nearest quarter-inch, not the nearest eighth-inch.

Sometimes the desire for consistency comes from tradition. For example, baseball players' hitting frequencies (batting averages) are found by dividing the number of hits by the number of times at bat. This number is first rounded to the nearest thousandth, and then reported as if the decimal point were not there. For example, the last man to hit over 40 percent in a season was Ted Williams in 1941 when he hit "406" (pronounced "four oh six").

Other times, consistency comes from a desire for uniformity in tables, charts, or graphs. Calculators round to a fixed-length decimal to fit calculations on the display (trailing 0s are usually truncated), and on some calculators the fixed length of decimals may be adjusted. Scientific notation is a well-defined procedure for writing numbers in a consistent format. *Everyday Mathematics* does not emphasize the need for children to make their estimates consistent. They see numbers all around them, however, that are written with just this goal in mind. You are advised to point out such instances when they arise.

8.1.3 Estimates Can Help in Problem Solving

Estimation can also be useful during problem solving, both before and after the answer is obtained. During the early phases of the problem-solving process, making an estimate can help in understanding the problem. Making an estimate helps clarify what is known and what is unknown, and can provide guidance toward finding the solution. Even if an estimate near the beginning of the problem-solving process turns out to be rather inaccurate, making one can be helpful, especially for difficult problems.

Once a solution is obtained, an estimate can be useful for checking its reasonableness. Looking back over the problem-solving process can be valuable, and estimating to verify the accuracy of a result is a good way to encourage such reflection. Estimating to check answers also emphasizes that results obtained in different ways should agree and, more generally, that mathematics makes sense.

8.2 Extreme Numbers

Very big and very small numbers—extreme numbers, you might call them—can be interesting to children. They appear in counts: the populations of countries, stars in galaxies, hairs on your head, cells in your brain, and so on. They appear in measurements: distances between solar systems, years since the dinosaurs, square miles in Antarctica, the speed of computers.

Extreme numbers can be difficult for some people to grasp, so relating them to familiar counts or measures can help. For example, it takes about 60 city blocks to cover one square mile. That means it would take about 6 million city blocks to cover the 104,000 square miles recorded as the area of Colorado. (The 104,000 square miles assumes Colorado is flat.) Such comparisons of a smaller, familiar measure to a much larger measure are applications of ratio comparison. Working and playing with extreme numbers illustrates the need for estimating and approximating. Big numbers may need to be estimated if they are unknown. This may be because the things with which they are associated cannot be counted or measured, or because the number is a large product or sum. Near the end of third grade, children are exposed to numbers in the millions when they first encounter population census figures.

It is not easy comparing large numbers to each other. For some people, comparing 1 to 1,000 can be visualized: a 1 cm cube can easily be compared to a $10 \times 10 \times 10$ cm block. Visualizing

in perspective

In *Everyday Mathematics* Grade 4, students extend the place-value system beyond millions and explore the relative sizes of millions, billions, and trillions. Students also compare big numbers by rounding to a consistent place value, writing the results with power-of-ten notations. In fifth grade, students are asked to think about big numbers that are unknown using guess-and-test strategies.

1,000,000 compared to 1,000,000,000, on the other hand, may not be quite as easy (unless you are comfortable with the 1 cm cube representing 1,000,000).

8.3 Estimates in Calculations

When considering how many $3.98 items you can afford to buy, it is easier to calculate using $4 as the price. This is an example of what we call *ballpark estimation.* In planning a trip and comparing costs of driving versus flying, for example, it is more realistic and easier to estimate. Your thinking might go like this: "The trip will be about 800 miles, my automobile gets about 25 miles per gallon, and gasoline costs about $1.80 per gallon; but there will be two days' extra driving and the motel will cost $80 and meals on the road about $50. On the other hand, the cheapest way to fly costs about $300, and I'll need to rent a car at the destination for five days at $60 per day . . . ."

Calculating by using estimates is often easier than calculating using exact numbers. It is less obvious that even with calculators and computers, estimating may make things a lot easier with no significant loss in the quality of the answers. In fact, answers derived using estimates may be more reasonable than exact ones. Even if exact answers are required and a calculator is used to find them, estimation can help check the results. Most of us have encountered a cashier who has entered the price of an item incorrectly, but did not know the total was off. Such occurrences are often used to support arguments that people depend too much on machines, that calculators should be banned from the classroom, and that children should master paper-and-pencil algorithms.

These arguments miss the point entirely. If pressed, few people would want the cashier to stop using a machine and do the calculations on paper. What the cashier needs are estimation skills to verify whether the machine total is somewhere in the neighborhood of being correct. If the machine total does not fit the estimate, then, obviously, the total should be recalculated. In the defense of the cashier, we must note that most traditional mathematics curricula don't teach estimation skills in conjunction with arithmetic operations. Such skills have sometimes been reviled as nothing more than trial and error. *Everyday Mathematics,* on the other hand, sees them as an integral component of a comprehensive and balanced approach to computation. Children are encouraged to compute either exactly or approximately, working either mentally, with paper and pencil, or with a calculator, depending on what is most appropriate for each situation.

8.4 Rounding

Estimation is often an educated guess at an unknown or unknowable value; rounding is an algorithm for approximating known numbers. Usually, the rounding is either up or down to get a number that is close to a known number but easier to understand or work with, where "close" and "easier" are determined by the context of a problem. In the following example, rounding makes estimation easier:

Example: You want to buy 4 cans of tennis balls, and each can of tennis balls costs $2.59. Estimate the least number of dollar bills you need in order to pay for your purchase.

Solution 1: Rounding up to $3 per can, a reasonable estimate for the cost of 4 cans is $4 \times \$3 = \$12$.

Solution 2: Rounding down to $2.50, a closer estimate to the cost of 4 cans is $11, because $4 \times \$2.50 = \$10$. So $4 \times \$2.59$ is a bit more than $10.

Which solution is right? Both are good applications of rounding. Although the second solution is closer to the exact cost, it is not necessarily a better estimate. Both solutions might be suggested and then compared with each other. A discussion may show that to estimate a calculation to a nearest dollar, you don't necessarily want to round to the nearest dollar first.

> in **perspective** The solutions to the examples above used two of the three traditional rounding algorithms taught more formally in *Everyday Mathematics* Grades 4–6. All three rounding algorithms require that a place value (ones, tens, tenths, and so on) first be picked as a target.

8.4.1 Rounding algorithms

• **Round up to the nearest** This algorithm is used to overestimate a value. *Example:* A school bus holds 28 students. How many school buses should be scheduled to take 300 students on a field trip? *Solution:* The target is a whole number of buses. $300/28 \rightarrow 10$ R20, so round up to 11 buses. The quotient 10 R20 means that 10 buses would leave 20 students behind, so 11 buses must be ordered.

• **Round down to the nearest** This algorithm is used to underestimate a value. *Example:* An elevator manufacturer tests the maximum weight an elevator can hold and finds the cable breaks at an average of 2,023.5 pounds. What should the posted weight limit be? *Solution:* The target is flexible, but is usually given in hundreds of pounds. Round down to be safe. Perhaps the limit should be posted as 1,500 pounds.

- **Round to the nearest** This algorithm is intended to be as fair as possible. The traditional version says to round up if the digit beyond the target place is 5 or greater, and to round down if the digit is less than 5. *Example:* What is 17.988 centimeters rounded to the nearest tenth? *Solution:* The 8 beyond the 9 in the tenths place is greater than 5, so round up to 18.0 centimeters.

8.5 Number Sense and Mathematical Connections

It is perhaps the single greatest goal of *Everyday Mathematics* that children completing the program have "number sense." People with number sense:

- have developed good mental-arithmetic skills along with reliable pencil-and-paper procedures for finding results they can't produce mentally
- are flexible in thinking about numbers and arithmetic and will look for shortcuts to make their efforts as efficient as possible
- can use number and arithmetic skills to solve problems in everyday situations
- are familiar with a variety of ways to communicate strategies and results
- can recognize unreasonable results when they see them in their own work or in the media

Number sense develops only with wide mathematical experience, including instruction and practice in specific techniques. But acquiring good number sense also depends on certain attitudes and beliefs. Chief among these is the belief that mathematics does make sense. That is, people with good number sense expect their mathematical knowledge to connect with their other knowledge, including their common sense and whatever they know about the situation at hand. Number sense thus depends on connections between various kinds of mathematical knowledge and between mathematics and other subjects.

Everyday Mathematics helps children develop number sense by encouraging them to build connections both within the *Everyday Mathematics* curriculum and between mathematics and other subjects in the curriculum. Having children work with number stories beginning in Kindergarten strengthens connections between mathematics and language arts. Many activities in *Everyday Mathematics* are specifically designed to show the student how mathematics applies to science and geography. Throughout *Everyday Mathematics,* there are connections between mathematics and history, including both the history of mathematics and how mathematics has shaped human endeavors. Finally, *Everyday Mathematics* connects mathematics to the community through efforts to share the authors' commitment to number sense with family members. Family Letters (found in the *Math Masters* book) explain how *Everyday Mathematics* introduces children not only to the traditional mathematics parents expect, but also to a richer mathematics curriculum that older family members may not have experienced. Home Links help parents understand the kinds of mathematics their children do in school and include ideas for parental involvement as well.

> **in perspective** Study Links, rather than Home Links, are used for Home-and-School communication in *Everyday Mathematics* Grades 4–6.

9

Patterns, Sequences, Functions, and Algebra

outline

9.1 **Visual Patterns** 182

9.2 **Odd and Even Number Patterns** 184

9.3 **Sequences** 184

    9.3.1 **Frames and Arrows** 185

    9.3.2 **Incomplete Number Lines** 187

    9.3.3 **Teaching with Sequences** 188

9.4 **Functions** 189

    9.4.1 **Function Machines** 190

    9.4.2 **"What's My Rule?"** 191

    9.4.3 **What Is a Function?** 192

    9.4.4 **Functions and Representations** 193

9.5 **Algebra** 195

Patterns can be found almost anywhere—in sounds, in movements, in shapes, in numbers, in graphs, in data. Patterns are especially important in mathematics; some people even define mathematics as the science of patterns.

Most of the patterns in *Everyday Mathematics* are either visual patterns or number patterns. Many of the visual patterns that students encounter are discussed in other sections of this manual. For example, pattern-based classifications of polygons are discussed in Essay 5, Geometry. Certain patterns in graphs and data sets are discussed in Essay 4, Data and Chance.

We do discuss visual patterns in this essay, but most of our attention is on number patterns and the arithmetic rules that generate them. We focus on two types of number patterns that are so important throughout mathematics that they have names: functions and sequences.

9.1 Visual Patterns

A major aim of *Everyday Mathematics* is for children to become aware of patterns of shapes and colors in their environment. Many pattern-recognition activities help children focus on geometric properties of shapes. Some examples follow.

- Make a pattern with craft sticks and ask your partner what would come next.

This type of sequence involves an understanding of the beauty and symmetry in parallel line segments and right-angle turns. What comes next? A horizontal triplet? A repetition of the first five triplets?

• Look at the pattern below and describe what would come next.

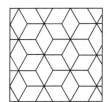 • • •

This puzzle introduces children to a sequence of concave hexagons, each of which is a turn by 90 degrees of the previous one. Or is it a slide of the first two repeated over and over? Or is it one sequence of horizontal shapes with another sequence of vertical ones placed on top? Without the need for formal names of the shapes, or definitions of the slides and turns involved, this kind of activity helps children become aware of relations of 2-dimensional objects and how those relations can be described.

• Color the diamond pattern with three colors.

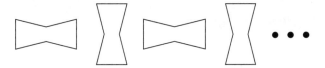

This pattern is a *tessellation*. Without knowing any of the names of the shapes, young children can get valuable experience with some rather sophisticated relations of polygons in the plane. In the example above, the result gives the impression of a pattern of stacked 3-dimensional cubes.

Everyday Mathematics engages children in many other activities with visual patterns. Patterns around the classroom or school include grilles on light fixtures, panes in windows, wires or slats in fences, milk cartons in crates, floor and ceiling tiles, patterns in magazine and newspaper pictures and advertisements, and so on. Home Links encourage children to find patterns at home and bring in examples. Visual patterns also appear frequently in Math Boxes and in *Minute Math+®*.

9.2 Odd and Even Number Patterns

For centuries, people have studied number patterns in a branch of mathematics called *number theory*. In this section, we address perhaps the simplest of these patterns, odd and even numbers. In the following sections, we discuss number sequences, functions, and algebra.

Odd and even numbers are simple, but can lead children to generalizations that are genuinely mathematical and of fundamental importance in number theory. For example, it is easy to observe that odd numbers of things always have one left over after pairing. Building on this simple observation, some children discover relationships such as the following:

- The sum of any two even numbers is even (there are no leftover pieces).
- The sum of an even number and an odd number is odd (the leftover piece remains).
- The sum of any two odd numbers is even (the leftovers pair up).

Similar patterns exist for differences of evens and odds and for products of evens and odds. Making generalizations based on observations of patterns is fundamental to mathematics and science, so when children discover and "prove" simple relationships about odd and even numbers, they are learning powerful ways of thinking about numbers that will serve them well throughout their mathematical careers.

Odd numbers of people or things can sometimes be a nuisance, since they may complicate equal sharing or make it impossible to get the same number on each of two teams. But odd numbers can sometimes be a convenience. Consider the insight reported by the parent of a first grader (see margin). Mathematicians would recognize this first grader's observation as a "theorem." As you list heights, weights, or other data in order, you and the children will find that this property of odd numbers makes it easier to identify a "middle value," which is a step toward understanding the data landmark known as the median. Although only a few primary-grade children can express such pattern-based properties, in time, many more will be able to "see" and "feel" them.

KEVIN: Odd numbers are neat. They always have a middle.

FATHER: What?

KEVIN: See *(pointing to the third of five sticks in a row),* always something in the middle. But with even numbers *(removing the third stick from the row),* there is just a space in the middle.

9.3 Sequences

A number sequence is a list of numbers. Many sequences are important enough to have names:

- whole numbers: 0, 1, 2, 3, 4, 5, 6, . . .
- odd numbers: 1, 3, 5, 7, 9, 11, . . .
- even numbers: 2, 4, 6, 8, 10, 12, . . .
- prime numbers: 2, 3, 5, 7, 11, 13, . . .
- square numbers: 1, 4, 9, 16, 25, 36, . . .

Many number sequences can be generated by repeated application of a rule. The whole numbers, for example, can be generated by starting with 0 and repeatedly applying the rule "Add 1." The even numbers can be generated by starting at 2 and applying the rule "Add 2."

Many number sequences can be linked to visual patterns. The square numbers, for example, can be modeled by a sequence of square arrays. The even numbers and triangular numbers can also be modeled by sequences of dot shapes. The interplay of number sequences and visual patterns is fertile ground for investigations in elementary school mathematics.

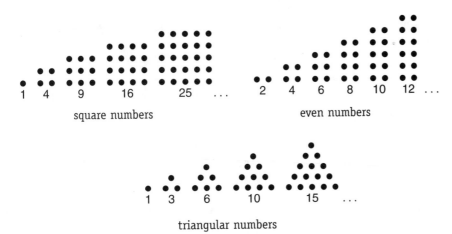

Patterns in many number sequences are accessible to children of any age. In primary grade *Everyday Mathematics,* children make sequences given a starting number and a rule such as "Add 3"; they find a rule given a sequence such as 5, 10, 15, 20, 25, . . . ; and then they fill in blanks on number lines with a given scale (rule) or one they invent. In *Kindergarten* through *Third Grade Everyday Mathematics,* many of these activities with sequences are presented through the Frames-and-Arrows routine.

9.3.1 Frames and Arrows

Frames-and-Arrows diagrams consist of frames connected by arrows. Each frame contains a number; each arrow represents a rule that determines which number goes in the next frame. The numbers in a Frames-and-Arrows diagram form a sequence; the arrow rule(s) represent the mathematical structure that generates the sequence. Frames-and-Arrows diagrams are also called chains. Here is a simple example of a Frames-and-Arrows diagram for the rule "Add 1":

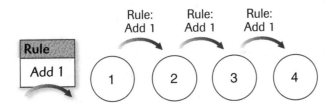

In Frames-and-Arrows problems, some information is missing. There are several kinds of problems:

- The rule is given. Some of the frames are empty. Fill in the blank frames.

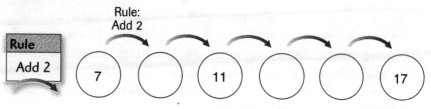

Solution: Write 9, 13, and 15 in the blank frames.

- The frames are filled in. The rule is missing. Find the rule

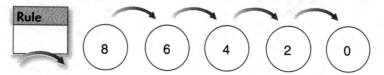

Solution: The rule is subtract 2, minus 2, or −2.

- Some of the frames are empty. The rule is missing. Find the rule and fill in the empty frames.

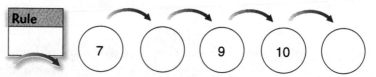

Solution: The rule is add 1. Write 8 and 11 in the empty frames.

A chain can have more than one arrow rule. If it does, the arrows for the rules must look different. For example, we can use a color arrow for one rule and a black arrow for the other rule:

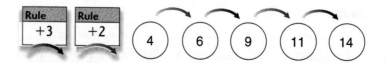

In the following example, the rules are given and the frames are filled in, but the arrows between frames are missing:

- Draw the arrows in the proper positions.

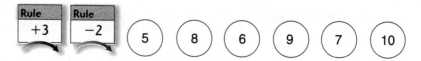

Solution: Draw the +3 arrow from 5 to 8, from 6 to 9, and from 7 to 10. Draw the −2 arrow from 8 to 6 and from 9 to 7.

The Frames-and-Arrows format is easily grasped by children and is highly flexible. *Everyday Mathematics* encourages you and your children to devise your own Frames-and-Arrows problems.

9.3.2 Incomplete Number Lines

In first and second grades, two uses of number lines are to keep track of days of the school year and to help with counting. Beginning in *First Grade Everyday Mathematics,* number lines are also used in a variation of Frames and Arrows. Children are given a number line with a sequence of blanks to fill in or tick marks to label. Like Frames-and-Arrows diagrams, such problems involve sequences in a different format. The scale of the number line—the distance between ticks—corresponds to the rule that governs the sequence. At first, we recommend that the numbers in the chain be whole numbers and the rule be "Add 1." Two types of problems appear:

1. Start with the familiar: Given two boundary points on a number line with scale 1, have the children fill in the blanks. For example:

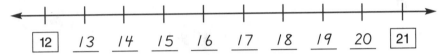

Note that the rule does not actually need to be stated in this type of problem, as the number of tick marks determines the scale.

2. Start in the middle: Given one or two numbers on a number line with scale 1, fill in the blanks in either direction. This encourages practice with both counting up and counting down.

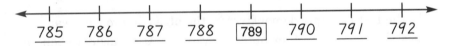

Note that in the second example children could use a scale other than 1. For example, they could decide to count by 10s, which would lead to the values 749 through 819. Don't push children to understand this early on, but don't penalize any child who realizes the possibilities. If you don't want to open this door for your children, be sure to label at least two tick marks on the given number line. The labeled points need not be consecutive. The best procedure for creating such problems is to complete the entire line and then erase all but one or two numbers—this ensures that the problem you create will have a reasonable answer.

Later, scales other than 1 are introduced in order to practice more sophisticated counting techniques and to use the number line as an extension of the numbering system to include fractions, decimals, and negative numbers. This increases the variety of problems that children see.

3. Begin with variations on the first kind of problem above: Given part of a number line on which two boundary points are labeled with whole numbers, children must skip count to fill in whole-number labels for points between the given points. For example:

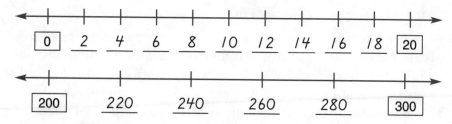

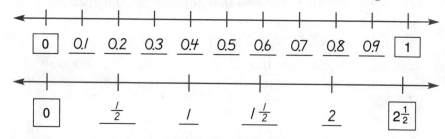

4. As part of their work with fractions and decimals, have children fill in missing labels on number lines such as the following:

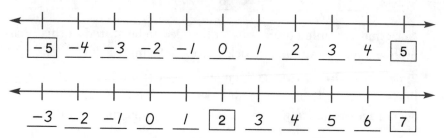

5. Extend the number line to the left of 0:

As the last example demonstrates, the above approaches can be used for any of the other number systems. Also consider open-ended problems where only one tick mark is labeled, but be prepared for a variety of scale choices. As this work with number lines continues, children will discover an amazing fact: Between any two points (numbers), another point (number) can always be found. The number line is thus doubly infinite. The entire number line contains infinitely many numbers, but even the smallest interval between two numbers also contains infinitely many numbers.

9.3.3 Teaching with Sequences

Many Frames-and-Arrows and incomplete-number-line problems have been incorporated into each grade's materials. Once you introduce these kinds of problems, use them often. Many different frame shapes are used for the Frames-and-Arrows routine. This helps children understand that it is the number sequence and its rules, not the shapes of the frames, that are important. A blackline master with a blank chain is included in *Math Masters* for you and the children to create your own Frames-and-Arrows problems.

Rules for sequence problems can become increasingly complicated. Toward the end of first grade, for example, you might use rules such as "double," "double and add 1," or "take half of" for Frames and

Arrows, and use numbers in the hundreds for number lines. Toward the end of third grade, rules might include "multiply by 10" or "add $1.25," with numbers in the thousands and negative numbers for number lines.

Scales for radio channels, for example, are nonlinear; scientists sometimes use nonlinear scales such as powers of ten to simplify graphing certain kinds of relationships.

Photography courtesy of Bill Lettow, ©1999

radio dial with nonlinear scale

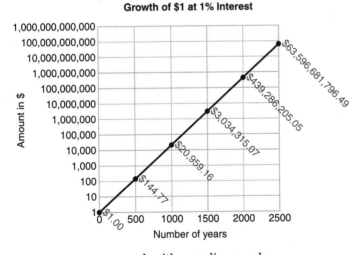

a graph with a nonlinear scale

9.4 Functions

Function is one of those everyday words that mathematicians use in a special way. Later, in Section 9.4.3, we will explain the mathematical definition of *function,* but first we want to discuss how *Everyday Mathematics* approaches this powerful idea in ways that even Kindergartners can understand.

9.4.1 Function Machines

Perhaps the best metaphor for understanding functions is the function machine. A function machine is an imaginary device that receives inputs and generates outputs. Here, for example, is a function machine that doubles any number put into it:

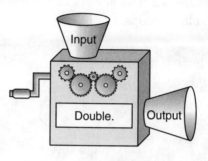

Rule: Double.

Input	Output
1	2
2	4
3	6
5	10
638	1276

Double Function

Rule: Always output 3

Input	Output
1	3
2	3
3	3
5	3
638	3

Constant Function

One can imagine putting a number into this machine, turning the crank, and getting another number out. For example, if 1 is put in, then 2 will come out. If 5 is put in, then 10 will come out. Whatever number goes in, twice that number will come out.

The inputs and outputs from a function machine can be recorded in a table. The table for the doubling machine above is shown next to the machine.

One important feature of a function machine is that it should always work the same: A function must always give the same output for any given input. If two rows in an input-output table have the same number in the input column, then they must also have the same number in the output column.

The function-machine metaphor captures the key features of functions that are studied in pre-college mathematics. There is a set of inputs, another set of outputs, and a rule associating each input with one certain output.

In the first four grades, *Everyday Mathematics* uses function machines and tables of values to approach functions. Function machines can be drawn very simply—the crank and gears in the doubling machine above are unnecessary ornamentation. Refer to the drawing in margin. Children use function machines to help

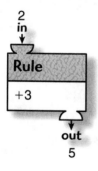

function machine

visualize how a rule associates each input value with an output value. A principal activity for developing this concept is called "What's My Rule?"

9.4.2 "What's My Rule?"

Simple "What's My Rule?" games begin in *Kindergarten Everyday Mathematics.* The first games are attribute or rule activities that sort children into a specified group. For example, children with hook-and-loop fasteners on their shoes belong to the group while children with laces, buckles, and so forth, do not. The teacher sorts the children without revealing his or her rule; the children have to guess what the sorting rule is. In first through third grades, this idea is extended to sorting numbers. For example, the teacher might draw a circle on the board and begin writing even numbers in the circle and odd numbers outside the circle. The children say numbers and try to guess where they go. Once they can reliably predict which numbers belong in the circle, they propose rules for the sorting. This can be repeated for one-digit numbers, numbers with zero in the ones place, numbers between 20 and 30, and so on.

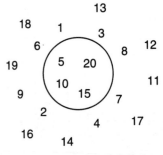

What's My Rule?

These "What's My Rule?" activities are eventually extended to include problems in which pairs of numbers are given and the task is to find the rule that relates the numbers in each pair. The same rule has to work for every pair. The first number can be considered the input to a function machine, the second number the output. The problem is to find the function machine's rule. The pairings can be displayed in a table of values.

In a "What's My Rule?" problem, two of the three parts (input, output, and rule) are known. The goal is to find the unknown part. There are several basic kinds of problems:

- The rule and the input numbers are known. Find the output numbers.

Rule: +10	
In	Out
39	
54	
163	

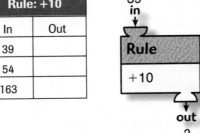

- The rule and the output numbers are known. Find the input numbers.

Rule: −6	
In	Out
	6
	10
	20

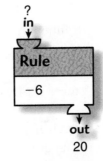

- The input and output numbers are known. Find the rule.

Rule: ?	
In	Out
55	60
85	90
103	108

85
in
↓

Rule
?

↓
out
90

Problems of more than one type can be combined. In the second example above, you also could give students the input value 26 while replacing the 20 with a blank. If you give enough input and output clues, children can fill in blanks as well as figure out the rule, as in the problem at the right.

Rule: ?	
In	Out
15	25
4	14
7	
	63

in
↓

Rule
?

↓
out

9.4.3 What Is a Function?

Like many ideas in mathematics, the concept of a function is simple yet powerful. The definition of *function* seems at first to be rather odd. According to a dictionary of mathematics, "A function is a set of ordered pairs (x, y) in which each value of x is paired with exactly one value of y." A few examples may help clarify what this means:

doubling: {(1, 2), (2, 4), (3, 6), (4, 8), . . .}

squaring: {(1, 1), (2, 4), (3, 9), (4, 16), . . .}

adding 1: { (1, 2), (2, 3), (3, 4), (4, 5), . . .}

In each of these sets of ordered pairs, each first number is paired with exactly one second number. According to the definition, then, each of these sets is a function.

This definition includes all the functions discussed so far in this essay, but you will note that there is no mention of a rule in the definition. The pairings in a function do not have to follow any rule; the only requirement is that each first value be paired with exactly one second value. If, for example, you matched every whole number less than 100 with a randomly chosen whole number less than 100, then you would have a function.

a function with no rule: {(1, 82), (2, 15), (3, 74), . . . , (99, 17), (100, 92)}

Such a function isn't very useful, but it is still a legitimate function. A more interesting example of a function with no rule is one that takes a date as the input and gives the closing stock price of IBM as output. If you could find a rule for such a function, you could strike it rich quite easily. Unfortunately, economists have proved that no such rule can exist—and if such a rule existed, someone would figure it out, use it to make money, and in the process invalidate the rule. The only way to find the closing price of IBM is to wait and see what the ticker says at the end of the day.

Don't worry about functions without rules. Most interesting functions are interesting precisely because they do have rules. All of the functions in *Everyday Mathematics* are associated with rules that are either given or may be deduced. To keep them interesting to children, many are taken from real life.

Also missing from the mathematical definition of *function* is any mention of numbers. In fact, functions do not have to involve numbers at all—all that is required is a set of inputs and a set of outputs. A function might take polygons in and output "triangle," "quadrangle," "pentagon," and so on. Another function might take triangles in and output "acute," "right," or "obtuse." All that is required is a set of inputs that are allowed (you can't put a polygon into a "Subtract 3" machine) and a set of outputs. A rule for associating a specific output with each input makes the function interesting, but, as noted above, such a rule is not required.

Many real-world situations involve functions. A bathroom scale is a function machine; stand on it and it outputs your weight. A gasoline pump has a built-in function machine; input an amount of gasoline and out comes the total cost, including tax. One way to think about science is as a search for functions that relate real-world variables.

Sequences can also be considered functions. Some sequences can be thought of as iterative functions, in which an output comes from applying a rule to the previous output (that is, to the previous number in the sequence), rather than to any arbitrary input value. For example, to get the next even number, just add 2 to the previous even number. Other sequences can't be approached in this way because there is no rule that gives the next term from the previous term. (Mathematicians call the numbers in a sequence the terms of the sequence.) The sequence of closing prices for IBM stock is an example of a sequence for which knowing all the previous terms is not enough to determine the next term. The even numbers, for example, correspond to the function in the table in the margin. Thinking of a sequence in this way can sometimes lead to a rule that will give any term in the sequence without having to find all the previous terms. Studying the table in the margin, for example, leads to a rule for finding any even number: To find the nth even number, simply double n.

In *Everyday Mathematics,* sequences are not treated as functions—it's easier to think of sequences as lists of numbers, often with a rule for generating the next term, as in Frames-and-Arrows diagrams. Activities with sequences, however, are quite helpful for developing children's understanding of functions.

9.4.4 Functions and Representations

Students of *Everyday Mathematics* approach functions concretely, pictorially, verbally (usually orally), and symbolically. Concrete

NOTE: Functions are not just restricted to two variables (a single input variable and a single output variable.) The speed of a falling object, for example, is a function of the force of gravity, the length of time the object has been falling, and air resistance. In *Everyday Mathematics,* however, we restrict ourselves to functions that involve only two variables.

Even Numbers	
Input	Output
1	2
2	4
3	6
4	8
5	10
. . .	. . .

activities include those in which children sort objects according to some measure or attribute. Lining up by height and ordering pattern blocks by shape, for example, are activities in which children explore patterns leading to functions.

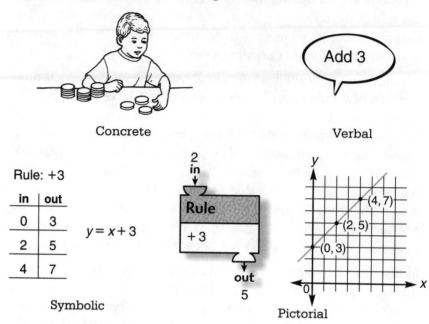

Concrete

Verbal

Rule: +3

in	out
0	3
2	5
4	7

$y = x + 3$

Symbolic

Pictorial

Frames-and-Arrows problems, incomplete number lines, and function machines are pictorial representations of functions and sequences. Graphs are particularly important pictorial representations that are investigated extensively throughout *Everyday Mathematics*.

Tables of values are an important kind of representation of functions in *Everyday Mathematics* Grades K–3. Many functions in real life are given as tables: the sports and business sections of the newspaper are filled with tables that represent functions of various sorts. The input could be a baseball team, for example, and the output the team batting average. Team standings, financial tables, weather tables, and so on, can all be considered functions. A great deal of the tabular information in almanacs and other reference books can also be thought of as functions.

Verbal representations for functions include rules like "double" or "add 5." These verbal representations can often be made more concise by using symbols like "+3" or "Output = Input +3," or even "$y = x + 3$". The symbolic representation of functions is explored more extensively in *Everyday Mathematics* Grades 4–6.

in **perspective**   In *Everyday Mathematics* Grades 4–6, children's work with tables, rules, and variables leads to representing functions with equations. The equations may in turn be graphed or used to generate more ordered pairs of values. Experiences with all of these representations of functions provide students with background for their junior and senior high school studies of more advanced algebra.

9.5 Algebra

Most adults probably remember algebra as a junior or senior high school course devoted to learning how to manipulate equations containing variables. But algebra is actually far more than symbol manipulation. Algebra can be thought of as generalized arithmetic, as a set of powerful problem-solving procedures, as a study of numerical relationships, or as a study of the structure of mathematics. The authors of *Everyday Mathematics* believe these are all valuable descriptions of algebra. Although the formal study of algebraic syntax is not appropriate for most elementary school children, students of *Everyday Mathematics* Grades K–3 engage in many activities involving algebra.

Algebra is the branch of mathematics that deals with variables and operations on variables. So, in a sense, as soon as first graders encounter problems like $8 + \_\_ = 12$ they are beginning algebra, as the blank is a kind of variable. Later in *Everyday Mathematics,* children experience variables as unknowns $(6 + x = 8)$, in formulas $(A = lw)$, in statements of mathematical properties $(a + b = b + a)$, and in functions $(y = x + 5)$. This experience with variables prepares children for success in algebra. (See Section 2.2.3 for a discussion of variables.)

Pattern tasks in *Everyday Mathematics* also involve mathematical processes that are fundamental in algebra. Among these are looking for patterns; making, testing, and proving conjectures about patterns; and representing patterns in several ways. Looking for patterns helps children develop modeling skills that are crucial to many applications of algebra. Making and justifying conjectures about patterns promotes habits of generalization and verification that will serve students to good advantage into algebra and beyond. Finally, working with multiple representations of functions— function machines, tables, rules, graphs, words, and symbols—will help students develop the conceptual competency required to support the symbolic skills vital for success in algebra.

Problem Solving

outline

10.1 **What Is Problem Solving?** 196
10.2 **Problem Representations** 197
10.3 **Mathematical Modeling** 199
10.4 **Teaching Problem Solving** 201
   10.4.1 **Learning Mathematical Modeling** 201

10.4.2 **Number Stories** 202
10.4.3 **Sharing Children's Strategies and Solutions** 204
10.4.4 **Problem Solving Strategies for Beginners** 205

In 1977, the National Council of Supervisors of Mathematics issued a position paper on basic skills. The first basic skill listed was problem solving: "Learning to solve problems is the principal reason for studying mathematics" (NCSM, 1977, p. 20). Ever since, problem solving has remained the top priority in school mathematics.

This essay is about problem solving and how *Everyday Mathematics* teaches it. Section 10.1 surveys various definitions of problem solving and explains what problem solving means in *Everyday Mathematics*. Section 10.2 discusses various ways mathematical ideas can be represented (concretely, pictorially, verbally, or symbolically) and what such representations have to do with problem solving. Section 10.3 explains what mathematical modeling is and its relationship with problem solving. Finally, Section 10.4 provides further details about teaching problem solving in *Everyday Mathematics* Grades K–3.

10.1 What Is Problem Solving?

In primary school mathematics books, "problem solving" often refers only to finding answers to printed "word problems." But problem solving is much more than that. In the NCSM position paper cited above, problem solving is defined as "the process of applying previously acquired knowledge to new and unfamiliar situations." In the discussion draft of *Principles and Standards for School Mathematics,* the National Council of Teachers of Mathematics states, "Problem solving means engaging in a task for which the solution method is not known in advance" (NCTM, 1998, p. 76). George Polya, whose book *How to Solve It* is a classic, wrote, "Solving a problem is finding the unknown means to a distinctly conceived end" (1980, p. 1).

These broader definitions of problem solving are not restricted to arithmetic and certainly not merely to "word problems" within arithmetic. Central to all of them is the idea that solution methods are not known in advance. A problem is not a problem if the problem solver knows exactly what to do right away. Problems for which the solution method is known ahead of time may be useful exercises. Indeed, a comprehensive curriculum like *Everyday Mathematics* must include many such exercises so that students can practice essential skills. But they are not genuine problems in the sense implied here.

In *Everyday Mathematics,* problem solving is broadly defined. Number stories (word problems) have their place, but problem solving permeates the entire curriculum. Children solve problems both in purely mathematical contexts, such as Frames and Arrows, and in real situations from the classroom and everyday life. Children also create and solve problems using information from posters, the teacher, and their own experience and imagination.

Everyday Mathematics defines problem solving as the process of modeling everyday situations using tools from mathematics. Mathematical modeling is discussed in detail in Section 10.3, but in a nutshell it means that expert problem solvers generally do one or more of a small number of things:

- identify what the problem is   ↑ *GOAL* ✲
- analyze what they know and seek out further data as necessary
- play with the data to discover patterns and meaning
- ask themselves what mathematical techniques can help find a solution
- look back after finding a tentative solution and think about whether the solution makes sense, and whether the solution method can be used to solve other problems

10.2 Problem Representations

but what works.

Often the key step in solving a problem is simply looking at it in the right way. Consider this problem: "How many handshakes are there when five people shake hands with one another?" One approach to solving this problem would be to find five people and have them shake hands, being careful to count each handshake. This approach is, to say the least, not very convenient. Another approach would be to make a list. If the people are represented by the letters A, B, C, D, and E, the handshakes could be listed as follows: A-B, A-C, A-D,

NOTE: The word *solution* in mathematics has two related meanings. One meaning is "the answer." The other is "how the answer was obtained; the solution method." Usually the context makes clear which meaning is intended.

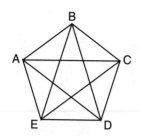

Figure 1. A Picture for Five People Shaking Hands

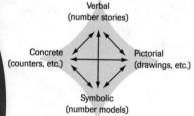

Figure 2. A Problem with Eggs

Four Problem-Solving REPRESENTATIONS

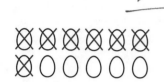

Verbal (number stories)

Concrete (counters, etc.)

Pictorial (drawings, etc.)

Symbolic (number models)

A-E, B-C, B-D, B-E, C-D, C-E, and D-E. Although this is practical for five people shaking hands, it looks like it might be troublesome for larger numbers. One might easily make a mistake in listing all the handshakes. Still another approach is to draw a picture of a pentagon with all its diagonals. Each corner stands for a person, and each line connecting two people stands for a handshake. Finding a mistake in such a figure may be easier than in a long list, though it might be a nuisance to draw such a figure for a lot of people.

Each of these solutions to the handshake problem depends on a different way of looking at the problem. One way used real people; another way involved a list; the third way made use of a drawing. Different ways of looking at a problem are called "problem representations." *Everyday Mathematics* Grades K–3 focuses on four basic kinds of problem representations: concrete, verbal, pictorial, and symbolic.

Suppose, for example, I need a dozen eggs to make egg salad, but when I take out my eggs I drop the carton on the floor. That's a concrete situation. A verbal description might make certain details explicit, like the fact that seven of the eggs are broken. A simple picture could show the sad condition of the eggs, and a number model could sum it up in symbols: $12 - 7 = 5$.

These varieties of problem representations can be diagrammed as shown in the margin. Note that arrows connect each kind of representation with each of the other kinds. Children and adults use all of these representations at one time or another, depending on the situation at hand. One of the aims of *Everyday Mathematics* is to increase children's facility with various kinds of representation. Variations and extensions of these four kinds of representations are featured as children move beyond third grade.

Another objective of *Everyday Mathematics* is to help children make easy translations among various ways of representing problems. Representations are closely related to solution strategies. Often, translating a problem into another representation is the key to solving it. Discussion of many different representations and solutions exposes children to methods they may like to try and teaches them that there are many ways to solve problems.

As you discuss problems and solutions, compare various representations and ask children to translate from one to another. For example, ask children to draw a picture for a problem given in words. If a child solves $25 + 36$ by counting up on a number grid, ask her to solve $35 + 42$ by just thinking about the grid rather than by using an actual grid. By encouraging multiple representations and translations among representations, you can help children develop into more powerful problem solvers.

As you observe children working with various representations, you can also determine their problem-solving strengths and weaknesses, which can, in turn, help you tailor activities to meet individual needs. You might observe, for example, that a certain child always uses counters to solve problems. This might lead you to suggest drawing a simple picture like the one of the eggs in Figure 2 on page 198. A child who is adept at drawing pictures might benefit from a suggestion to try using a number grid.

10.3 Mathematical Modeling

A mathematical model is something mathematical that corresponds to something in the real world. A sphere is a model for a basketball. The sentence "$22 + 1 = 23$" is a model for the number of children in a classroom when a new student arrives. The formula "$d = (5\ hours) \times (50\ miles/hour)$" is a model for the distance a car travels in 5 hours at 50 mph, and the more general formula $d = rt$ is a model for links among distance, rate, and time. Specialists in science and industry spend much of their time building and testing mathematical models of real-world systems. Other people do mathematical modeling whenever they use mathematics to solve a problem.

Mathematical modeling is the process of translating a real situation into the language of mathematics. After the situation is translated into mathematics, a solution is found using mathematical techniques; finally, the solution is translated back into the real world. This process is illustrated in Figure 4.

Figure 4 is an oversimplification. Mathematical modeling is usually more complicated. It often involves some or all of the following steps:

- Formulate or confront a problem. Try to understand your problem. What do you want to find out? Imagine what the answer would look like if you had one.

- Examine the information that is given and seek additional data as necessary. Discard information that is not necessary. Sort the data you have.

- Explore the data. Represent the data in various ways, perhaps by drawing a picture, making a graph, or writing a number model. Play with the data.

- Do the math. Carry out the arithmetic, algebra, geometry, statistics, or whatever else is necessary to find an answer.

- Check the answer against the original problem situation to see if it makes sense. Compare your answer to someone else's or to an answer you obtain in another way. Think about the method you used. Can the same method be used in other, similar problems? Is there another method that works? Compare various solutions and methods.

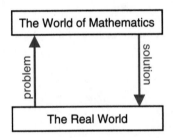

Figure 4. Mathematical Modeling

The diagram shows five boxes connected by arrows in a star pattern:

- What is given? Is more information needed? Is there extra information?
- What is the problem? Understand the problem.
- Play with the data. Represent the problem in various ways.
- Examine the solution. Does the answer make sense? Does the solution generalize?
- What math can help? How can an answer be found? Find an answer.

Figure 5. The Process of Mathematical Modeling

The process of mathematical modelling can actually begin anywhere and go anywhere. The lines in Figure 5 are meant to show this.

Often, for example, mathematical modeling begins with data. Suppose you are a baseball fan and are studying tables of baseball statistics. As you explore the data, you might notice that it appears that in inter-league games the National League usually beats the American League. This might lead you to ask whether this is actually true. By adding up the total wins for each league you might find that the National League does win more often. If you wished, you could test your answer when the next set of inter-league games takes place.

Though not quite in the order that they appear in the list above, this baseball situation involves all five phases of the mathematical modeling process. Sometimes, only a few of the phases are involved. An expert problem solver might see the solution to a problem instantly and simply have to check that it's correct. Sometimes it may be necessary to cycle repeatedly among phases—playing with the data, finding more data, playing with the new data, and so on— before a solution can be found.

Mathematical modeling involves abstraction. The number model "100 − 79 = 21" could be an abstraction from the action of buying a 79-cent candy bar with a dollar bill. The modeling process involves both a real situation and an abstract mathematical model of that situation. (Even a mathematical model that uses concrete physical objects, such as base-10 blocks, is abstract in the sense that it omits many of the original situation's details that are irrelevant to the problem.) Because it is abstract, a single mathematical model can apply to many different real-world situations. For example, the formula for the area of a rectangle,

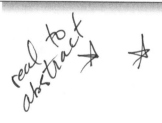
real to abstract

NOTE: In *Everyday Mathematics,* the problem-solving process often begins with information being given on a journal page or in a table. Children use the information to make up their own problems, which they or their classmates solve.

$A = lw$ (area equals length times width), applies to all real-world rectangles. This versatility is part of what makes mathematics such a powerful problem-solving tool.

Because they are abstract, however, mathematical models can become disconnected from the situation they are meant to model. Often, children crank through a mathematical process, arrive at an answer that makes no sense, and are completely unconcerned that they have produced nonsense. Making frequent connections between the real situation and the abstract model can help keep the process on track. Questions children should ask themselves are: What does this number refer to? What does this graph say about the problem situation? Does this solution make sense?

One reason for making ballpark estimates is to be sure the problem-solving process is on track. If the process gives a solution that doesn't agree with the ballpark estimate, then something is wrong either with the estimate or with the solution. Making ballpark estimates is an excellent way to reinforce connections between mathematical abstractions and real-world situations.

10.4 Teaching Problem Solving

Often when you are trying to learn something complicated, it is a good idea to focus on just one part. A pianist might play a difficult passage over and over again; a chef in training might practice making a roux until it's just right; a golfer might spend hours working on eight-foot putts. Practicing just one part at a time helps develop component skills that are essential for mastery of the entire complex activity, whether it's piano playing, cooking, or golf.

As the diagram in Figure 5 illustrates, problem solving is a complex activity. Children can benefit from practicing each of the parts—formulating problems, playing with data, and so on. Many of the exercises in *Everyday Mathematics* aim to provide practice in specific parts of the problem-solving process. Such instruction can be effective in teaching children how to manage each individual phase of the process, but successful problem solving in real-life requires experience in navigating among the phases, just as cooking a fine meal requires successfully orchestrating many separate steps.

10.4.1 Learning Mathematical Modeling

Despite the fact that problems in everyday life, science, and business can be complex, people who make their living solving mathematical problems follow certain simple procedures, whether their models involve arithmetic, algebra, geometry, statistics, calculus, or other branches of mathematics. These procedures are suggested by the diagram on page 200, Figure 5, a version of which is introduced to students in *Fourth Grade Everyday Mathematics*.

As discussed in Section 10.3, a person working on a problem might "visit" some or all of the nodes of this diagram. If the process is successful—an answer is obtained—the expert always visits the "Check" node to test the accuracy, quality, and utility of the answer, and possibly explore whether the solution method can be applied to other problems. This, in turn, may lead the expert back to the "What is the problem?" node to start the process over again.

During their years in school, children learn can how to be effective in each separate phase of the mathematical-modeling process. In *Everyday Mathematics,* for example, children become skilled at counting, measuring, calculating, estimating, looking up information, and many other specific skills that are useful in solving problems. It takes years of experience, however, to become expert at navigating among the nodes. Knowing when to abandon an approach that's not working and go back to playing with the data, for example, is a skill that experience alone furnishes.

As children progress through *Everyday Mathematics* and confront problems that are more complex and less routine, they grow both in their problem-solving skills and in their ability to manage the problem-solving process. Recent research carried out by Karen Fuson at Northwestern University shows that the problem-solving skills of *Everyday Mathematics* students are far above the levels American students traditionally achieve and are on a par with high-achieving international student populations. Many other researchers have found similar results. Problem solving is a real strength of *Everyday Mathematics.*

10.4.2 Number Stories

Everyday Mathematics aims to help students deal with real, age-appropriate problems, not merely with simplified and artificial textbook problems. The authors' research shows that young children have impressive but largely untapped problem-solving abilities. One way *Everyday Mathematics* works to expand these abilities is through the use of number stories.

Number stories are stories which involve numbers and a question. The stories may be written, oral, pictorial, or even dramatic. Number stories are created by both the teacher and the children. The stories may be designed to practice specific problem-solving techniques—the teacher might tell a parts-and-total number story, for example, in order to introduce or practice the parts-and-total diagram—or the stories may arise spontaneously from classroom situations.

As early as Kindergarten, children create number stories based on everyday experiences. In *Everyday Mathematics* Grades K–3, many of the children's stories are based on journal pages that present a range of numerical data related to real situations (animal measures, shopping for groceries, vending machines, and so on). Problem posing—making up problems—is a part of the problem-solving process that is often ignored in school mathematics, yet identifying

NOTE: See Section 2.1 in the Operations and Facts essay for a discussion of common types of problem situations, including change, comparison, and parts-and-total situations, which lead to various types of addition and subtraction problems, and area, rate, and other situations, which lead to multiplication and division problems.

NOTE: Some teachers say a number story involves numbers and has an "ending" rather than a question. This sanctions stories that give the answer.

and defining the problem is often the crucial first step toward a solution. Problem posing also leads to a high level of enthusiasm and involvement because the children feel they have ownership of the problems they create themselves. Since the information presented tends to cover a wide range of difficulty, all members of the class will have opportunities to participate.

Children enjoy hearing and telling number stories. You might consider devoting an occasional language arts lesson to working with number stories. Creating, sharing, and discussing number stories can help develop children's communication and listening skills as well as their problem-solving abilities. The careful reading required for solving number stories helps children develop skills that will serve them to good advantage when they deal with technical text as they grow older.

Number stories provide a bridge from natural to symbolic language. Children in Kindergarten and first grade can be helped across that bridge by the following simple procedure:

- Introduce number stories. Use a situation that is familiar to the children. Keep the stories short and the language simple. (When children tell their own stories, this is not always easy to do!) Whenever possible, draw pictures or diagrams to illustrate the stories. Modeling with concrete objects is effective with all ages, and essential with younger children.

- Begin to include occasional mathematical terms in your comments on children's stories. For example, "You told an addition story. You had 5 candies and then you added 3 more."

- Begin writing number models underneath your illustrations as you discuss the stories. Relate the numbers and other symbols (+, −, =) in the number models to quantities and actions in the stories. (For example, "This '5' is for the candies you started with. '+3' means you got three more, '8' tells how many you ended up with, and '=' means that 8 is the same as 5 and 3 more.") Help children understand how the symbols fit the problem situation. Explain that by using mathematics symbols you can write a number story more quickly and easily. If you wrote it in words, it would take a long time and fill the board.

NOTE: See Sections 2.1 and 2.2 for discussions of situation diagrams and number models.

- Children may begin writing number models to fit stories. Often more than one number model can fit a given number story. Some first grade children may begin to use diagrams for parts-and-total, change, and comparison stories, though this is not expected until second grade.

When children begin to write number stories depends on their writing skills. Many first grade teachers report that their children enjoy trying to put their stories into words. For most children, it appears that skill at writing stories develops later than the ability to write number models using +, −, and =. Although you may give children the opportunity to write number stories at an early age, do not expect this from most of them until second grade, or even third grade for some; they are asked to write, swap stories, and solve stories for each other in *Third Grade Everyday Mathematics*. Younger children can tell or dictate stories before they can write them themselves or they can draw pictures and write a few words or numbers for their stories.

10.4.3 Sharing Children's Strategies and Solutions

Research indicates that children develop a variety of problem-solving strategies if they are given the opportunity to share their ideas with their peers. Number stories are an excellent context for developing habits of sharing. If this sharing takes place in an open, receptive environment, children will learn that inventing creative, innovative ways of solving problems is acceptable in mathematics. The practice of gathering children together to share solutions after individual or group problem solving continues throughout *Everyday Mathematics*.

Teachers who ask children to solve stories in many ways and who take time for children to share and compare their solution methods find that their students develop strong, flexible, and independent calculation skills and problem-solving strategies. When teachers explore multiple representations and encourage multiple solution strategies with number stories involving small numbers, children become able to work with much larger numbers than they would normally be able to handle. Children develop a better understanding of various mathematical processes when asked to think and strategize rather than when they are merely asked to repeat the steps of a standard written algorithm.

Blair Chewning, an *Everyday Mathematics* teacher from Virginia, has provided an example of the powerful results that this approach can yield. In April 1993, Ms. Chewning read in the Richmond *Times-Dispatch* that on a recent national mathematics test, 40% of eighth grade students failed to perform at even a basic level. The following problem was given as an example of a "basic problem" for Grade 8:

> Jill needs to earn $45 for a class trip. She earns $2 each day on Mondays, Tuesdays, and Wednesdays. She earns $3 each day on Thursdays, Fridays, and Saturdays. She does not work on Sundays. How many weeks will it take her to earn $45?

Ms. Chewning was teaching second grade at the time, using *Everyday Mathematics*, and decided to see how her students would handle this problem. This is what she reported:

> Every single student attempted the problem, which was presented as optional. Such risk-takers they have become! Two students, using mental math only, presented me with the correct answer by the time I had

in **perspective**

In *Fifth Grade Everyday Mathematics,* students are encouraged to communicate with one another and with the teacher using more writing than in previous grades. Writing provides an opportunity for students to analyze their own thinking and reflect upon their thoughts. It affords them an opportunity to organize information for themselves. It also gives the teacher a great additional way to assess students' understanding of ideas and concepts.

completed writing the number story on the board. A total of 82% of the students, using a variety of strategies (see below), successfully solved the problem in less than five minutes. Of the three students who struggled, two were right on track, making only minor computational errors, and the third achieved success after extensive trial and error.

Needless to say, I was astounded. While I had expected them to be successful to some extent, I had not anticipated the speed and comfort with which they approached the task.

Thank you, *Everyday Mathematics*. The skills your program fosters empowered my second graders to soar higher than they or their teacher thought possible. They wore the "hats" of eighth-graders quite proudly that day and would seem to suggest that our math future is anything but bleak.

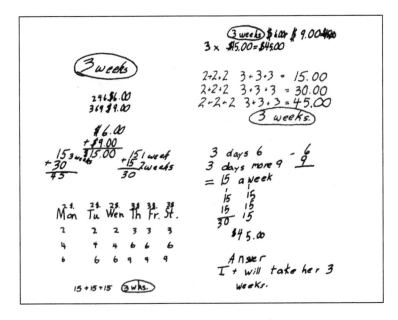

10.4.4 Problem-Solving Strategies for Beginners

The diagram of the problem-solving process in Figure 5 on page 200 fits what experts actually do when they solve problems, but is too complicated to be of much help for beginners. On the other hand, many elementary school mathematics textbooks include long lists of strategies and tips—but these lists are often little help even with simple real-life problems, and are essentially useless for dealing with complicated problems on public policy and the workplace.

Children need a guide that is more useful than a list of tips but simpler than a diagram of expert behavior. To this end, *Everyday Mathematics* Grades K–3 outlines general guidelines for managing problem solving, such as the one in the margin.

Guide to Solving Number Stories

1. What do you know from reading the story?

2. What do you want to find out?

3. What do you need to do? Do it, then record what you did. If you can, write a number model that fits the problem.

4. Answer the question.

5. Check. Ask, "Does my answer make sense? How do I know?"

Because problems from everyday life are usually complicated, the first need is often to simplify the situation and figure out exactly what is known and what is to be found out. Number stories in daily life, for example, often contain many irrelevant numbers. Sometimes relevant numbers are missing and must be inferred or derived from what is known. Often, the problem solver must deal not only with just a few counts or measures but with large sets of data. Considerable effort may be required to make the data consistent in format and to devise a display that suggests useful patterns or interesting questions. The process seldom follows one predictable step after another.

Children should feel comfortable sharing their thinking and strategies, which is why *Everyday Mathematics* suggests the gradual introduction to number stories described in Section 10.4.2. Children should share their strategies, record their solutions (both correct and incorrect) on the board. Draw pictures and write number models to illustrate children's solutions. In later grades, children can record their own solutions on the board for whole-class discussion and analysis.

Examining students' solutions can be extremely valuable, but care should be taken to ensure that children are not embarrassed if their efforts fall short. Children with correct answers are usually happy to share their models and their strategies with the class, but discussing incorrect answers can also be very instructive. Here are some suggestions for dealing with wrong answers:

- Emphasize that it is OK to make mistakes. In fact, errors are inevitable. What is not OK is failing to learn from one's mistakes.

- Frame discussions of incorrect solutions by saying, "Some children in last year's class did _____ [Describe the incorrect approach.] Why do you think they did that? How would you help them see their mistake?"

- Emphasize that answers obtained using different methods should agree, so if there is not agreement, something may be wrong. Press the children to resolve the dilemma.

- Compare and contrast different strategies and help the children see advantages and disadvantages of each. An incorrect method may have some good ideas that can be used to improve another method.

At the beginning of each school year, *Everyday Mathematics* builds in specific occasions for this kind of interaction. Many other opportunities materialize over the course of the year. Eventually, with practice, children will become comfortable sharing their strategies and will be able to talk about them freely and fluently, listen to one another attentively, revise their own strategies and adopt new ones based on these discussions. That, at least, is what *Everyday Mathematics* is aiming for.

References

National Council of Supervisors of Mathematics. (1977). Position paper on basic skills. *Arithmetic Teacher* 25 (1): 19–22.

National Council of Supervisors of Mathematics. (1988). Essential mathematics for the 21st century: The position of the National Council of Supervisors of Mathematics. Minneapolis: Author.

National Council of Teachers of Mathematics. (1980). An agenda for action: Recommendations for school mathematics of the 1980s. Reston, VA: Author.

National Council of Teachers of Mathematics. (1989). Curriculum and evaluation standards for school mathematics. Reston, VA: Author.

National Council of Teachers of Mathematics. (1998). Principles and standards for school mathematics: Discussion draft. Reston, VA: Author.

Polya, George. *How to Solve It.* Princeton University Press, (1988).

Glossary

absolute value (1) The distance between a number and 0 on the number line. (2) The larger of a number and its opposite. The absolute value of a positive number is the number itself, and the absolute value of a negative number is the opposite of the number. The absolute value of 0 is 0. The notation for the absolute value of n is |n|.

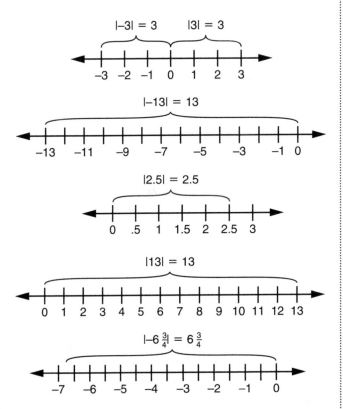

accurate As near as possible to a true result. For example, an accurate measure or count is one with little or no error. Compare to *precise*.

acre In the U.S. customary system, a unit of area equal to 43,560 square feet, roughly the size of a football field. A square mile is 640 acres. See *Table of Measures*. See Section 6.5 of the Measurement essay.

acute angle An angle with a measure greater than 0° and less than 90°. See *angle*. See Section 5.4 of the Geometry essay.

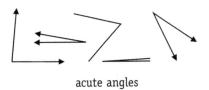

acute angles

acute triangle A triangle with the measures of all angles less than 90°. See *triangle*. See Section 5.4 of the Geometry essay.

acute triangle

addend One of two or more numbers that are added. For example, in 5 + 3 + 1, the addends are 5, 3, and 1. See *addition*.

addition A mathematical operation based on putting together two or more quantities. Numbers being added are called *addends*; the result of addition is called the *sum*. For example, in 12 + 33 = 45, the addends are 12 and 33 and the sum is 45. Subtraction "undoes" addition: 12 + 33 = 45 can be "undone" by either 45 − 12 = 33 or 45 − 33 = 12. See Sections 2.1 of the Operations and Facts essay and 3.2 of the Algorithms and Mental Arithmetic essay.

addition fact Two 1-digit numbers and their sum, such as 9 + 7 = 16. See *arithmetic facts*. See Section 2.3 of the Operations and Facts essay.

additive inverses Two numbers whose sum is 0. The additive inverse of a number is also called its *opposite*. For example, 3 and −3 are additive inverses because 3 + (−3) = 0.

add–up subtraction A subtraction procedure in which the difference is found by adding up from the smaller number. For example, to solve 87 − 49, start at 49, add 30 to reach 79, and then add 8 more to reach 87. The difference is 30 + 8 = 38. See Section 3.2 of the Algorithms and Mental Arithmetic essay for further discussion and other subtraction algorithms.

adjacent angles Two angles with a common side and vertex that do not otherwise overlap. See Section 5.4 of the Geometry essay.

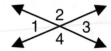

Angles 1 and 2, 2 and 3, 3 and 4, and 4 and 1 are pairs of adjacent angles.

algebra (1) A school subject, usually studied in eighth or ninth grade. (2) The use of letters of the alphabet to represent numbers in equations, formulas, and rules. (3) A set of rules and properties for a number system. See Section 2.2 of the Operations and Facts essay and Section 9.5 of the Patterns, Sequences, Functions, and Algebra essay.

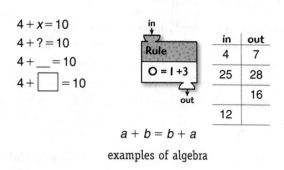

Area = length × width
$A = l \times w$

$4 + x = 10$
$4 + ? = 10$
$4 + \underline{} = 10$
$4 + \square = 10$

$a + b = b + a$

examples of algebra

algebraic expression An expression that contains a variable. For example, if Maria is 2 inches taller than Joe and if the variable M represents Maria's height, then the expression $M - 2$ represents Joe's height. See *algebra*. See Section 2.2 of the Operations and Facts essay and Section 9.5 of the Patterns, Sequences, Functions, and Algebra essay.

algebraic order of operations Same as *Order of Operations.*

algorithm A set of step-by-step instructions for doing something, such as carrying out a computation or solving a problem. The most common algorithms are those for basic arithmetic computations, but there are many others. Some mathematicians and many computer scientists spend a lot of time trying to find more efficient algorithms for solving problems. See Sections 3.1 and 3.2 of the Algorithms and Mental Arithmetic essay.

altitude (1) In a geometric figure, a line segment from any vertex that is perpendicular to the line containing the opposite side or to the plane containing the opposite face. (2) The length of this segment. (3) The perpendicular distance from one side of a figure to a parallel side or from a vertex to the opposite side; the height. See *height of a parallelogram, height of a rectangle, height of a triangle,* and *height of a 3-dimensional figure.* See Sections 5.4 and 5.5 of the Geometry essay.

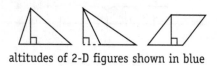

altitudes of 2-D figures shown in blue

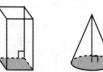

altitudes of 3-dimensional figures shown in blue

(4) Geography: Distance above sea level. Same as *elevation.*

A.M. The abbreviation for *ante meridiem,* which means "before the middle of the day;" from midnight to noon.

analog clock A clock that shows the time by the positions of the hour and minute hands. Compare to *digital clock.* See Section 7.2 of the Reference Frames essay.

analog clock

-angle A suffix meaning angle, or corner.

angle A figure formed by two rays or two line segments with a common endpoint. The common endpoint is called the *vertex of the angle.* The rays or segments are called the *sides of the angle.* An angle is measured by a number of degrees between 0 and 360, which can be thought of as the amount of rotation around the vertex from one side to the other. Angles can be represented by rotating one side while the other is kept stationary. Angles are named either by a single capital letter naming the vertex or by three letters, two naming points on the sides with the vertex letter between them. See *acute angle*, *obtuse angle*, *reflex angle*, *right angle*, and *straight angle*. See Section 5.4 of the Geometry essay.

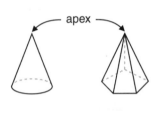

$\angle A$ $\angle BCD$

angles

apex In a pyramid or cone, the vertex opposite the base. In a pyramid, all the non-base faces meet at the apex. See Section 5.5 of the Geometry essay.

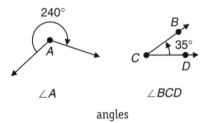

apex

arc Part of a circle, from one point on the circle to another. For example, a semicircle is an arc with endpoints that are the endpoints of a diameter of the circle. An arc is named by its endpoints. See Section 5.4 of the Geometry essay for a discussion of circles.

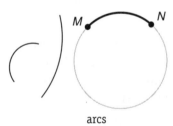

arcs

area A measure of a bounded surface. The boundary might be a triangle or rectangle in a plane or the boundaries of a state or country on the earth's surface. Area is expressed in square units such as square miles, square inches, or square centimeters, and can be thought of as the approximate number of non-overlapping squares that will "tile" or "cover" the surface within the boundary. See Section 6.5 of the Measurement essay.

40 square units   21 square units

The area of the United States is about 3,800,000 square miles.

arithmetic facts The basic arithmetic facts are the addition facts (addends 9 or less); the subtraction facts that are the inverses of these; the multiplication facts (factors 9 or less); and the division facts that are inverses of these, except there is no division by zero. There are:

100 addition facts, from $0 + 0 = 0$ to $9 + 9 = 18$
100 subtraction facts, from $0 - 0 = 0$ to $18 - 9 = 9$
100 multiplication facts, from $0 \times 0 = 0$ to $9 \times 9 = 81$
90 division facts, from $0/1 = 0$ to $81/9 = 9$

An extended arithmetic fact involves a multiple of 10 (or 100, 1,000, . . .) of one or both addends or factors in a basic fact or use of a basic fact to get a relatively simple new result. See Section 2.3 of the Operations and Facts essay.

$2 + 3 = 5$ so $20 + 30 = 50, 500 - 300 = 200$
$4 \times 6 = 24$, so $400 \times 6 = 2400, 240/60 = 4$
$5 + 7 = 12$, so $15 + 7 = 22$

extended facts

arm span The distance from fingertip to fingertip of a person's outstretched arms. Same as *fathom*. A fathom is standardized at 6 feet, or 2 yards. See Section 6.1 of the Measurement essay.

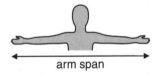

arm span

array A rectangular arrangement of objects in rows and columns. An array can be used to model multiplication. See Section 2.1 of the Operations and Facts essay and Section 6.5 of the Measurement essay.

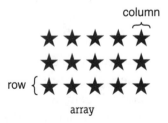

column

row {

array

arrow path In *Everyday Mathematics*, a route to follow on a number grid. Solving number-grid

glossary

puzzles with arrow paths requires using the patterns on the grid. After sufficient practice, arrow paths may be drawn by themselves, without the number grid. See Section 1.4 of the Number and Counting essay.

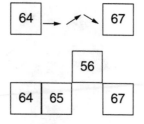

arrow rule In *Everyday Mathematics*, the operation that determines the number that goes into the next frame in a Frames-and-Arrows diagram. See *Frames and Arrows*. See Section 9.3 of the Patterns, Sequences, Functions, and Algebra essay.

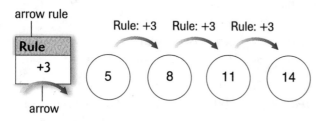

arrows In *Everyday Mathematics*, the links representing the rule that determines which numbers go in the frames of a Frames-and-Arrows diagram. See *arrow rule*. See Section 9.3 of the Patterns, Sequences, Functions, and Algebra essay.

associative property A property of addition and multiplication (but not of subtraction or division) that says that changing the grouping of the elements being added or multiplied will not change the sum or product.

For addition: $(a + b) + c = a + (b + c)$, so $(4 + 3) + 7 = 4 + (3 + 7)$.
For multiplication: $(a \times b) \times c = a \times (b \times c)$, so $(4 \times 3) \times 7 = 4 \times (3 \times 7)$.

attribute A feature of an object or a common feature of a set of objects. Examples of attributes include size, shape, color, and number of sides. See *property*.

average (1) A central, or typical, value of a set of numbers. In statistics, and in *Everyday Mathematics*, several different averages are defined, including the mean, the median, and the mode. (2) "Average" is usually assumed to refer to the mean, which is determined by finding the sum of all of the numbers in a set and then dividing that sum by the

number of numbers in the set. See Section 4.1 of the Data and Chance Essay.

axis (1) Either of the two number lines used to form a coordinate grid. Plural: *axes*. See Section 5.9 of the Geometry essay and Section 7.3 of the Reference Frames essay.
(2) A line about which a solid figure rotates. See Section 5.8 of the Geometry essay.

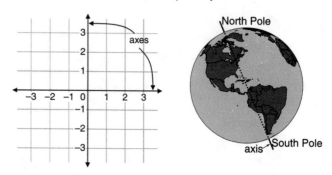

ballpark estimate A rough estimate. A ballpark estimate can serve as a check on the reasonableness of an answer obtained through some other procedure, or it can be made when an exact figure is unnecessary or impossible to obtain. See Sections 8.1 and 8.3 of the Estimation and Number Sense essay and Section 10.3 of the Problem Solving essay.

bank draft A written order for the exchange of money. $1,000 bills are no longer in existence so $1,000 bank drafts are issued. People can exchange $1,000 bank drafts for smaller bills (for example 10 bills of $100 each).

bar graph A graph that shows the relationships among data by the use of bars to represent quantities. See Section 4.1 of the Data and Chance essay.

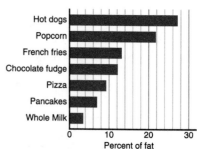

bar graphs

base (1) Geometry: Any side of a polygon, usually used for area computations along with the "altitude" perpendicular to it. See *base of a parallelogram*, *base of a rectangle*, and *base of a triangle*. See *altitude*. See Section 5.4 of the Geometry essay.

Bases are shown in blue, altitudes in grey.

(2) Geometry: Either of two parallel and congruent faces that define the shape of a prism or cylinder, or the face that defines the shape of a cone or pyramid. See *base of a 3-dimensional figure*. See Section 5.5 of the Geometry essay.

Bases are shown in blue.

(3) Arithmetic: The number which is to be raised to some power in exponential notation. For example, in the expression 2^3, 2 is the base and 3 is the exponent, which indicates that the 2 is to be used as a factor three times:

$$2^3 = 2 \times 2 \times 2 = 8.$$

exponential notation

See *exponential notation*. See Section 2.2 of the Operations and Facts essay.

(4) Arithmetic: The foundation number for a numeration system. For example, our ordinary number system is a base-ten place-value system, with 1, 10, 100, 1,000, and other powers of 10 as the values of the places in whole numbers. In electronics and computers, bases of two, eight, or sixteen are usual, instead of base ten. See Section 1.7 of the Number and Counting essay.

$$356 = 300 + 50 + 6$$

base-ten number

base of a parallelogram One of the sides of a parallelogram; also, the length of this side. In calculating area, the base is used along with the height, or altitude, which is measured on a perpendicular to the side opposite the base. See

altitude or *height of a parallelogram*. See Section 5.4 of the Geometry essay.

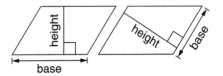

base of a rectangle One of the sides of a rectangle; also, the length of this side. In calculating area, the base is used along with the height, or altitude, of the rectangle. See *altitude* or *height of a rectangle*. See Section 5.4 of the Geometry essay.

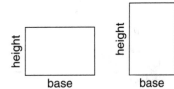

base of a 3-dimensional figure A special face of a 3-dimensional figure. The shape of a base is used for naming and classifying certain polyhedra, including pyramids and prisms. The height, or altitude, is the length of a line segment that is perpendicular to a base and extends from that base to an opposite face or vertex or to a parallel plane containing that face or vertex. See *base* and *altitude*, or *height of a 3-dimensional figure*. See Section 5.5 of the Geometry essay.

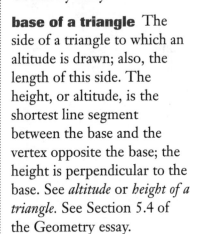

base of a triangle The side of a triangle to which an altitude is drawn; also, the length of this side. The height, or altitude, is the shortest line segment between the base and the vertex opposite the base; the height is perpendicular to the base. See *altitude* or *height of a triangle*. See Section 5.4 of the Geometry essay.

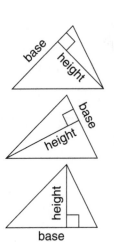

base-10 shorthand In *Everyday Mathematics,* a system used to represent base-10 blocks. See Section 1.7 of the Number and Counting essay and Base-10 Blocks in the Tools section of the Management Guide.

Name	Base-10 block	Base-10 shorthand
cube	▫	▪
long				
flat		□
big cube		◳

benchmark An important count or measure that can be used to evaluate the reasonableness of other counts, measures, or estimates. A benchmark for land area is that a football field is about one acre. A benchmark for length is that the width of a man's thumb is about one inch. See Section 6.1 of the Measurement essay.

big cube In *Everyday Mathematics,* the term for the base-10 block cube that measures 10 cm by 10 cm by 10 cm. A big cube is worth 1,000 cm cubes. See Section 1.7 of the Number and Counting essay and Base-10 Blocks in the Tools section of the Management Guide.

big cube

bisect To divide a segment, angle, or figure into two parts of equal measure.

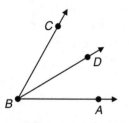

Ray *BD* bisects Angle *ABC.*

broken-line graph A graph in which data points are connected by a line or line segments. Same as *line graph.* See Section 4.1 of the Data and Chance essay.

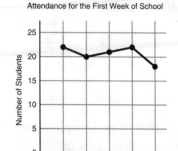

broken-line graph

calendar (1) A reference frame used to keep track of the passage of time. Many different calendars exist, including the Gregorian calendar that most of the Western world currently uses, the Hebrew calendar, the Islamic calendar, and others. See Section 7.2 of the Reference Frames essay.
(2) The concrete representation of such a reference frame, on which appointments, special days, and other markings can be made.
(3) A schedule or listing of events

August 2000						
Sunday	Monday	Tuesday	Wednesday	Thursday	Friday	Saturday
		1 Dr's appt. 3:00	2	3	4	5
6	7	8	9	10	11	12
13 Mom's b-day	14	15	16	17	18	19
20	21	22	23	24	25	26
27	28	29	30	31		

calibrate To divide or mark something, such as a thermometer, with gradations.

capacity (1) A measure of how much a container can hold, usually in such units as *quart, gallon, cup,* or *liter.* See *volume.* See Section 6.6 of the Measurement essay.
(2) The maximum weight that a scale can measure.

cartographer A person who makes maps.

Celsius The temperature scale on which pure water at sea level freezes at 0° and boils at 100°. The Celsius scale is used in the metric system. A less common name for this scale is "centigrade", because there are 100 units between the freezing and boiling points of water. Compare to *Fahrenheit*. See Section 7.1 of the Reference Frames essay.

census An official count of population and the recording of such data as age, sex, income, education, and so on.

center Of a circle: The point in the plane of a circle equally distant from all points on the circle. See Section 5.4 of the Geometry essay.

Of a sphere: The point equally distant from all points on the sphere. See Section 5.5 of the Geometry essay.

cent (1) One-hundredth, (with a penny, $\frac{1}{100}$ of a dollar). The word comes from the Latin word *centesimus*, which means a hundredth part. (2) A prefix meaning one hundred, as in century.

centi- In the metric system, a prefix meaning one hundredth. For example, a centimeter is $\frac{1}{100}$ of a meter. (Centi- can also mean one hundred, as in "centipede," an arthropod with many legs.)

centimeter (cm) In the metric system, a unit of length equivalent to 10 millimeters, $\frac{1}{10}$ of a decimeter, and $\frac{1}{100}$ of a meter. See Table of Measures. See Section 6.2 of the Measurement essay.

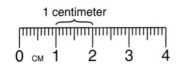

chance The possibility of an outcome occurring in an uncertain event. For example, in tossing a coin there is an equal chance of getting heads or tails. See Section 4.2 of the Data and Chance essay.

change diagram In *Everyday Mathematics*, a diagram used to represent situations in which quantities are either increased or decreased. The

diagram includes the starting quantity, the ending quantity, and the amount of change. See *situation diagram*. See Section 2.1 of the Operations and Facts essay.

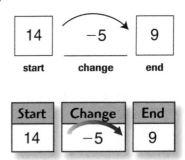

change diagrams for 14 − 5 = 9

circle The set of all points in a plane that are equidistant from a given point in the plane called the *center* of the circle. The distance from the center to the circle is the *radius*. The circle is the boundary only. A circle together with its interior is called a *disk* or a *circular region*. See Section 5.4 of the Geometry essay.

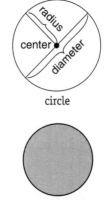

circle

circular region

circle graph A graph in which a circle and its interior are divided into parts to represent the parts of a set of data. The circle represents the whole set of data. Same as *pie graph*. See Section 4.1 of the Data and Chance essay.

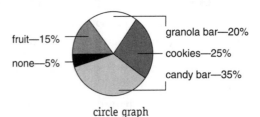

circle graph

circumference The distance around a circle or the maximum distance around a sphere. See Sections 5.4 and 5.5 of the Geometry essay.

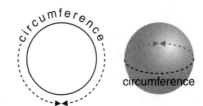

glossary

Class Data Pad In *Everyday Mathematics*, a large pad of paper where data collected by the class can be stored for use (and reuse) throughout the year. Data recorded on the Class Data Pad can be used for analysis, graphing, and generating number stories. See Section 4.1 of the Data and Chance essay. See the Organizing Routines and Displays section in the Management Guide.

clockwise A rotation in the same direction that the hands of a standard analog clock move; turning to the right.

clutch (of eggs) A nest of eggs.

column A vertical arrangement of objects or numbers in an array or a table.

column addition An addition procedure in which vertical lines drawn between digits make place value more explicit. See Section 3.2 of the Algorithms and Mental Arithmetic essay for further discussion and for information on other addition algorithms.

common denominator Any nonzero number that is a multiple of the denominators of two or more fractions. For example, the fractions $\frac{1}{2}$ and $\frac{2}{3}$ have common denominators 6, 12, 18, and so on. See *denominator*.

common factor Any number that is a factor of two or more numbers. The common factors of 18 and 24 are 1, 2, 3, and 6. See *factors*.

commutative property A property of addition and multiplication (but not of subtraction or division) that says that changing the order of the elements being added or multiplied will not change the sum or product.

For addition: $a + b = b + a$, so $5 + 10 = 10 + 5$.
For multiplication: $a \times b = b \times a$,
so $5 \times 10 = 10 \times 5$.

See *turn-around facts*. See Section 2.3 of the Operations and Facts essay.

comparison diagram In *Everyday Mathematics*, a diagram used to represent situations in which two quantities are compared. Comparison diagrams can be helpful in solving certain one-step addition and subtraction problems. See *situation diagram*. See Section 2.1 of the Operations and Facts essay.

Comparison Diagrams for $12 = 9 + N$

complementary angles Two angles whose measures total 90°. See Section 5.4 of the Geometry essay.

Angles 1 and 2 are complementary angles.

composite number A whole number that has more than two factors. For example, 10 is a composite number because it has more than two factors: 1, 2, 5, and 10. A composite number is divisible by at least three whole numbers. Compare to *prime number*.

concave polygon A polygon in which at least one vertex is "pushed in." The term "non-convex" is a more formal synonym for concave. Compare *convex polygon*. See Section 5.4 of the Geometry essay.

concave polygon

concentric circles Circles that have the same center but radii of different lengths. See Section 5.4 of the Geometry essay.

concentric circles

cone A 3-dimensional shape having a circular base, a curved lateral surface, and one vertex, called the apex. See Section 5.5 of the Geometry essay.

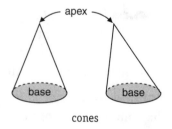

cones

congruent figures Two figures that are the same size and shape. If you put one figure on top of the other, they will match exactly. Congruent figures are also said to be congruent to each other. See Section 5.7 of the Geometry essay.

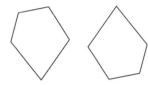

congruent pentagons   congruent prisms

consecutive Following one another in an uninterrupted order. For example, A, B, C, and D are four consecutive letters of the alphabet; 6, 7, 8, 9, and 10 are five consecutive whole numbers.

consecutive angles Two angles in a polygon that share a common side. See Section 5.4 of the Geometry essay.

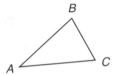

Angles *A* and *B*, *B* and *C*, and *C* and *A*
are pairs of consecutive angles

constant A value that does not change. For example, the ratio of the circumference of a circle to its diameter is a famous constant, π. In the number sentence $3x = y$, 3 is a constant.

contour line A curve on a map through places where a measurement (such as temperature, elevation, air pressure, or growing season) is constant.

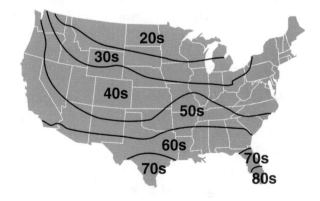

conversion fact A fixed relationship, such as 1 yard = 3 feet or 1 inch = 2.54 centimeters, that can be used to convert measurements within or between systems of measurement. See Section 6.2 of the Measurement essay.

convex polygon A polygon in which all vertices are "pushed outward." A line segment connecting any two points of a convex polygon lies entirely within or on the polygon. Compare to *concave polygon*. See Section 5.4 of the Geometry essay.

convex polygon

coordinate A number used to locate a point on a number line, or one of two numbers used to locate a point on a coordinate grid. See Section 5.9 of the Geometry essay.

coordinate grid A device for locating points in a plane by means of ordered pairs of numbers. A rectangular coordinate grid is formed by two number lines that intersect at right angles at their zero points. See Section 5.9 of the Geometry essay and Section 7.3 of the Reference Frames essay.

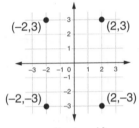

coordinate grid

corner Of an angle: A point at which two rays or line segments meet.
Of a polygon: A point at which two sides meet.
Of a polyhedron: A point where three or more edges meet.
Same as *vertex*. See Sections 5.3–5.5 of the Geometry essay.

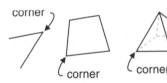

counterclockwise A rotation in the opposite direction as that of the hands of a standard analog clock; a turning to the left.

counting numbers The numbers used to count things. The set of counting numbers is {1, 2, 3, 4, . . .}. Sometimes 0 is included. Counting numbers are also in the set of integers, the set of rational numbers, and the set of real numbers, but those sets also include numbers that are not counting numbers. See Section 1.2 of the Number and Counting essay.

cross section A shape formed by the intersection of a plane and a geometric solid. See Section 5.5 of the Geometry essay.

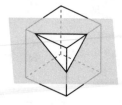

cross section of a cube

cube (1) A polyhedron with six square faces. One of the five regular polyhedra. See *regular polyhedron*. See Section 5.5 of the Geometry essay.

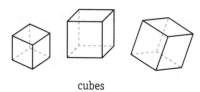

cubes

(2) In *Everyday Mathematics*, the term for the smaller cube of the base-10 blocks, measuring 1 cm on each edge. See Section 1.7 of the Number and Counting essay and Base-10 Blocks in the Tools section of the Management Guide.

cm cube

cubic centimeter (cm³) A metric unit of volume; the volume of a cube that is 1 centimeter on a side. 1 cubic centimeter is equal to 1 milliliter. See Table of Measures. See Sections 6.2 and 6.6 of the Measurement essay.

cubic unit A unit used in measuring volume. Common cubic units include cubic centimeters, cubic inches, cubic feet, and cubic meters. See Section 6.6 of the Measurement essay.

cubit An ancient unit of length, measured from the point of the elbow to the end of the middle finger. The cubit has been standardized at various times to be between 18 and 22 inches. The Latin word *cubitum* means "elbow." See Section 6.1 of the Measurement essay.

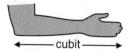

cubit

cup In the U.S. customary system, a unit of capacity equal to 8 fluid ounces; $\frac{1}{2}$ pint. See Table of Measures. See Sections 6.2 and 6.6 of the Measurement essay.

curved surface (1) A surface that does not lie in a plane; for example, a sphere or the lateral surface of a cylinder.
(2) A non-base surface of a cone or cylinder. See Section 5.5 of the Geometry essay.

customary system The measuring system used most often in the United States, in contrast to the metric system used nearly everywhere else. Units for length include inch, foot, yard, and mile; units for weight include ounce and pound; units for capacity (amount of liquid or other pourable substance a container can hold) include cup, pint, quart, and gallon; units for temperature include degrees Fahrenheit. See Section 6.2 of the Measurement essay.

cylinder A 3-dimensional shape having a curved surface and parallel congruent circular or elliptical bases. A can is a common object shaped like a cylinder. See Section 5.5 of the Geometry essay.

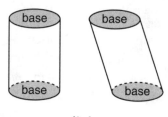

cylinders

data Information gathered by observing, counting, or measuring. Strictly, *data* is the plural of *datum*, but *data* is often used as a singular word. See Section 4.1 of the Data and Chance essay.

deca- Prefix meaning ten.

deci- Prefix meaning one-tenth.

decimal A number written in standard notation containing a decimal point, as in 2.54. A decimal that ends, such as 2.54, is called a terminating decimal. Some decimals continue a pattern without end; for example, 0.333. . . or 0.$\overline{3}$ which is equal to $\frac{1}{3}$. Such decimals are called repeating decimals. A terminating decimal can be thought of as a repeating decimal in which 0 repeats. See Section 1.6 of the Number and Counting essay.

decimal point The mark that separates the whole number from the fraction in decimal notation; in expressing money, it separates the dollars from the cents. In the U.S., a period is used; in Europe and elsewhere, a comma is used.

decimeter (dm) In the metric system, a unit of length equivalent to $\frac{1}{10}$ of a meter or 10 centimeters. See Table of Measures. See Section 6.2 of the Measurement essay.

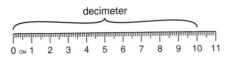
decimeter

shown at 50% of actual size

degree (°) (1) A unit of measure for angles based on dividing one complete circle (rotation) into 360 equal parts. See Section 5.4 of the Geometry essay. (2) A unit for measuring temperature change on either the Celsius or Fahrenheit scale. See Section 7.1 of the Reference Frames essay. The small, raised symbol ° is called the degree symbol.

degree Celsius (°C) Unit for marking Celsius thermometers or for measuring differences in temperature in the metric system. On the Celsius scale, pure water at sea level freezes at 0° and boils at 100°. See *Celsius*. See Section 7.1 of the Reference Frames essay.

degree Fahrenheit (°F) Unit for marking Fahrenheit thermometers or measuring differences in temperature in the U.S. Customary system. On the Fahrenheit scale, pure water at sea level freezes at 32°F and boils at 212°F, and a saturated salt solution freezes as 0°F. See *Fahrenheit*. See Section 7.1 of the Reference Frames essay.

denominator In a fraction, the number written below the line or to the right of the slash. In the fraction $\frac{a}{b}$ or a/b, b is the denominator. In a part-whole fraction, it is the number of equal parts into which the whole (or ONE) has been divided. See *part-whole fraction*. Compare to *numerator*. See Section 1.6 of the Number and Counting essay.

diagonal (1) A line of objects or numbers from upper left to lower right, or from lower left to upper

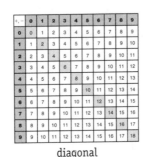
diagonal

right in an array or a table. (2) A line segment joining two non-adjacent vertices of a polygon. See Section 5.4 of the Geometry essay. (3) A line segment joining two vertices of different faces of a polyhedron. See Section 5.5 of the Geometry essay.

diameter A line segment that passes through the center of a circle or sphere and has endpoints on the circle or sphere; also, the length of such a line segment. The diameter of a circle or sphere is twice the length of the radius. See *circle* and *sphere*. See Sections 5.4 and 5.5 of the Geometry essay.

difference The amount by which one number is greater or less than another number; the result of subtracting one number from another. For example, in $12 - 5 = 7$, 7 is the difference between 5 and 12. See *subtraction*.

digit In the base-10 numeration system, one of the symbols 0, 1, 2, 3, 4, 5, 6, 7, 8, 9, which can be used to write any number. For example, the numeral 145 is made up of the digits 1, 4, and 5. See Section 1.7 of the Number and Counting essay.

digital clock A clock that shows the time with numbers to represent hours and minutes, with a colon separating the two. Compare to *analog clock*. See Section 7.2 of the Reference Frames essay.

digital clock

dimension (1) A measure in one direction of an object, especially length, width, or height. The dimensions of a box might be 24 cm by 20 cm by 10 cm. (2) The number of coordinates necessary to fix a point in a geometric space. Thus a line has one dimension since one coordinate suffices to locate a point on a line. A plane or the surface of a sphere has two dimensions since two coordinates are necessary to locate a point. Space has three dimensions because three coordinates are required to locate a point in space. See Section 5.1 of the Geometry essay.

displace To move something from one position to another.

distributive property A property that relates two operations on numbers, usually multiplication and addition or multiplication and subtraction. This property gets its name because it "distributes" the factor outside the parentheses over the two terms within the parentheses.

For multiplication over addition:
$a \times (x + y) = (a \times x) + (a \times y)$,
so $2 \times (5 + 3) = (2 \times 5) + (2 \times 3) = 10 + 6 = 16$
For multiplication over subtraction:
$a \times (x - y) = (a \times x) - (a \times y)$
so $2 \times (5 - 3) = (2 \times 5) - (2 \times 3) = 10 - 6 = 4$

dividend In division, the number that is being divided. For example, in $35 \div 5 = 7$, the dividend is 35. See *division*.

```
        divisor
dividend  ↓  quotient
     ↘    ↓   ↙
      35/5 = 7
```

```
        divisor
dividend  ↓  quotient
     ↘    ↓   ↙
      40 ÷ 8 = 5
```

```
quotient ──→ 3
divisor ──→ 12)36 ←── dividend
```

divisibility test A procedure to determine whether a whole number can be divided evenly by another whole number, without actually doing the division. For example, to check whether a number is divisible by 3, check whether the sum of its digits is divisible by 3. Since the sum of the digits of 51 is divisible by 3 ($5 + 1 = 6$, which is divisible by 3), 51 passes the divisibility test for 3, and we know that 51 is divisible by 3.

divisible One whole number is divisible by another whole number if the result of the division is a whole number with remainder 0. For example, 28 is divisible by 7, because 28 divided by 7 is 4 with remainder 0. If a number n is divisible by a number d, then d is a factor of n. See *factors*.

division The operation used to solve equal-sharing problems. Division is used to find how a total amount can be separated into an equal number of groups, or into groups of equal size; the inverse of multiplication. For example, $24 \div 4$ can mean "How many 4s in 24?" and is an inverse of the product $6 \times 4 = 24$. If $a \div b$ results in a whole number, a is said to be divisible by b, as in the example $24 \div 4$. Otherwise, depending on the nature of the problem being solved, $a \div b$ can be expressed using fractions, decimals, or as a whole number quotient and a remainder. See the examples below. See *dividend*, *divisor*, and *quotient*. See Sections 2.1 of the Operations and Facts essay and 3.2 of the Algorithms and Mental Arithmetic essay.

$$25 \div 4 = 6\tfrac{1}{4} \qquad 6\tfrac{1}{4} \times 4 = 25$$
$$25 \div 4 = 6.25 \qquad 6.25 \times 4 = 25$$
$$25 \div 4 \rightarrow 6\ R1 \qquad 6 \times 4 + 1 = 25$$

dividend ÷ divisor = quotient

$$\frac{\text{dividend}}{\text{divisor}} = \text{quotient}$$

dividend ÷ divisor → quotient with remainder

division symbols The number a divided by the number b is expressed in print in a variety of ways: $a \div b$, $\frac{a}{b}$ and a/b are used in *Everyday Mathematics*; $b\overline{)a}$ is used to set up the "long division" algorithm; $a:b$ is sometimes used in Europe; $a \div b$ is rarely used except in school mathematics text books. See Section 2.2 of the Operations and Facts essay.

divisor In division, the number that divides another number. For example, in $35 \div 7 = 5$, the divisor is 7. See *division*.

```
        divisor
dividend  ↓  quotient
     ↘    ↓   ↙
      35/5 = 7
```

```
        divisor
dividend  ↓  quotient
     ↘    ↓   ↙
      40 ÷ 8 = 5
```

```
quotient ──→ 3
divisor ──→ 12)36 ←── dividend
```

dodecahedron A polyhedron with 12 faces. If each face is a regular pentagon, it is one of the 5 regular polyhedra. See *regular polyhedron*. See Section 5.5 of the Geometry essay.

decagonal prism

irregular dodecahedron

regular dodecahedron

dollar The basic unit of money in the U.S. money system, equal to 100 cents.

double Two times an amount; an amount added to itself.

doubles fact An addition or multiplication fact without a turn-around partner. A doubles fact names the sum or product of a 1-digit number added to or multiplied by itself, such as $4 + 4 = 8$ or $3 \times 3 = 9$.

edge A line segment where two faces of a polyhedron meet. See Section 5.5 of the Geometry essay.

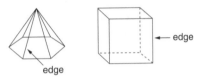

edge

elevation The height above sea level. Same as *altitude*.

ellipse A closed, oval plane figure. An ellipse is the path of a point that moves in a plane so that the sum of its distances from two fixed points in the plane is constant. Each of the fixed points is called a focus of the ellipse.

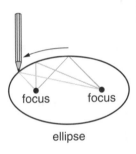

ellipse

embedded figure A figure entirely enclosed within another figure.

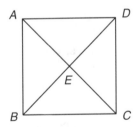

Triangle *ADE* is embedded in Square *ABCD*.

endpoint A point at the end of a line segment or ray. A line segment is named for its two endpoints. "Segment $\overline{LT}$" or "segment $\overline{TL}$" is the line segment between points L and T. See *ray* and *line*. See Section 5.3 of the Geometry essay.

endpoints

enlarge To increase the size of an object or figure. See Section 5.6 of the Geometry essay.

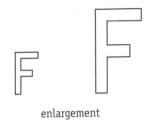

enlargement

equal-grouping story A number story involving separating something into equal groups. In these problems, the total and the number in each group are known. For example, "How many tables seating 4 persons each are needed for 52 people?" is an equal-grouping story. Often division can be used to solve equal-grouping stories. See *measurement division* or *quotitive division*. See Section 2.1 of the Operations and Facts essay.

equal groups Sets with the same number of elements, such as cars with 5 passengers, rows with 6 chairs, boxes each containing 100 clips, and so on. See Section 2.1 of the Operations and Facts essay.

equal-sharing story A number story involving sharing something equally. In these problems, the total and the number of groups are known. For example: "There are 10 brownies to share equally among 4 children. How many brownies will each child get?" is an equal-sharing story. Often division can be used to solve equal-sharing stories. Same as *partitive division*. See Section 2.1 of the Operations and Facts essay.

equation A mathematical sentence that asserts the equality of two quantities. See Section 2.2 of the Operations and Facts essay.

equilateral polygon A polygon in which all sides are the same length. See Section 5.4 of the Geometry essay.

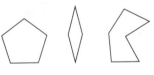

equilateral polygons

equilateral triangle A triangle in which all three sides are the same length and all three angles have the same measure. See *triangle*. See Section 5.4 of the Geometry essay.

equilateral triangle

equivalent Equal in value, though possibly different in form. For example, $\frac{1}{2}$, 0.5, and 50% are all equivalent. See Sections 1.5 and 1.6 of the Number and Counting essay.

equivalent equations Equations that have the same solution(s). For example, $2 + x = 4$ and $6 + x = 8$ are equivalent equations; their solution is 2. See Section 2.2 of the Operations and Facts essay.

Equivalent equations
$$x + 3 = 7$$
$$3 + x = 7$$
$$7 = x + 3$$
$$2x + 6 = 14$$
$$x = 4$$

equivalent fractions Fractions that have different numerators and denominators but name the same amount. See Section 1.6 of the Number and Counting essay.

equivalent names Different ways of naming the same number. For example: $2 + 6$, $4 + 4$, $12 - 4$, $18 - 10$, $100 - 92$, $5 + 1 + 2$, eight, VIII, and ⫫⫫ /// are all equivalent names for 8. See *name-collection box*. See Section 1.5 of the Number and Counting essay.

equivalent ratios Ratios that make the same comparison. Equivalent ratios can be expressed by equivalent fractions. For example, $\frac{1}{2}$ and $\frac{4}{8}$ are equivalent ratios. See *equivalent fractions*. See Section 1.6 of the Number and Counting essay.

estimate (1) A close, rather than exact, answer; an approximate answer to a computation; a number close to another number.
(2) To make an estimate. See the Estimation and Number Sense essay.

European subtraction A subtraction procedure common in Europe and in certain parts of the United States. The method involves increasing the smaller number rather than regrouping. The method is as efficient as the traditional procedure once children have practiced using it. See Section 3.2 of the Algorithms and Mental Arithmetic essay for further discussion and other subtraction algorithms.

even number A whole number that can be evenly divided by 2. It has 0, 2, 4, 6, or 8 in the ones place. Compare to *odd number*. See Section 9.2 of the Patterns, Sequences, Functions, and Algebra essay.

event In probability, the result of a random process such as rolling a die or tossing a coin. For example, the dice throw of 5 is an event, as is a coin landing heads-side up when tossed. See Sections 4.2 and 4.3 of the Data and Chance essay.

expanded notation A way of expressing a number as the sum of the values of each digit. For example, in expanded notation, 356 is written $300 + 50 + 6$. Compare to *standard notation*, *scientific notation*, and *number-and-word notation*. See Section 1.7 of the Number and Counting essay.

Exploration In *Everyday Mathematics*, an independent or small-group activity that may involve concept development, manipulatives, data collection, problem solving, games, and skill reviews. See page 8 in the Management Guide for more information.

exponent The number of times a factor is to be repeated, denoted by a superscript. In 2^5, the exponent is 5. See *exponential notation*. See Section 2.2 of the Operations and Facts essay. Compare to *base*.

exponential notation A shorthand way of representing repeated multiplication of the same factor. For example, 2^3 is exponential notation for $2 \times 2 \times 2$. The small, raised 3, called the *exponent*, indicates how many times the number 2, called the *base*, is used as a *factor*. See Section 2.2 of the Operations and Facts essay.

$$2^3 = 2 \times 2 \times 2 = 8$$
$$4^5 = 4 \times 4 \times 4 \times 4 \times 4 = 1024$$
exponential notation

expression A group of mathematical symbols (numbers, operation signs, variables, grouping symbols) that represent or can represent a number if values are assigned to any variables that the expression contains. See Section 2.2 of the Operations and Facts essay.

$2 + 3$
$\sqrt{2ab}$
πr^2

expressions

extended fact A variation of a basic arithmetic fact involving multiples of 10, 100, and so on. For example, $30 + 70 = 100$, $40 \times 5 = 200$, and $560 \div 7 = 80$ are extended facts. See *arithmetic facts*. See Section 2.3 of the Operations and Facts essay.

face (1) Any of the polygonal regions that form 3-dimensional prisms, pyramids, or polyhedra. Some special faces are called bases. See *base*.

(2) Curved surface that forms part or all of a cylinder, cone, or sphere. See Section 5.5 of the Geometry essay.

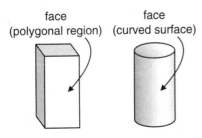

face (polygonal region) face (curved surface)

fact A basic number combination, such as $3 + 5 = 8$ or $7 \times 5 = 35$. See *arithmetic facts*. See Section 2.3 of the Operations and Facts essay.

fact extensions Calculations with larger numbers using knowledge of basic facts. For example, knowing the basic fact $5 + 8 = 13$ makes it easy to solve problems like $50 + 80 = ?$ and $65 + ? = 73$. Fact extensions can also be applied to basic subtraction, multiplication, and division facts.

fact family A collection of related addition and subtraction facts, or multiplication and division facts, made from the same numbers.
For 5, 6, and 11, the addition/subtraction family consists of $5 + 6 = 11$, $6 + 5 = 11$, $11 - 5 = 6$, and $11 - 6 = 5$.
For 5, 7, and 35, the multiplication/division family consists of $5 \times 7 = 35$, $7 \times 5 = 35$, $35 \div 7 = 5$, and $35 \div 5 = 7$. See *number family*. See Section 2.3 of the Operations and Facts essay.

fact habits In *Everyday Mathematics*, a term used to refer to number-fact reflexes; automaticity in knowing basic addition, subtraction, multiplication, and division facts. See Section 2.3 of the Operations and Facts essay.

fact power In *Everyday Mathematics*, a term that refers to the ability to recall basic number facts automatically without having to figure them out. See Section 2.3 of the Operations and Facts essay.

factor (1) A number being multiplied in a multiplication number model. In the number model $6 \times 0.5 = 3$, 6 and 0.5 are factors and 3 is the product. See *multiplication*. (2) A whole number that can divide another whole number without a remainder. For example, 4 and 7 are both factors of 28 because 28 is divisible by both 4 and by 7.

(3) To represent a number as a product of factors. To factor 21, for example, is to write it as 7×3.

factor pair Two whole-number factors of a number whose product is that number. A number may have more than one factor pair. For example, the factor pairs for 24 are 1 and 24, 2 and 12, 3 and 8, and 4 and 6.

factor rainbow A way to show factor pairs in a list of all the factors of a number. A factor rainbow can be used to check whether a list of factors is correct.

factor rainbow for 24

factor string A name for a number written as a product of at least two whole-number factors other than 1. For example, a factor string for the number 24 is $2 \times 3 \times 4$. This factor string has three factors, so its length is 3. By convention, the number 1 is not allowed in factor strings. For example, $1 \times 2 \times 3 \times 4$ is not a factor string for 24 because it contains the number 1.

factor tree A method used to determine the prime factorization of a number. The original number is represented as a product of factors, and each of those factors is represented as a product of factors, and so on, until the factors are all prime numbers. Factor trees are drawn upside down, with the root at the top and the leaves at the bottom.
See *prime factorization*.

```
      30
      /\
    6 * 5
    /\  \
  2 * 3 * 5
```
factor tree for 30

factorial A product of a whole number and all smaller whole numbers except 0. An exclamation point, !, is used to denote factorials. For example:
$3! = 3 \times 2 \times 1 = 6$
3! is read as "three factorial."
$4! = 4 \times 3 \times 2 \times 1 = 24$
4! is read as "four factorial."
For any number N,
$N! = N \times (N - 1) \times (N - 2) \times \ldots \times 1$
$N!$ is read as "N factorial."

Fact Triangle A triangular flash card labeled with the numbers of a fact family that children can use to practice addition/subtraction and multiplication/

division facts. The two 1-digit numbers and their sum or product (marked with a dot) appear in the corners of each triangle. See *fact family*. See Section 2.3 of the Operations and Facts essay.

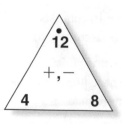

Facts Table A chart of rows and columns, also known as an Addition/Subtraction Facts Table or a Multiplication/Division Facts Table, which records addition and subtraction or multiplication and division facts.

Fahrenheit The temperature scale on which pure water at sea level freezes at 32° and boils at 212° and on which a saturated salt solution freezes at 0°. The Fahrenheit scale is widely used in the U.S. but in few other places. Compare to *Celsius*. See Section 7.1 of the Reference Frames essay.

fair game A game in which every player has the same chance of winning. If any player has an advantage or disadvantage at the beginning (through for example, playing first), the game is not fair. See Section 4.2 of the Data and Chance essay.

fathom A unit used mainly by people who work with boats and ships to measure depths under water and lengths of cables. A fathom is now defined as 6 feet. See *arm span*. See Section 6.1 of the Measurement essay.

fathom

figurate numbers Numbers that can be shown by dots arranged in specific geometric patterns. Square numbers and triangular numbers are examples of figurate numbers.

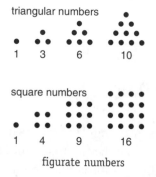

triangular numbers
1   3   6   10

square numbers
1   4   9   16

figurate numbers

flat In *Everyday Mathematics*, the term for the base-10 block consisting of 100 cm cubes. See Section 1.7 of the Number and Counting essay and Base-10 Blocks in the Tools section of the Management Guide.

flat

flip An informal name for a reflection transformation. See *reflection* and *transformation*. See Section 5.6 of the Geometry essay.

fluid ounce In the U.S. customary system, a unit of capacity equal to $\frac{1}{16}$ of a pint. One fluid ounce is 29.574 milliliters. See Table of Measures. See Sections 6.2 and 6.6 of the Measurement essay.

foot (ft) In the U.S. customary system, a unit of length equivalent to 12 inches or $\frac{1}{3}$ of a yard. See Table of Measures. See Section 6.2 of the Measurement essay.

formula A general rule for finding the value of something. A formula is often written symbolically using letters, called variables, to stand for the quantities involved. For example, a formula for distance traveled can be written as $d = s \times t$, where d stands for distance, s for speed, and t for time. See Section 2.2 of the Operations and Facts essay.

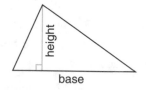
height
base
Area of triangle = 1/2 base × height
$A = 1/2\ b \times h$

fraction A number in the form $\frac{a}{b}$ or a/b, where a and b are whole numbers and b is not 0. Fractions are used in many contexts—to name part of an object or part of a collection of objects, to compare two quantities, and to represent division. For example, $\frac{12}{6}$ can mean 12 divided by 6, and $\frac{2}{3}$ can be thought of as 2 divided by 3. See *numerator* and *denominator*. See Section 1.6 of the Number and Counting essay and Section 2.1 of the Operations and Facts essay.

frames In *Everyday Mathematics*, the empty shapes in which numbers are written in a Frames-and-Arrows diagram. See *Frames and Arrows*. See Section 9.3 of the Patterns, Sequences, Functions, and Algebra essay.

Frames and Arrows In *Everyday Mathematics*, these are diagrams used to represent number sequences—lists of numbers often generated by one or more rules. The diagrams consist of *frames* in which numbers are written and *arrows* that represent the rule(s) for moving from one frame to the next. Frames-and-Arrows diagrams are also called chains. See Section 9.3 of the Patterns, Sequences, Functions, and Algebra essay.

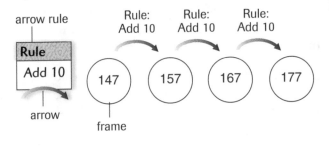

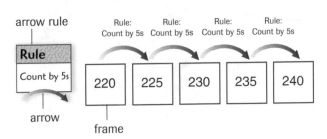

frequency (1) The number of times a value occurs in a set of data. See Section 4.1 of the Data and Chance essay. (2) The number of vibrations per second of a sound wave; more generally, the number of repetitions per unit of time.

frequency graph A graph showing how often each value in a data set occurs. See Section 4.1 of the Data and Chance essay.

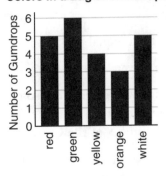

frequency graph

frequency table A chart on which data are tallied to find the frequency of given events or values. See Section 4.1 of the Data and Chance essay.

Color	Number of Gumdrops
red	ＩＩＩＩ
green	ＩＩＩＩ Ｉ
yellow	ＩＩＩＩ
orange	ＩＩＩ
white	ＩＩＩＩ

frenquency table

fulcrum (1) The center support of a pan balance.

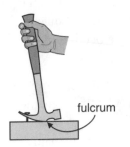

fulcrum

(2) The support on which a lever turns.

fulcrum

(3) The point on a mobile at which a rod is suspended.

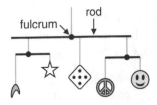

function A set of ordered pairs of numbers, usually connected by a rule, such that each first number is paired with exactly one second number. A function can be shown in a table, as points on a coordinate graph, or by a rule. For example, for a function with a rule of "double," 1 is paired with 2, 2 is paired with 4, 3 is paired with 6, and so on. See Section 9.4 of the Patterns, Sequences, Functions, and Algebra essay.

function machine In *Everyday Mathematics*, an imaginary machine programmed to process numbers according to a certain rule. A number (input) is put into the machine and is then transformed into a second number (output) through the application of a rule. See *function*. See Section 9.4 of the Patterns, Sequences, Functions, and Algebra essay.

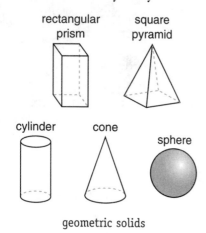

in	out
1	2
2	4
3	6
5	10
20	40
300	600

function machine with input/output table

furlong A unit of measure equal to one eighth of a mile. Today, furlongs are most commonly used in horse racing.

gallon (gal) In the U.S. customary system, a unit of capacity equal to 4 quarts. See Table of Measures. See Sections 6.2 and 6.6 of the Measurement essay.

geometric solid A 3-dimensional shape bounded by surfaces. Common geometric solids include the *rectangular prism*, *square-based pyramid*, *cylinder*, *cone*, and *sphere*. Despite its name, a geometric solid in *Everyday Mathematics* is defined as the surface only (it is "hollow") and does not include the points in its interior. Sometimes, however, in informal discussion and in certain dictionaries, a solid is defined as both the surface and its interior. See Section 5.5 of the Geometry essay.

rectangular prism   square pyramid

cylinder   cone

sphere

geometric solids

geometry The study of spatial objects and their properties and relationships. The word geometry is derived from the Greek words for "earth" and "measure." See the Geometry essay.

girth The distance around a 3-dimensional object.

-gon A suffix meaning angle. For example, a hexagon is a plane figure with six angles—one at each vertex.

gram In the metric system, a unit of mass equal to $\frac{1}{1,000}$ of a kilogram. See Table of Measures.

greatest common factor The largest factor that two or more numbers have in common. For example, the common factors of 24 and 36 are 1, 2, 3, 4, 6, and 12. Thus, the greatest common factor of 24 and 36 is 12.

great span The distance from the tip of the thumb to the tip of the little finger (pinkie), when the hand is stretched as far as possible. The great span averages about 9 inches for adults. Same as *hand span*. Compare to *normal span*. See Section 6.1 of the Measurement essay.

great span

grouping symbols Symbols, such as parentheses ( ), brackets [ ], or braces { }, that indicate the order in which operations in an expression are to be done. For example, in the expression (3 + 4) × [(8 + 2) / 5], the operations within the grouping symbols are to be done first, beginning with the innermost grouping symbols and proceeding outward. Thus, the expression above first becomes (3 + 4) × [10/5], then 7 × 2, and then 14, which is the correct result if the grouping symbols are adhered to. See Section 2.2 of the Operations and Facts essay.

half One of two equal parts.

hand span Same as *great span*.

height A measure of how tall something is. In geometry height is the same as *altitude*. See Sections 5.4 and 5.5 of the Geometry essay.

height of a parallelogram The length of the shortest line segment between a base and the line containing the opposite side. The height is perpendicular to the

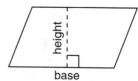

base

glossary

base. Also, the line segment itself. See *altitude* and *base of a parallelogram*. See Section 5.4 of the Geometry essay.

height of a rectangle The length of the side perpendicular to the base of a rectangle. See *altitude* and *base of a rectangle*. See Section 5.4 of the Geometry essay.

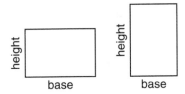

height of a 3-dimensional figure The length of the line segment from a vertex of a 3-dimensional figure perpendicular to the plane containing the opposite side, or base. See *altitude* and *base of a 3-dimensional figure*. See Section 5.5 of the Geometry essay.

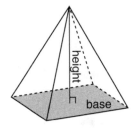

height of a triangle The length of any of the segments from a vertex perpendicular to a line containing the opposite side. See *altitude* and *base of a triangle*. See Section 5.4 of the Geometry essay.

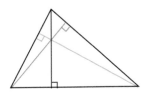

The heights of the triangle are indicated in blue.

hepta- A prefix meaning seven.

heptagon A 7-sided polygon. See Section 5.4 of the Geometry essay.

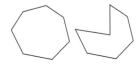

heptagons

hexa- Prefix meaning six.

hexagon A 6-sided polygon. See Section 5.4 of the Geometry essay.

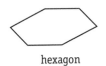

hexagon

Home Link In *Everyday Mathematics*, a suggested follow-up or enrichment activity to be done at home. See page 12 in the Management Guide for more information.

horizon Where the earth and sky appear to meet; if nothing is in the way, as when looking out to sea, the horizon looks like a line.

horizontal Positioned in a left-to-right orientation. Parallel to the line of the horizon.

hypotenuse In a right triangle, the side opposite the right angle.

icosahedron A polyhedron with 20 faces. One of the five regular polyhedra is an icosahedron with triangular faces. See *regular polyhedron*. See Section 5.5 of the Geometry essay.

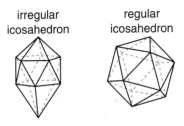

irregular icosahedron   regular icosahedron

image A figure that is produced by a transformation of another figure. See *transformation*. Compare to *preimage*. See Section 5.6 of the Geometry essay.

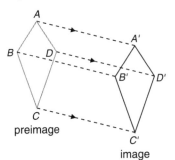

preimage   image

improper fraction A term for a fraction whose numerator is greater than or equal to its denominator. An improper fraction names a number greater than or equal to 1. For example, $\frac{4}{3}$, $\frac{5}{2}$, $\frac{4}{4}$, and $\frac{24}{12}$ are all improper fractions. In *Everyday Mathematics*, improper fractions are sometimes called "top-heavy" fractions.

inch (in.) In the U.S. customary system, a unit of length equal to $\frac{1}{12}$ of a foot and equivalent to 2.54 centimeters. See Table of Measures. See Section 6.2 of the Measurement essay.

indirect measurement Methods for determining heights, distances, and other quantities that cannot be measured directly.

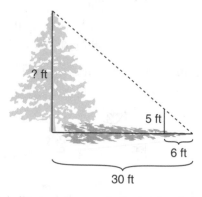

Using indirect measurement, the height of the tree is found to be 25 ft.

inequality A number sentence stating that two quantities are not equal or might not be equal. Relation symbols for inequalities include $\neq$, $<$, $>$, $\leq$, and $\geq$. See Section 2.2 of the Operations and Facts essay.

input (1) A number inserted into an imaginary function machine, which processes numbers according to a designated rule. See *function machine*. Compare to *output*. (2) A number operated on by a function rule to produce an output. See *function*. See Section 9.4 of the Patterns, Sequences, Functions, and Algebra essay.

inscribed polygon A polygon whose vertices are all points on a circle.

inscribed square

integer A number in the set {. . . –4, –3, –2, –1, 0, 1, 2, 3, 4, . . .}. All integers are rational numbers, but not all rational numbers are integers. (For example, $-\frac{1}{2}$, is a rational number but is not an integer.) All whole numbers are integers, but not all integers are whole numbers. (For example, -3 is an integer, but not a whole number.) Compare to *whole number, rational number, irrational number,* and *real number.* See Section 1.2 of the Number and Counting essay.

interior The set of all points in a plane "inside" a closed 2-dimensional figure, such as a polygon or circle. Also, the set of all points in space "inside" a closed 3-dimensional figure, such as a polyhedron or sphere. The interior is usually not considered to be part of the figure. See Sections 5.4 and 5.5 of the Geometry essay.

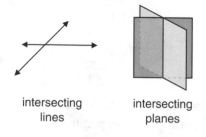

intersect To share a common point or points.

intersecting Sharing a common point or points.

intersecting lines   intersecting planes

interval (1) A set of numbers between two numbers *a* and *b*, which may include one or both of *a* and *b*. (2) A part of a number line, including all numbers between two points.

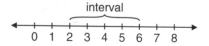

irrational numbers Numbers that cannot be written as fractions such that both the numerator and denominator are integers and the denominator is not zero. For example, $\sqrt{2}$ and π are irrational numbers. An irrational number can be represented by a nonterminating, nonrepeating decimal. For example, the decimal for π, 3.141592653. . . , continues without a repeating pattern. The number 1.10100100010000. . . is also irrational: although there is a pattern in the decimal, it does not repeat. See Section 1.2 of the Number and Counting essay.

isometry transformation A transformation such as a translation (slide), a reflection (flip), a rotation (turn), or a combination of these that preserves distances between corresponding points and angle measures. As a result, isometries preserve both the shape and the size of figures, but not necessarily position or orientation. (From Greek *isometros*, of equal measure.) See *transformation*, *translation*, *reflection*, and *rotation*. See Section 5.6 of the Geometry essay.

slide turn reflection

isometry transformations

isosceles trapezoid A trapezoid whose non-parallel sides are the same length. See *trapezoid*. See Section 5.4 of the Geometry essay.

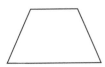

isocsceles trapezoid

isosceles triangle Triangle with at least two sides that are the same length and at least two angles that are the same measure. See *triangle*. See Section 5.4 of the Geometry essay.

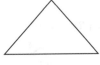

isocsceles triangle

juxtapose To place side by side in an expression. Juxtaposition often indicates multiplication. For example, 5n means 5 × n, and *ab* means a × b. See Section 2.2 of the Operations and Facts essay.

key sequence A set of instructions for performing a particular calculation or function with a calculator. See page 27 in the Management Guide.

797 [×] 389 [=]

key sequence

kilo- A prefix meaning thousand.

kilogram In the metric system, the fundamental unit of mass; it is equal to 1,000 grams. The kilogram is defined in terms of actual objects stored in special vaults in Paris, Washington DC, and elsewhere. 1 kilogram equals approximately 2.2 pounds. See *weight*. See Table of Measures. See Sections 6.2 and 6.7 of the Measurement essay.

kilometer In the metric system, a unit of length equal to 1,000 meters. One kilometer equals about 0.62 mile. See Table of Measures. See Section 6.2 of the Measurement essay.

kite A quadrilateral with exactly two pairs of adjacent sides that are the same length. (A rhombus is not a kite.) Compare to *rhombus*. See Section 5.4 of the Geometry essay.

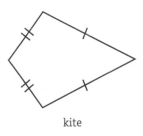

kite

label A descriptive word or phrase used to put a number or numbers in context. Using a label reinforces the idea that numbers refer to something. Flags, snowballs, and scary monsters are examples of labels. See Sections 2.1 and 2.3 of the Operations and Facts essay.

landmark A notable feature of a data set. Landmarks include *median*, *mode*, *maximum*, *minimum*, and *range*. See Section 4.1 of the Data and Chance essay.

lattice multiplication An algorithm for multiplying multidigit numbers. Lattice multiplication is a very old method, requiring little more than a knowledge of basic multiplication facts and the ability to add strings of 1-digit numbers. Once the lattice is drawn, the method is highly efficient and can be used to multiply very large numbers, including numbers too large to enter into calculators. See Section 3.2 of the Algorithms and Mental Arithmetic essay for further discussion and other multiplication algorithms.

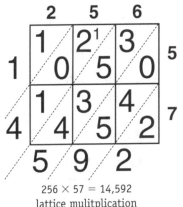

256 × 57 = 14,592
lattice mulitplication

least common denominator The least common multiple of the denominators of every fraction in a given collection. For example, the least common denominator of $\frac{1}{2}$, $\frac{4}{5}$, and $\frac{3}{8}$ is 40. See *least common multiple*.

least common multiple The smallest number that is a multiple of two or more numbers. For example, while some common multiples of 6 and 8 are 24, 48, and 72, the least common multiple of 6 and 8 is 24.

left-to-right subtraction A subtraction procedure which works left to right in several steps. For example, to solve $94 - 57$, first subtract 50 from 94 to obtain 44, and then 7 from 44 to obtain 37. The method is especially suited to mental arithmetic. See Section 3.2 of the Algorithms and Mental Arithmetic essay for further discussion and other subtraction algorithms.

leg of a right triangle A side of a right triangle that is not the hypotenuse. Compare to *hypotenuse*.

length of a rectangle Usually, but not necessarily, the longer dimension of a rectangle or a rectangular object.

like fractions Fractions with the same denominator.

line A straight path that extends infinitely in opposite directions. See Section 5.3 of the Geometry essay.

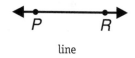

line

line graph A graph in which data points are connected by a line or line segments. Same as *broken line graph*. See Section 4.1 of the Data and Chance essay.

line of symmetry A line that divides a figure into two halves that are mirror images of each other. Each point in one of the halves of the figure is the same distance from the line of symmetry as

the corresponding point in the other half. A figure may have any number of lines of symmetry. For example, a parallelogram that is not a rectangle has no lines of symmetry. A square has four lines of symmetry. A circle has infinitely many lines of symmetry. See *line symmetry*. See Section 5.8 of the Geometry essay.

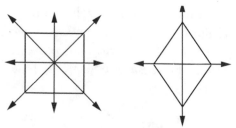

lines of symmetry are shown in blue

line plot A sketch of data in which check marks, X's, or other marks above a number line show the frequency of each value. See Section 4.1 of the Data and Chance essay.

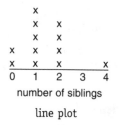

number of siblings

line plot

line segment A straight path joining two points. The points are called the *endpoints* of the line segment. See Section 5.3 of the Geometry essay.

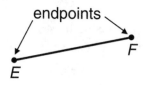

line segment

line symmetry A figure has line symmetry if a line can be drawn through it so that it is divided into two parts with both parts looking exactly alike, but facing in opposite directions. See *line of symmetry*. Compare to *rotational symmetry*. See Section 5.8 of the Geometry essay.

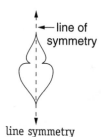

line symmetry

glossary

liter (L) In the metric system, a unit of capacity equal to the volume of a cube that measures 10 centimeters on a side. 1 L = 1,000 mL = 1,000 cm³. A liter is a little larger than a quart. See Table of Measures. See Sections 6.2 and 6.6 of the Measurement Essay.

long In *Everyday Mathematics*, the term for the base-10 block consisting of 10 cm cubes. Sometimes called a rod. See Section 1.7 of the Number and Counting essay and Base-10 Blocks in the Tools section of the Management Guide.

a long

lowest terms Same as *simplest form*. See Section 1.6 of the Number and Counting essay.

magnitude estimate A very rough estimate of the size of a numerical result—whether it is in the 1s, 10s, 100s, 1000s, and so on. For example, the U.S. national debt per person is in the tens of thousands of dollars. In *Everyday Mathematics*, children are often asked to give order of magnitude estimates for problems like "How many dimes in $200?" or "How many halves are in 30?" Same as *order of magnitude estimate*. See Section 8.2 of the Estimation and Number Sense essay.

map direction symbol A symbol on a map that identifies north, south, east, and west. Sometimes only north is indicated.

```
        N
        |
W ——————◇—————— E
        |
        S
```

map direction symbol

map legend A diagram that explains the symbols, markings, and colors on a map. Also called a map key.

map scale A device for relating distances on a map to corresponding distances in the real world. One inch on a map, for example, might correspond to 1 mile in the real world. A map scale is often represented by a labeled line segment, similar to a ruler; by a ratio of distances (for example $\frac{1}{63,380}$ when an inch represents a mile); or by an incorrect

use of the = symbol (as in "1 inch = 1 mile"). See Section 7.3 of the Reference Frames essay.

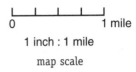

1 inch : 1 mile

map scale

mass A measure of the amount of material in an object. The mass of an object is the same on Earth as it is in outer space. Metric units for mass include grams and kilograms. In everyday life, these units are also used for weight. Compare to *weight*. See Section 6.7 of the Measurement essay.

Math Boxes In *Everyday Mathematics*, a format to provide review problems and to practice skills. A set of Math Boxes for each lesson are in the student Math Journals. See page 12 in the Management Guide for more information.

mathematics A study of relationships among numbers, shapes, systems, and patterns. Among other things, mathematics is used to count and measure things, to discover similarities and differences, to solve problems, and to learn about and organize the world.

Math Journal In *Everyday Mathematics*, a student record of mathematical discoveries and experiences. Journal pages provide visual models for conceptual understanding, problem material, and activities for individuals and small groups.

Math Master In *Everyday Mathematics*, a page ready for duplicating. Most masters are used by children in carrying out suggested activities. Some masters are used more than once during the school year.

Math Message In *Everyday Mathematics*, an activity for children to complete before the start of a lesson. Math Messages may be problems that introduce the day's lesson, directions to follow, sentences to complete or correct, review exercises, or reading assignments. See page 13 in the Management Guide for more information.

maximum The largest amount; the greatest number in a set of data. Compare to *minimum*. See Section 4.1 of the Data and Chance essay.

mean A typical or central value for a set of numbers, often called the average. It is calculated by finding the sum of all the numbers in the set and then dividing the sum by the number of numbers. See *average*. Compare to *median* and *mode*. See Section 4.1 of the Data and Chance essay.

measurement division A phrase often used in teacher training courses to indicate the use of division in equal-shares situations in which the total amount and the size of the shares are known and the number of shares is to be found. For example, "How many tables seating 4 people each are needed for 52 people?" is a measurement division problem. Same as *quotitive division*. In *Everyday Mathematics*, the term "equal-grouping story" describes measurement division problems. See *equal-grouping story*. Compare to *partitive division* and *equal-sharing story*. See Section 2.1 of the Operations and Facts essay.

measurement unit The reference unit used when measuring. Basic units include meters (length), grams (mass or weight), liters (capacity), seconds (elapsed time), and degrees Celsius (change of temperature). Compound units include square centimeters (area) and kilometers per hour (speed). See the Measurement essay.

median The middle value in a set of data when the data are listed in order from least to greatest (or greatest to least). If there is an even number of data points, the median is the mean of the two middle values. The median is also known as the *middle value*. Compare to *mean* and *mode*. See Section 4.1 of the Data and Chance essay.

memory keys Keys to manage a calculator's memory. The memory keys are commonly labeled [M+], [M−], and [MRC]. The [M+] key is used to add a number to the number stored in the calculator's memory; the [M−] key is used to subtract a number from the number in memory. The [MRC] key, pressed once, displays the number currently stored in memory. When the [MRC] key is pressed twice, the calculator's memory is cleared.

mental arithmetic Computations done by people "in their heads," either in whole or in part. In *Everyday Mathematics*, children develop a variety of strategies for doing arithmetic—calculating mentally, using paper and pencil, drawing pictures, counting jumps on a number grid, and so on. See Section 3.3 of the Algorithms and Mental Arithmetic essay, Section 8.5 of the Estimation and

Number Sense essay and Section 10.4 of the Problem Solving essay.

Mental Math and Reflexes In *Everyday Mathematics*, exercises (usually oral), suggested at the start of most lessons. They are designed to strengthen children's number sense and to review and advance essential basic skills. See Section 3.3 of the Algorithms and Mental Arithmetic essay. See page 13 in the Management Guide for more information.

meter (m) In the metric system, the fundamental unit of length from which other metric units of length are derived. Originally, the meter was defined as $\frac{1}{10,000,000}$ of the distance from the North Pole to the equator along a meridian passing through Paris. Today, the meter is defined as the distance light will travel in a vacuum in $\frac{1}{299,792,458}$ seconds. One meter is equal to 10 decimeters, 100 centimeters, and 1,000 millimeters. See Section 6.2 of the Measurement essay.

metric system A measurement system based on the base-10 numeration system and used in most countries around the world. Units for linear measure (length, distance) include millimeter, centimeter, meter, and kilometer; units for mass (weight) include gram and kilogram; units for capacity include milliliter and liter; and the unit for temperature change is degrees Celsius. See Section 6.2 of the Measurement essay.

middle value Same as *median*. See Section 4.1 of the Data and Chance essay.

midpoint A point halfway between two other points.

mile (mi) In the U.S. customary system, a unit of length equal to 5,280 feet or 1,760 yards; about 1,609 meters.

milli- A prefix meaning one thousandth, especially in measures.

milliliter (mL) In the metric system, a unit of capacity equal to $\frac{1}{1,000}$ of a liter; 1 cubic centimeter. See Sections 6.2 and 6.6 of the Measurement essay.

millimeter (mm) In the metric system, a unit of length equivalent to $\frac{1}{10}$ of a centimeter or $\frac{1}{1,000}$ of a meter. See Section 6.2 of the Measurement essay.

millisecond (ms or msec) A unit of time equal to $\frac{1}{1,000}$ of a second.

minimum The smallest amount; the smallest number in a set of data. Compare to *maximum*. See Section 4.1 of the Data and Chance essay.

minuend The number that is reduced in subtraction. For example, in $19 - 5 = 14$, the minuend is 19. See *subtraction*.

mixed number A number that is written using both a whole number and a fraction. For example, $2\frac{1}{4}$ is a mixed number equal to $2 + \frac{1}{4}$.

modal Of or relating to the mode. The most common value in a data set is the modal value. See *mode*. See Section 4.1 of the Data and Chance essay.

mode The value or values that occur most often in a set of data. Compare to *median* and *mean*. In the data set 3, 4, 4, 4, 5, 5, 6, the mode is 4. See Section 4.1 of the Data and Chance essay.

multiples (1) Repeated groups of the same amount. Multiples of a number are the products of that number and the numbers 1, 2, 3, ... For example, the multiples of 7 are 7, 14, 21, 28, . . . (2) Products of a number and an integer. The multiples of 7 are . . . , -21, -14, -7, 0, 7, 14, 21, ...

multiplication The operation used with whole numbers to find the total number of things in several equal groups or the number of things in a rectangular array. Multiplication is used with whole numbers, fractions, or decimals to find areas, enlargements or reduction of quantities, and to "check" division results. Numbers being multiplied are called factors; the result of multiplication is called the product. See Section 2.1 of the Operations and Facts essay and Section 3.2 of the Algorithms and Mental Arithmetic essay.

multiplication diagram A diagram used to represent numbers in which several equal groups are being considered together. The diagram has three parts: a number of groups, a number in each group, and a total number. Also called multiplication/division diagram and *rate diagram*.

rows	chairs per row	total chairs
15	25	?

multiplication fact The product of two 1-digit numbers, such as $6 \times 7 = 42$. See *arithmetic fact*. See Section 2.3 of the Operations and Facts essay.

multiplication symbols The number *a* multiplied by the number *b* is expressed in print in a variety of ways. Mathematics textbooks and *Second* and *Third Grade Everyday Mathematics* use "$\times$" to indicate multiplication ($a \times b$). In fourth grade, *Everyday Mathematics* begins to use the * symbol for multiplication ($a*b$). Other common ways to signify multiplication are through the use of a raised dot (for example, $a \bullet b$) and by juxtaposition (ab), which is common in formulas. See *juxtapose*. See *multiplication*. See Section 2.2 of the Operations and Facts essay.

multiplicative inverses Two numbers whose product is 1. Multiplicative inverses are also called *reciprocals* of each other. See *reciprocal*.

name-collection box In *Everyday Mathematics*, a box-like diagram tagged with a given number and used for collecting equivalent names for that number. See *equivalent names*. See Section 1.5 of the Number and Counting essay. See page 14 in the Management Guide for more information.

25	37 − 12	20 + 5

HHT HHT HHT HHT HHT

twenty-five

veinticinco

negative number A number less than 0.

negative rational numbers Numbers less than 0 that can be written as a fraction or a terminating or repeating decimal. See *rational numbers*. See Section 1.2 of the Number and Counting essay.

net weight The weight of the contents of a container, not including the weight of the container.

***n*-gon** A polygon with *n* sides. For example, a 5-gon is a pentagon and an 8-gon is an octagon. Polygons with large numbers of sides are usually named only as *n*-gons such as 13-gon and 100-gon, etc. See Section 5.4 of the Geometry essay.

nona- A prefix meaning nine (rarely used).

normal span The distance from the end of the thumb to the end of the index (first) finger of an outstretched hand. For estimating lengths, many people can adjust this distance to approximately 6 inches or 20 centimeters. Same as *span*. Compare to *great span*.

***n*-to-1 ratio** A ratio of a number to 1. Every ratio can be converted to an n-to-1 ratio. For example, to convert the ratio of 3 girls to 2 boys to an n-to-1 ratio, divide 3 by 2. The n-to-1 ratio is 1.5 to 1.

number-and-word notation A notation consisting of the significant digits of a large number and words for the place value. For example, 27 billion is written in number-and-word notation. See *significant digits*.

number family Any triplet of numbers consisting of two addends and their sum or two factors and their product. For example, 5, 17, and 22 are an addition/subtraction number family. See *fact family*. See Section 2.3 of the Operations and Facts essay.

number grid In *Everyday Mathematics*, a table in which consecutive numbers are arranged in rows, usually 10 columns per row. A move from one

									0
1	2	3	4	5	6	7	8	9	10
11	12	13	14	15	16	17	18	19	20
21	22	23	24	25	26	27	28	29	30
31	32	33	34	35	36	37	38	39	40
41	42	43	44	45	46	47	48	49	50
51	52	53	54	55	56	57	58	59	60
61	62	63	64	65	66	67	68	69	70
71	72	73	74	75	76	77	78	79	80
81	82	83	84	85	86	87	88	89	90
91	92	93	94	95	96	97	98	99	100
101	102	103	104	105	106	107	108	109	110

number grid

number to the next within a row is a change of 1; a move from one number to the next within a column is a change of 10. See Section 1.4 of the Number and Counting essay.

number-grid puzzle In *Everyday Mathematics*, a piece of a number grid in which some, but not all, of the numbers are missing. Number-grid puzzles are used for practice with place-value concepts. See Section 1.4 of the Number and Counting essay.

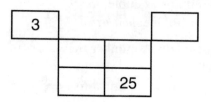

number-grid puzzle

number line A line on which points correspond to numbers, used as a frame of reference for counting and numeration activities. Every number has a point on the line, and every point has a number. See Sections 1.2 and 1.4 of the Number and Counting essay.

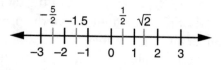

number line

number model A number sentence that models or fits a situation. For example, the situations "Sally had $5 and then she earned $8," "A young plant 5 cm high grew 8 cm," and "Harry is 8 years older than his 5-year-old sister Sally" can all be modeled by the number sentence $5 + 8 = 13$. See Section 2.2 of the Operations and Facts essay and Sections 10.3 and 10.4 of the Problem Solving essay.

number scroll In *Everyday Mathematics*, number-grid pages taped together. See *number grid*. See Section 1.4 of the Number and Counting essay.

number scroll

number sentence A sentence made up of at least two numbers or expressions and a single relation symbol (=, <, >, ≠, ≤, or ≥). Number sentences usually contain at least one operation symbol. They may also have grouping symbols, such as parentheses. If a number sentence contains one or more variables, it is called an open sentence. See *open sentence*. See Section 2.2 of the Operations and Facts essay.

$$5 + 5 = 10$$
$$a \times b \geq 16$$
$$[(x + y)/2] - 4 < 20$$

number sentences

number sequence A list of numbers, often generated by some rule. See *Frames and Arrows*, which generate number sequences. See Section 9.3 of the Patterns, Sequences, Functions, and Algebra essay.

1, 2, 3, 4, 5, 6, . . .
1, 4, 9, 16, 25, 36, . . .
1, 2, 1, 2, 1, 2, 1, 2, . . .
1, 3, 5, 7, 9, 11, 13, 15, 17, . . .

number sequences

number story A story that contains a problem that can be solved using one or more of the four basic arithmetic operations or by sorting out relations, such as equals, is less than, or is greater than. See Section 10.4 of the Problem Solving essay.

numeration A method of numbering or of reading and writing numbers. In *Everyday Mathematics*, numeration activities include counting, writing numbers, identifying equivalent forms for name-collection boxes, exchanging coins (such as, 5 pennies for 1 nickel), and renaming numbers in computation.

numerator In a fraction, the number written above the line or to the left of the slash. In a part-whole fraction, where the whole is divided into a number of equal parts, the numerator names the number of equal parts being considered. In the fraction $\frac{a}{b}$ or a/b, a is the numerator. See *part-whole fraction*. Compare to *denominator*. See Section 1.6 of the Number and Counting essay.

obtuse angle An angle with a measure more than 90° and less than 180°. See *angle*. See Section 5.4 of the Geometry essay.

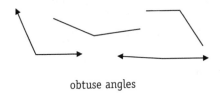

obtuse angles

obtuse triangle A triangle with an angle larger than 90°. See *triangle*. See Section 5.4 of the Geometry essay.

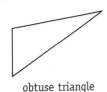

obtuse triangle

octa- A prefix meaning eight.

octagon An 8-sided polygon. See Section 5.4 of the Geometry essay.

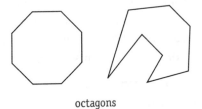

octagons

octahedron A polyhedron with eight faces. One of the five regular polyhedra is an octahedron with eight triangular faces. See *regular polyhedron*. See Section 5.5 of the Geometry essay.

odd number A whole number that cannot be evenly divided by 2. Compare to *even number*. See Section 9.2 of the Patterns, Sequences, Functions, and Algebra essay.

ONE In *Everyday Mathematics*, a way of denoting the unit whole in part-whole fractions and other similar situations. Same as *whole, unit whole*. See *part-whole fraction*. See Section 1.6 of the Number and Counting essay.

one-dimensional (1-D) (1) A figure such as a line segment or part of a curve that, roughly speaking, has length, but no width or depth. (2) A figure such as a line in which one can locate any point with just one number in a coordinate system. Compare to *2-D* and *3-D*. See Sections 5.1 and 5.3 of the Geometry essay.

open sentence A number sentence in which one or more variables hold the place of missing numbers. For example, the number sentences $9 + \_\_ = 15$ and $\_\_ - 4 < 10$ are open. As an introduction to algebra, *Everyday Mathematics* regards a ? symbol or a blank or a frame as a variable in the "place holder" sense, in for example, "missing addend" problems. See Section 2.2 of the Operations and Facts essay.

$$9 + ? = 15 \qquad 5 - ? \geq 3$$
$$9 + \_\_ = 15 \qquad 5 - \_\_ \geq 3$$
$$9 + \boxed{} = 15 \qquad 5 - \boxed{} \geq 3$$
$$9 + x = 15 \qquad 5 - x \geq 3$$

open sentences

operation An action performed on one or two numbers producing a single number result. See *addition*, *subtraction*, *multiplication*, and *division* for definitions of the four basic "binary" operations. See *opposite of a number* and *square root of a number* for information on operations on single numbers that produce another single number result. See Section 2.1 of the Operations and Facts essay.

operation diagram Same as *situation diagram*. See Section 2.1 of the Operations and Facts essay.

operation symbol A symbol used in number sentences to stand for a particular mathematical operation. The operation symbols most often used in school mathematics are:

+ for addition
− for subtraction
×, *, and • for multiplication
÷ and / for division

See Section 2.2 of the Operations and Facts essay.

opposite angles (1) Of a quadrilateral: angles that do not share a common side.

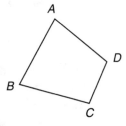

Angles *A* and *C* and Angles *B* and *D* are pairs of opposite angles.

(2) Of a triangle: an angle is opposite the side of a triangle that is not one of the sides of the angle.

Angle *C* is opposite Side *AB*.

(3) When two lines intersect, the angles that do not share a common side are opposite angles. Opposite angles have equal measures. Also called *vertical angles*.

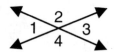

Angles 2 and 4 and Angles 1 and 3 are pairs of opposite, or vertical, angles.

opposite change algorithm Same as *rename-addends algorithm*. See Section 3.2 of the Operations and Facts essay for further discussion and other addition algorithms.

opposite of a number A number that is the same distance from zero on the number line as the given number, but on the opposite side of zero. The opposite of any number *n* is written as (op)*n* or −*n*. If n is a negative number, (op)*n* or −*n* will be a positive number. For example, if n = −5, then −*n*, or (op)n, is (op)−5 = 5. The sum of a number and its opposite is zero. Same as *additive inverse*. See Section 1.2 of the Number and Counting essay.

opposite side (1) Of a quadrilateral: sides that do not share a common vertex. (2) Of a triangle: a side is opposite an angle of the triangle if it is not part of that angle. See *opposite angles*.

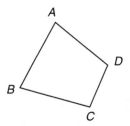

Sides *AB* and *CD* and Sides *AD* and *BC* are pairs of opposite sides.

order of magnitude estimate Same as magnitude estimate. See Section 8.2 of the Estimation essay.

order of magnitude increase A ten-fold increase in a value. See Section 1.7 of the Number and Counting essay and Section 8.2 of the Estimation essay.

order of operations Rules that tell the order in which operations should be done in an expression. The conventional order of operations is:
1. Carry out operations inside parentheses and other grouping symbols. Work out from the innermost set of grouping symbols, using rules 2 − 4.
2. Carry out any exponentiation (raising to powers, such as 5^2).
3. Carry out multiplications and divisions in order from left to right.
4. Carry out additions and subtractions in order from left to right.
See Section 2.2 of the Operations and Facts.

$5 \times 4 − 6 \times 3 + 2 = $
$20 − 18 + 2 = $
$2 + 2 = 4$

$5^2 + (3 \times 4 − 2) \div 5 = $
$5^2 + (12 − 2) \div 5 = $
$5^2 + 10 \div 5 = $
$25 + 10 \div 5 = $
$25 + 2 = 27$

order of operations

ordered pair (1) A pair of numbers used to locate a point on a coordinate grid. The first number corresponds to position along the horizontal axis, and the second number corresponds to position along the vertical axis.
See Section 5.9 of the Geometry essay and Section 7.3 of the Reference Frames essay.
(2) Any pair of objects or numbers in a particular order.

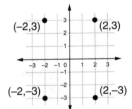

ordered pairs

orders of magnitude Positive powers of ten: 10, 100, 1,000, and so on. See Section 1.7 of the Number and Counting essay and Section 8.2 of the Estimation and Number Sense essay.

ordinal number A number used to express position or order in a series, such as first, third, and tenth. Generally, ordinal numbers are used to name dates as in, "May fifth" (rather than "May five"). See Section 1.2 of the Number and Counting essay.

origin The point at which the x-axis and y-axis intersect on a coordinate grid. See Section 5.9 of the Geometry essay and Section 7.3 of the Reference Frames essay.

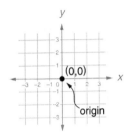

ounce (oz) (1) In the U.S. customary system, a unit of weight equal to $\frac{1}{16}$ of a pound. One ounce is about 28.35 grams. (2) In the U.S. customary system, a *fluid ounce* is a unit of capacity equal to $\frac{1}{16}$ of a pint. One fluid ounce equals 29.574 milliliters. See Table of Measures. See Sections 6.2, 6.6, and 6.7 of the Measurement essay.

outcome A possible result of a random process. Heads and tails are the two possible outcomes of tossing a coin. See Sections 4.2 and 4.3 of the Data and Chance essay.

output (1) The number resulting from the application of a rule used by an imaginary function machine to process numbers. See *function machine*. Compare to *input*. See Section 9.4 of the Patterns, Sequences, Functions, and Algebra essay.
(2) A number resulting from the application of a function rule to a given input number. See *function*.

pan balance A device used to weigh objects or compare their weights. See Section 6.3 of the Measurement essay.

pan balance

parabola The curve formed by the surface of a right circular cone when it intersects a plane that is parallel to a side of the cone. A parabola can also be defined as the curve formed by all of the points in a plane that are the same distance from a line and a point not on that line.

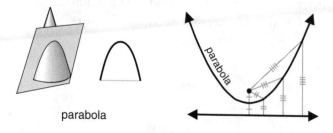

parabola

parallel Lines, rays, line segments, and planes that are equidistant at all points, no matter how far extended; never meeting. See Section 5.7 of the Geometry essay.

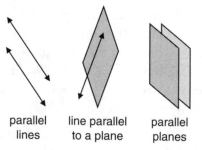

| parallel lines | line parallel to a plane | parallel planes |

parallelogram A quadrilateral that has two pairs of parallel sides and opposite sides that are congruent. All rectangles are parallelograms, but not all parallelograms are rectangles because parallelograms do not need to have right angles. See *opposite side* and *rectangle*. See Section 5.4 of the Geometry essay.

parallels Lines of latitude on maps or globes.

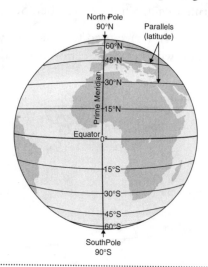

parentheses Grouping symbols ( ) that are used in multi-operation number models to indicate which operation(s) should be done first, as in $a \div (b + c)$. Other grouping symbols include brackets [ ] and braces { }. See *grouping symbols*. See Section 2.2 of the Operations and Facts essay.

part-whole fraction A fraction used when an object or a collection is divided into parts. In *Everyday Mathematics*, the object or collection is called the ONE, or the whole. Many common models for fractions are part-whole including pizzas, rectangles, and circles. See Section 1.6 of the Number and Counting essay.

partial differences algorithm A subtraction procedure in which differences are computed for each place separately and then added to yield the final answer. See Section 3.2 of the Algorithms and Mental Arithmetic essay for further discussion and other subtraction algorithms.

$$
\begin{array}{r}
932 \\
- 356 \\
\end{array}
$$

1. Subtract 100s: 900 − 300   600
2. Subtract 10s: 30 − 50   − 20
3. Subtract 1s: 2 − 6   − 4
4. Add the partial differences   576
   (600 − 20 − 4, done mentally)

partial differences algorithm

partial products algorithm A multiplication procedure in which products of the digits of two factors are computed separately and then added to yield the final product. See Section 3.2 of the Algorithms and Mental Arithmetic essay for further discussion and other multiplication algorithms.

$$
\begin{array}{r}
67 \\
\times 53 \\
\end{array}
$$

50 × 60	3000
50 × 7	350
3 × 60	180
3 × 7	+ 21
	3551

partial products algorithm

partial sums algorithm An addition procedure in which sums are computed for each place separately and then added to yield a final sum. See Section 3.2 of the Algorithms and Mental

Arithmetic essay for further discussion and other addition algorithms.

$$
\begin{array}{r}
268 \\
+\ 483 \\
\hline
600 \\
140 \\
+\ \ 11 \\
\hline
751
\end{array}
$$

1. Add 100s.
2. Adds 10s.
3. Add 1s.
4. Add partial sums.

partial sums algorithm

partitive division A phrase often used in teacher training courses to indicate the use of division in equal-shares situations in which the total amount and the number of shares are known and the size of the shares is to be found. For example, "If $10 is shared by 4 people, how much does each person get?" is a partitive division problem. In *Everyday Mathematics*, the term "equal-sharing story" is used to describe partitive division problems. See *equal-sharing story*. Compare to *measurement division* and *equal-grouping story*. See Section 2.1 of the Operations and Facts essay.

parts-and-total diagram In *Everyday Mathematics*, a diagram used to represent problems in which two or more quantities are combined to form a total quantity. It is often used when the parts are known and the total is unknown. It can also be used when the total and one or more parts are known, but one part is unknown. See *situation diagram*. See Section 2.1 of the Operations and Facts essay.

13	
8	?

Total	
13	
Part	**Part**
8	

parts-and-total diagrams for $13 = 8 + N$

pattern A model or plan by which elements can be arranged so that what comes next can be predicted. See Sections 9.1–9.4 of the Patterns, Sequences, Functions, and Algebra essay.

Pattern-Block Template In *Everyday Mathematics*, a sheet of plastic with geometric shapes cut out, used to draw patterns and designs.

penta- A prefix meaning five.

pentagon A 5-sided polygon. See Section 5.4 of the Geometry essay.

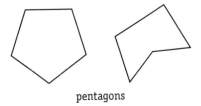

pentagons

per *In each* or *for each*, as in ten chairs per row or six tickets per family.

per capita Per person.

percent (%) Per hundred, or out of a hundred. 1% means $\frac{1}{100}$ or 0.01. For example, "48% of the students in the school are boys" means that out of every 100 students in the school, 48 are boys. See Section 1.6 of the Number and Counting essay.

perimeter The distance around a closed plane figure or region. *Peri-* comes from the Greek word for "around," and *meter* comes from the Greek word for "measure"; perimeter means "around measure." See Section 6.4 of the Measurement essay.

perpendicular Two rays, lines, line segments, or planes that form right angles are perpendicular to each other. See Section 5.7 of the Geometry essay.

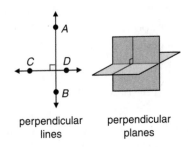

perpendicular lines   perpendicular planes

perspective drawing A method of drawing that accurately represents a 3-dimensional object on a 2-dimensional surface. See Section 5.1 of the Geometry essay.

pi (π) The ratio of the circumference of a circle to its diameter. Pi, which is approximately 3.14, is the same for every circle. Pi is also the ratio of a circle's area to the square of its radius. Also written as the Greek letter π. See Section 5.4 of the Geometry essay.

3.1415926535897932384

The first 20 digits of pi

glossary

pictograph A graph constructed with pictures or symbols. A pictograph makes it possible to compare at a glance the relative amounts of two or more counts or measures. See Section 4.1 of the Data and Chance essay.

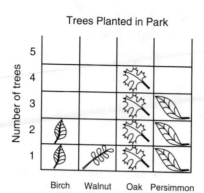

Trees Planted in Park

pie graph A graph in which a circle (the "pie") and its interior are divided into parts to represent the parts of a set of data. The circle and its interior represent the entire set of data. Same as *circle graph*. See Section 4.1 of the Data and Chance essay.

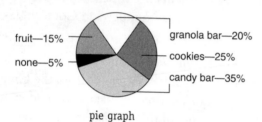

fruit—15%
none—5%
granola bar—20%
cookies—25%
candy bar—35%

pie graph

pint In the U.S. customary system, a unit of capacity equal to 2 cups or 16 fluid ounces. A handy saying to remember is "A pint's a pound the world around," which refers to the fact that a pint of water *weighs* about 1 pound (or 16 ounces). See Table of Measures. See Sections 6.2 and 6.6 of the Measurement essay.

place value The relative worth of each digit in a number, which is determined by its position. Each place has a value ten times that of the place to its right and one-tenth of the value of the place to its left. See Section 1.7 of the Number and Counting essay.

thousands	hundreds	tens	ones	tenths	hundredths

a place-value chart

plane A 2-dimensional flat surface that extends forever. See Section 5.4 of the Geometry essay.

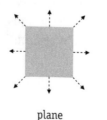

plane

plane figure A figure that can be entirely contained in a single plane. For example, triangles, squares, pentagons, circles, and parabolas are plane figures; cones, cubes, and prisms are not. See *2-dimensional*. See Section 5.4 of the Geometry essay.

P.M. An abbreviation for *post meridiem*, which means "after the middle of the day"; from noon to midnight

point An exact location in space. Points are usually labeled with capital letters. See Section 5.2 of the Geometry essay.

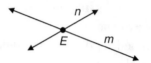

Lines *m* and *n* intersect at point E.

poly- A prefix meaning many.

polygon A closed plane figure formed by three or more line segments that meet only at their endpoints. The word comes from Greek: *Poly* means many and *gon* (from *gonia*) means angle. See Section 5.4 of the Geometry essay.

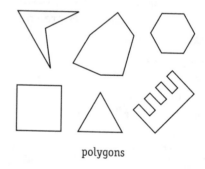

polygons

polyhedron A closed 3-dimensional shape, all of whose surfaces (faces) are flat. Each face consists of a polygon and its interior. See Section 5.5 of the Geometry essay.

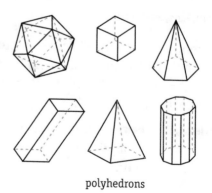

polyhedrons

population (1) The total number of people living within a certain geographical area.
(2) In data collection, the collection of people or objects that is the focus of study. The population is often larger than the target audience for a given survey, in which case a smaller, representative sample is considered. See *sample*.

population density The number of people living in a given area; usually given as a rate, such as "876 people per square mile."

positive number A number greater than 0; a number to the right of 0 on a horizontal number line or above 0 on a thermometer or other vertical number line. See Section 1.2 of the Number and Counting essay.

positive rational numbers A number greater than 0 that can be written as a fraction or a terminating or repeating decimal. For example, 7, 4/3, 1/1000, 0.01, 8.125, and 5.111… are positive rational numbers. See *rational number*. See Section 1.2 of the Number and Counting essay.

poster In *Everyday Mathematics*, a page displaying a collection of numerical data. The poster may be used as a source of data for developing number stories in lessons following the lesson in which it is introduced. See page 42 in the Management Guide for more information.

pound (lb) In the U.S. customary system, a unit of weight equal to 16 ounces (oz) and defined as 0.45359237 kilograms. See Table of Measures. See Sections 6.2 and 6.7 of the Measurement essay.

power (1) The exponent to which a "base" number is raised in exponential notation; the number a in n^a, where n is the base. If n is any number and a is a positive whole number, a tells how many times to use n as a factor in a product. For example, $5^3 = 5 \times 5 \times 5 = 125$, and is read "5 to the third power." See *power of 10* for more examples, including examples in which a is a negative integer.
(2) The result of a "powering" or "exponential" operation x^y. In mathematics beyond grades K–4, exponentiation goes beyond repeated multiplication because y can be a fraction or a decimal. See Section 2.2 of the Operations and Facts essay.

$$4^5 = 4 \times 4 \times 4 \times 4 \times 4 = 1024$$
$$10^2 = 10 \times 10 = 100$$
$$4^{1/2} = \sqrt{4}$$

power of 10 (1) A whole number that can be written as a product using only 10 as a factor; also called a positive power of 10. For example, 100 is equal to 10×10, or 10^2. 100 can also be called ten squared, the second power of 10, or 10 to the second power. (2) More generally, any number that can be written as a product using only 10s or $\frac{1}{10}$s as factors. For example, 0.01 is equal to 0.1×0.1, or 10^{-2}. Other powers of 10 include $10^1 = 10$ and $10^0 = 1$. See *power*.

powers key The $[y^x]$ key on a calculator, used to calculate powers. Keying in 4 $[y^x]$ 5 gives 4 raised to the fifth power, or 4^5, which equals $4 \times 4 \times 4 \times 4 \times 4$, or 1,024. See *power*.

precise In everyday language, a fine measurement or scale. The smaller the unit, or fraction of a unit used, the more precise the measurement or scale. For example, a measurement to the nearest inch is more precise than a measurement to the nearest foot. A ruler with 1/16-inch markings is said to be more precise than a ruler with 1/4-inch markings. Compare to *accurate*.

preimage A geometric figure that is operated on by a transformation—such as a reflection, rotation, or translation—to produce another figure. See *transformation*. Compare to *image*. See Section 5.6 of the Geometry essay.

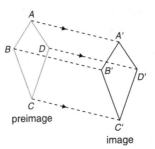

prime factorization A whole number expressed as a product of prime factors. For example, the prime factorization of 24 is $2 \times 2 \times 2 \times 3$. See *prime number*.

prime number A whole number greater than 1 that has exactly two whole-number factors, 1 and itself. For example, 7 is a prime number because its only factors are 1 and 7. The first five prime numbers are 2, 3, 5, 7, and 11. Compare to *composite number*.

prism A polyhedron with two parallel faces (bases) that are the same size and shape and other faces that are bounded by parallelograms (which are often rectangles). Prisms are classified according to the shape of the two parallel bases. See Section 5.5 of the Geometry essay.

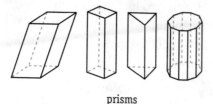

prisms

probability A number from 0 to 1 that indicates the likelihood that an event will happen. The closer a probability is to 1, the more likely it is that the event will happen. The closer a probability is to 0, the less likely it is that the event will happen. For example, the probability that a fair coin will show heads is 1/2. See *event*. See Section 4.2 of the Data and Chance essay.

product The result of a multiplication. In the number model $4 \times 3 = 12$, the product is 12. See *multiplication*.

Project In *Everyday Mathematics*, a thematic activity to be completed in one or more days by small groups or by the whole class. Projects often involve collecting and analyzing data and are usually cross-curricular in nature. See page 16 in the Management Guide for more information.

proper factor Any whole-number factor of a number except the number itself. For example, the factors of 10 are 1, 2, 5, and 10, but the proper factors of 10 are 1, 2, and 5.

proper fraction The traditional term for a fraction in which the numerator is less than the denominator; a proper fraction names a number less than 1. For example, 3/4, 2/5, and 12/24 are proper fractions. Compare to *improper fraction*, or *top-heavy fraction*.

property A feature of an object. For example, size, shape, color, and number of sides are all properties. Same as *attribute*.

protractor A tool used for measuring or drawing angles. When measuring an angle, the vertex of the angle should be at the center of the protractor and one side aligned with the 0° mark. A half-circle

protractor can be used to measure or draw angles up to 180°, a full-circle protractor to measure or draw angles up to 360°.

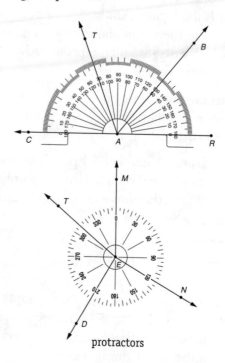

protractors

pyramid A polyhedron in which one face (the base) is a polygon and all the other faces are triangles with a common vertex called the *apex*. Pyramids are classified according to the shapes of their bases. See Section 5.5 of the Geometry essay.

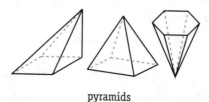

pyramids

Pythagorean theorem The proposition that for any right triangle, the area of the square on the hypotenuse is equal to the sum of the areas of the squares on the other two sides.

Symbolically, the theorem can be stated as follows: If the legs of a right triangle have lengths a and b, and the hypotenuse has length c, then $a^2 + b^2 = c^2$.

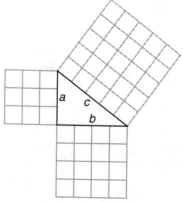

Pythagorean theorem

quad- A prefix meaning four.

quadrangle Same as *quadrilateral*. See Section 5.4 of the Geometry essay.

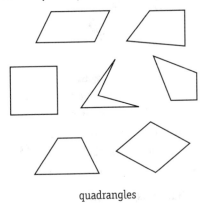

quadrangles

quadrant Any of the four sections into which a rectangular coordinate grid is divided by the intersection of the *x* and *y* axes. The quadrants are numbered 1 through 4, beginning at the upper right (where *x* and *y* coordinates are positive) and going counterclockwise.

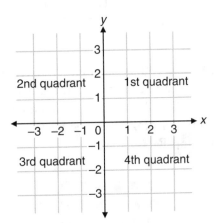

quadrilateral A 4-sided polygon. Same as *quadrangle*. See Section 5.4 of the Geometry essay.

quadruple Four times an amount.

quart In the U.S. customary system, a unit of capacity equal to 32 fluid ounces, 2 pints, or 4 cups. See Table of Measures.

quotient The result of dividing one number by another number; the number of equal shares. In the division model in $10 \div 5 = 2$, the quotient is 2. See *division*.

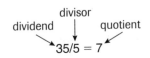

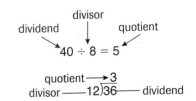

quotitive division Same as *measurement division*. See Section 2.1 of the Operations and Facts essay.

radius A line segment from the center of a circle (or sphere) to any point on the circle (or sphere); also, the length of such a line segment. See Sections 5.4 and 5.5 of the Geometry essay.

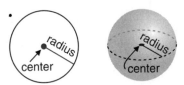

random Not predictable with respect to individual outcomes. Flipping a fair coin is a random process because the outcome of an individual flip cannot be predicted. See Section 4.2 of the Data and Chance essay.

random number A number produced by a random process, such as rolling a die or spinning a spinner. See Sections 4.2 and 4.3 of the Data and Chance essay.

random sampling Selecting a sample from a population in a way that allows all members of the population the same chance of being included.

range The difference between the greatest and least values in a set of data. See Section 4.1 of the Data and Chance essay.

rate A comparison by division of two quantities with unlike units. For example, traveling 100 miles in 2 hours can be expressed as 100 mi/2 hr or 50 miles per hour. In this case, the rate compares distance (miles) to time (hours). Compare to *ratio*. See Section 1.6 of the Number and Counting essay and Section 2.1 of the Operations and Facts essay.

rate diagram A tool used to represent rate situations in which a total count or measure and the size of several equal groups are being considered. The diagram has three parts: the number of groups, the number in each group, and the total number. Rate diagrams can be helpful in solving multiplication and division problems involving rates. Also called *multiplication diagram*. See *situation diagram*. See Section 2.1 of the Operations and Facts essay.

rows	chairs per row	chairs
6	4	?

hours	miles per hour	miles
2	25	?

rate diagrams

rate table A means of displaying rate information. See *rate*.

miles	35	70	105	140	175	210
gallons	1	2	3	4	5	6

rate table

rate unit A unit, used to describe a rate, made up of two different units. For example, miles per hour, dollars per pound, and words per minute are all rate units. See *rate*. See Section 1.6 of the Number and Counting essay.

ratio A comparison by division of two quantities with the same units. Ratios can be expressed as fractions, decimals, or percents, as well as in words. Ratios can also be written with a colon between the two numbers being compared. For example, if a team wins 3 games out of 5 games played, the ratio of wins to total games is $\frac{3}{5}$, 3/5, 0.6, 60%, 3 to 5, or 3:5 (read "three to five"). Compare to *rate*. See Section 1.6 of the Number and Counting essay and Section 2.1 of the Operations and Facts essay.

rational number Any number that can be represented in the form *a/b*, where *a* and *b* are integers and $b \neq 0$. A rational number can always be represented by either a terminating decimal or a repeating decimal. For example, 2/3, −2/3, 0.5, −0.5, and 0.3333. . . are all rational numbers. See Section 1.2 of the Number and Counting essay.

ray A straight path that extends infinitely from a point, called its *endpoint*. See Section 5.3 of the Geometry essay.

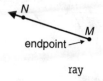

ray

real number Any rational or irrational number. For every real number there is a corresponding point on the number line, and for every point on the number line there is a real number. See Section 1.2 of the Number and Counting essay.

reciprocal Same as *multiplicative inverse*.

rectangle A parallelogram whose angles are all right angles. See *parallelogram*. See Section 5.4 of the Geometry essay.

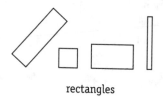

rectangles

rectangular array A rectangular arrangement of objects in rows and columns such that each row has the same number of objects and each column has the same number of objects. See Section 2.1 of the Operations and Facts essay.

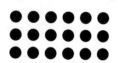

rectangular array

rectangular prism (1) In common usage, a prism whose faces (including the bases) are all rectangles. Many packing boxes have the shape of rectangular prisms. (2) More generally, any prism with rectangular bases, some of the faces of which might be non-rectangle parallelograms. See Section 5.5 of the Geometry essay.

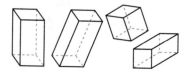

rectangular prisms

rectangular pyramid A pyramid whose base is a rectangle. See Section 5.5 of the Geometry essay.

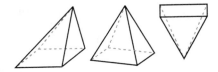

rectangular pyramids

reduce (1) To make an object or shape smaller. (2) To reduce fractions: To put into simplest form. See *simplest form*. See Section 1.6 of the Number and Counting essay.

reference frame A system for locating numbers within a given context, often with reference to an arbitrarily set 0-point. Examples of reference frames are number lines, timelines, calendar systems, temperature scales, and rectangular coordinate systems, including those on maps. See the Reference Frames essay.

reflection A transformation that "flips" a picture or object so that it becomes a mirror image of the original (preimage). Same as *flip*. See *transformation*. See Section 5.6 of the Geometry essay.

reflection

reflex angle An angle with a measure between 180° and 360°. See *angle*. See Section 5.4 of the Geometry essay.

reflex angle

regular polygon A polygon whose sides are the same length and whose angles are all equal. See Section 5.4 of the Geometry essay.

regular polygons

regular polyhedron A polyhedron whose faces are all congruent regular polygons and with the same number of faces meeting at every vertex, all at the same angle. There are five regular polyhedrons; they are also known as the Platonic solids:

tetrahedron: 4 faces, each formed by an equilateral triangle

cube: 6 faces, each formed by a square

octahedron: 8 faces, each formed by an equilateral triangle

dodecahedron: 12 faces, each formed by a regular pentagon

icosahedron: 20 faces, each formed by an equilateral triangle

See Section 5.5 of the Geometry essay.

tetrahedron   cube   octahedron

dodecahedron   icosahedron

regular tessellation A tessellation made up of only one kind of regular polygon. There are only three regular tessellations. See *tessellation*.

the three regular tessellations

relation symbol A symbol used to express a relationship between two quantities. Some relation symbols used in number sentences include:

= for "is equal to," ≠ for "is not equal to," < for "is less than," > for "is greater than," ≤ for "is less than or equal to," and ≥ for "is greater than or equal to."

See Section 2.2 of the Operations and Facts essay.

remainder An amount left over when things are divided into equal shares. In the division number model $16 \div 3$, there are 5 groups of 3, and the remainder is 1, usually denoted R1. See Section 2.2 of the Operations and Facts essay.

glossary

rename-addends algorithm An addition procedure in which both addends are changed by equal amounts in opposite directions. For example, $73 + 29 = (73 - 1) + (29 + 1) = 72 + 30 = 102$. Same as *opposite change algorithm*. See Section 3.2 of the Algorithms and Mental Arithmetic essay for further discussion and other addition algorithms.

repeating decimal A decimal in which one digit, or a group of digits, is repeated without end. For example, 0.3333. . . and $0.\overline{147}$ are repeating decimals. See *decimal*. Compare to *terminating decimal*.

rhombus A parallelogram with all sides the same length. The angles may be right angles, in which case the rhombus is a square. See Section 5.4 of the Geometry essay.

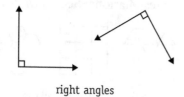

rhombuses

right angle A square corner; a 90° angle. See *angle*. See Section 5.4 of the Geometry essay.

right angles

right triangle A triangle that has a right angle. See *triangle*. See Section 5.4 of the Geometry essay.

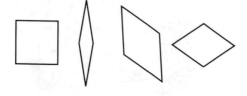

right triangle

Roman numerals Symbols from an ancient Roman system of numeration. Roman numerals are the letters that are used alone and in combination to represent numbers in this ancient system. Roman numerals are still found on clocks, building cornerstones, preliminary pages in books, and other places.

Roman Numerals

I = 1	XX = 20 (2 tens)	CC = 200
II = 2	XXX = 30 (3 tens)	CCC = 300
III = 3	XL = 40 (50 less 10)	CD = 400
IV = 4	L = 50	D = 500
V = 5	LX = 60 (50 plus 10)	CM = 900
VI = 6	LXX = 70 (50 plus 20)	M = 1,000
VII = 7	LXXX = 80 (50 plus 30)	$\overline{X}$ = 10,000
VIII = 8	XC = 90 (100 less 10)	$\overline{C}$ = 100,000
IX = 9	C = 100	∞ = 100,000,000
X = 10		or infinity

rotation A transformation that "turns" an object around a fixed point or axis. The point or axis, called the *center* or *axis of rotation*, can be inside or outside of the original image. Same as *turn*. See *transformation*. See Section 5.6 of the Geometry essay.

rotation

rotational symmetry (1) In a plane, a figure has rotational symmetry if it can be rotated less than one full turn around a point so that the resulting figure (the image) exactly matches the original figure (the preimage). Compare to *line symmetry*. See Section 5.8 of the Geometry essay.

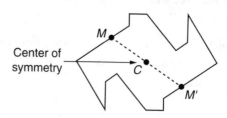

2-D shape with rotational symmetry

(2) A 3-D figure has rotational symmetry if it can be rotated less than a full turn around an axis so that the resulting figure exactly matches the original figure.

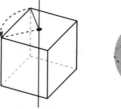

3-D shapes with rotational symmetry

round (1) Arithmetic: To express a number in a simplified way. Examples of rounding include expressing a measure of weight to the nearest pound and expressing an amount of money to the nearest dollar. See Section 3.3 of the Algorithms and Mental Arithmetic essay and Section 8.4 of the Estimation essay. (2) Geometry: Circular in shape.

row A horizontal arrangement of objects or numbers in an array or table.

same change algorithm A subtraction procedure in which the same change is made to both numbers. For example, $87 - 34 = (87 - 4) - (34 - 4) = 83 - 30 = 53$. See Section 3.2 of the Algorithms and Mental Arithmetic essay for other subtraction algorithms.

sample A part of a population intended to represent the nature of the whole.

scale (1) The ratio of the distance on a map, globe, or drawing to the actual distance. See *scale factor*. See Section 2.1 of the Operations and Facts essay and Section 7.3 of the Reference Frames essay.

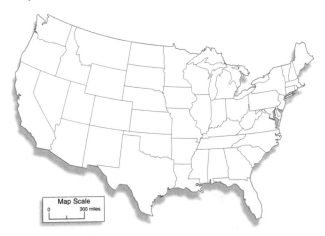

(2) A number line on a thermometer used for measuring temperature. (3) An instrument for measuring weight.

scale drawing A drawing that represents an object or area in fixed proportion to its actual size. The proportion is called the scale factor. For example, if an actual object measures 33 yards by 22 yards, a scale drawing of it might measure 33 centimeters by 22 centimeters, with all of the proportions between the drawing and the actual object being the same. A map is a scale drawing of a

geographical region. See *scale factor*. See Section 2.1 of the Operations and Facts essay and Section 7.3 of the Reference Frames essay.

woodpecker (8 in.) shown in $\frac{1}{4}$ scale

scale factor The ratio between the size of an object and the size of a representation of that object (such as a scale drawing or model). See *scale*, *scale drawing*, and *scale model*. See Section 2.1 of the Operations and Facts essay.

scale model A model that represents an object or display in fixed proportion to its actual size. The proportion is called the scale factor. For example, many model trains or airplanes are scale models of actual vehicles. See *scale factor*. See Section 2.1 of the Operations and Facts essay.

scalene triangle A triangle with sides of three different lengths and angles of three different sizes. See *triangle*. See Section 5.4 of the Geometry essay.

scientific calculator A calculator that displays very large or very small numbers in scientific notation and has powering, square root, change-of-sign, and reciprocal keys. Scientific calculators usually carry out operations in accordance with the conventional order of operations. See *scientific notation* and *order of operations*. See the section on calculators in the Management Guide.

scientific notation A system for representing numbers in which a number is written as the product of a number between 1 and 10 and a power of 10. Scientific notation allows writing big and small numbers with only a few symbols. For example, 4,300,000 in scientific notation is 4.3×10^6, and 0.00001 in scientific notation is 1×10^{-5}. Compare to *standard notation* and *expanded notation*. See Section 8.1 of the Estimation essay.

second (1) A unit of time. There are 60 seconds in a minute. (2) An ordinal number in the sequence first, second, third, . . .

sector A region bounded by an arc and two radii of a circle, which resembles a slice of pizza. See Section 5.4 of the Geometry essay for a discussion of circles.

semicircle Half of a circle, bounded by the circumference and the ends of a diameter. In common usage, the diameter is often included as a boundary of a semicircle, making it a closed figure that is half of a circular region. See *circle*. See Section 5.4 of the Geometry essay.

semicircle

set A collection or group of objects, numbers, or other items.

side Any one of the line segments that make up a polygon. See Section 5.4 of the Geometry essay.

significant digits The digits in a number that are considered to convey useful and reliable information. A number with more significant digits is more precise than a number with fewer significant digits. In general, calculations cannot produce results with more significant digits than the original numbers. See *scientific notation*. See Section 8.1 of the Estimation and Number Sense essay.

similar figures Figures that are exactly the same shape but not necessarily the same size. See Section 5.7 of the Geometry essay.

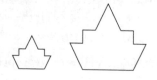

similar figures

simplest form Of fractions: Having numerator and denominator with no common factors (other than 1). For example, $\frac{10}{15}$ and $\frac{2}{3}$ are equivalent fractions. However, $\frac{10}{15}$ is not in simplest form because the numerator and denominator can each be divided by 5; $\frac{2}{3}$ is in simplest form because 2 and 3 have no common factors (other than 1). If the numerator is greater than the denominator, writing in simplest form usually requires rewriting as a mixed number in which the fraction part is in

simplest form. Same as *lowest terms*. See Section 1.6 of the Number and Counting essay.

simplify To express a fraction in simplest form, or lowest terms. See *simplest form*. See Section 1.6 of the Number and Counting essay.

situation diagram One of various diagrams used to organize information in simple problem situations. Same as *operation diagram*. See *change diagram, comparison diagram, parts-and-total diagram, multiplication diagram,* and *rate diagram.* See Section 2.1 of the Operations and Facts essay.

size change An enlargement or reduction of an original.

size-change factor A number that indicates the amount of enlargement or reduction. See *size change*.

slanted cylinder, cone, prism, or pyramid Three-dimensional figures that are "tilted." Slanted cylinders and prisms have lateral faces or surfaces that are not perpendicular to their bases. Slanted cones and pyramids have apexes that are not directly above the centers of their bases. Also known as *oblique* cylinders, cones, prisms, and pyramids. See Section 5.5 of the Geometry essay.

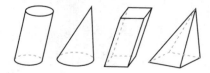

slanted cylinder, cone, prism, and pyramid

slate A lap-sized (about 8″ × 11″) chalkboard or whiteboard that children use in *Everyday Mathematics* for a variety of purposes, including recording responses during group exercises and informal group assessments. See page 16 in the Management Guide for more information.

slide An informal name for a translation transformation. See *translation* and *transformation*. See Section 5.6 of the Geometry essay.

solution of an open sentence A value or values for the variable(s) in an open sentence which make the sentence true. For example, the open sentence 4 + __ = 10 has the solution 6. See *open sentence*. See Section 2.2 of the Operations and Facts essay.

solution set The set of all solutions of an equation or inequality. For example, the solution

glossary

set of $x^2 = 25$ is $\{5, -5\}$ since substitution of either 5 or -5 for x makes the sentence true. See Section 2.2 of the Operations and Facts essay.

span Same as *normal span*.

speed A rate that compares distance traveled with the time taken to travel that distance. See *rate*. See Sections 1.6 of the Number and Counting essay and 2.1 of the Operations and Facts essay.

sphere A 3-dimensional shape whose curved surface is, at all points, a given distance from its center point. A ball is shaped like a sphere. A sphere is hollow; it does not include the points in its interior. See Section 5.5 of the Geometry essay.

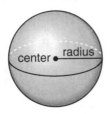

sphere

square A rectangle whose sides are all the same length. See Section 5.4 of the Geometry essay.

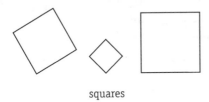

squares

square array A rectangular array with the same number of rows as columns. For example, 16 objects will form a square array with 4 objects in each row and 4 objects in each column. See Sections 2.1 and 2.2 of the Operations and Facts essay.

square array

square number A number that is the product of a whole number and itself; a whole number to the second power. For example, 25 is a square number, because $25 = 5 \times 5$. A square number can be represented by a square array. See *square array*. See Section 2.2 of the Operations and Facts essay.

square of a number The product of a number and itself; symbolized by a raised 2. For example, $3.5^2 = 3.5 \times 3.5 = 12.25$. See Section 2.2 of the Operations and Facts essay.

square pyramid A pyramid with a square base.

square root of a number The square root of a number n is a number which, when multiplied by itself, results in the number n. For example, 4 is a square root of 16, because $4 \times 4 = 16$. Normally, square root refers to the positive square root, but the opposite of a positive square root is also a square root. For example, -4 is also a square root of 16 because $(-4) \times (-4) = 16$. See Section 1.2 of the Number and Counting essay.

square unit A unit used to measure area. A square unit represents a square with the measure of each side being one of that unit. For example, a square inch represents a square that measures one inch on each side. See Section 6.5 of the Measurement essay.

square units

standard notation The most familiar way of representing whole numbers, integers, and decimals. Standard notation is ordinary base-10 place-value numeration. For example, standard notation for three hundred fifty six is 356. Compare to *expanded notation* and *scientific notation*. See Section 1.7 of the Number and Counting essay.

standard unit A unit of measure that has been defined by a recognized authority, such as a government or a standards organization. For example, inches, meters, miles, seconds, pounds, grams, and acres are all standard units. See Section 6.2 of the Measurement essay.

stem-and-leaf plot A display of data in which digits with larger place values are "stems" and digits with smaller place values are "leaves." See Section 4.1 of the Data and Chance essay.

Data List: 24, 24, 25, 26, 27, 27, 31, 31, 32, 32, 36, 36, 41, 41, 43, 45, 48, 50, 52

Stems 10's	Leaves 1's
2	4 4 5 6 7 7
3	1 1 2 2 6 6
4	1 1 3 5 8
5	0 2

stem-and-leaf plot

step graph A graph that looks like steps because the values are the same for an interval and then change (or "step") for another interval. Step graphs are particularly common when the horizontal axis represents time.

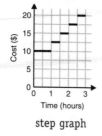

step graph

straight angle An angle with a measure of 180°. See *angle*. See Section 5.4 of the Geometry essay.

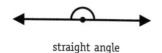

straight angle

straightedge A tool used to draw line segments. A straightedge does not have measure marks on it, so if a ruler is used as a straightedge the markings on it must be ignored.

substitute To replace one thing with another; in a formula, to replace variables with numerical values. For example, if $b = 4.5$ and $h = 8.5$, then these values can be substituted in the formula $A = b \times h$ to yield $A = 4.5 \times 8.5 = 38.25$. See Section 2.2 of the Operations and Facts essay.

subtraction The operation used to find how many are left when some are taken away or when a given quantity is decreased, or when comparing quantities. The number being subtracted is called the *subtrahend*; the number it is subtracted from is called the *minuend*; and the result of subtraction is called the *difference*. For example, in $45 - 12 = 33$, the minuend is 45, the subtrahend is 12, and the difference is 33. Addition "undoes" subtraction: $45 - 12 = 33$ can be "undone" by $12 + 33 = 45$. See Section 2.1 of the Operations and Facts essay and Section 3.2 of the Algorithms and Mental Arithmetic essay.

subtrahend In subtraction, the number that is being taken away from another. For example, in $15 - 5 = 10$, the subtrahend is 5. See *subtraction*.

sum The result of adding two or more numbers. For example, in $5 + 3 = 8$, the sum is 8. See *addition*.

supplementary angles Two angles whose measures total 180°. See Section 5.4 of the Geometry essay.

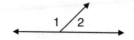

∠1 and ∠2 are supplementary angles.

surface area A measure of the surface of a 3-dimensional figure. The surface area of a polyhedron is the sum of the areas of its faces. See *area*. See Section 6.5 of the Measurement essay.

survey A study that collects data. For example, surveys are used to find out about people's characteristics, behaviors, interests, opinions, and so on. In *Everyday Mathematics*, surveys are used to generate data for graphing and analysis. See Section 4.1 of the Data and Chance essay.

symmetry The property of exact balance in a figure; having the same size and shape across a dividing line or around a point. See *line symmetry* and *rotational symmetry*. See Section 5.8 of the Geometry essay.

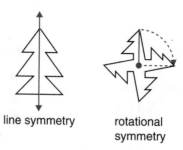

line symmetry   rotational symmetry

tally A vertical mark (卌 ////) used to keep track of a count. See Section 4.1 of the Data and Chance essay.

temperature A measure of how hot or cold something is, usually expressed in degrees Celsius or degrees Fahrenheit. The Celsius and Fahrenheit temperature scales are different reference frames for temperature. See *reference frame*. See Section 7.1 of the Reference Frames essay.

template In *Everyday Mathematics*, a sheet of plastic with geometric shapes cut out of it, used to draw patterns and designs. See *Pattern-Block Template*. See Section 5.10 of the Geometry essay.

term In an algebraic expression or equation, a number or a product of a number and one or more variables. For example, in the expression $5y + 3k - 8$, the terms are $5y$, $3k$, and 8. See Section 2.2 of the Operations and Facts essay.

terminating decimal A decimal that ends. Alternatively, a decimal in which all digits to the right of a certain place are 0s. For example, 0.5 and 0.125 are terminating decimals. See *decimal*. Compare to *repeating decimal*.

tessellate To make a tessellation. See *tessellation*.

tessellation An arrangement of closed shapes that covers a surface completely without overlaps or gaps. Same as *tiling*. See *tile*.

tessellation

tetrahedron A polyhedron with four faces, all of which are triangles. If each face is an equilateral triangle, this tetrahedron is one of the five regular polyhedra. See *regular polyhedron*. See Section 5.5 of the Geometry essay.

regular tetrahedron   irregular tetrahedrons

theorem A mathematical statement that can be proved to be true (or, sometimes, a statement that is proposed and needs to be proved). For example, the Pythagorean theorem states that if the legs of a right triangle have lengths a and b and the hypotenuse has length c, then $a^2 + b^2 = c^2$. The Pythagorean theorem has been proved in hundreds of ways over the past 2,500 years.

three-dimensional (3-D) (1) A figure in space that cannot be contained in a plane. Examples include prisms, pyramids, or sphere, all of which, roughly speaking, have length, width, and height. Other examples include pairs of perpendicular planes or sets of lines that are not all in the same plane. (2) A figure or surface on which any point can be located with three numbers in a coordinate system. Compare to *1-D* and *2-D*. See Section 5.5 of the Geometry essay.

tile A shape used in a tessellation. If only one shape is repeated in a tessellation, the tessellation is called a same-tile tessellation.

tiling An arrangement of closed shapes that covers a surface completely without overlaps or gaps. See *tessellation*. Also, the act of making a tessellation.

time line A device for showing in sequence when events took place. A time line is a number line with the numbers naming years, days, and so on. See *reference frame*. See Section 7.2 of the Reference Frames essay.

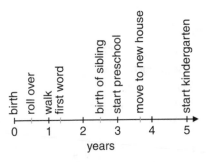

timeline of a young child's milestones

tool kit In *Everyday Mathematics*, a bag or a box containing a calculator, measuring tools, and manipulatives often used in the program. See page 36 in the Management Guide for more information.

top-heavy fraction A term used in *Everyday Mathematics* for a fraction that names a number greater than or equal to 1; a fraction whose numerator is not less than its denominator. Examples of top-heavy fractions are $\frac{7}{3}$, $\frac{5}{5}$, $\frac{9}{7}$, and $\frac{16}{4}$. Same as *improper fraction*.

trade-first subtraction A subtraction procedure in which all necessary trades are done before any subtractions are carried out. Doing so simplifies the algorithm since the user can concentrate on one thing at a time. See Section 3.2 of the Algorithms and Mental Arithmetic essay for further discussion and other subtraction algorithms.

transformation An operation on a geometric figure that produces a new figure, called the *image*, from the original figure, called the *preimage*. Transformations are sometimes thought of as "motions" that move a figure from one place to another and sometimes change its size or shape. The study of transformations is called *transformation geometry.* See *isometry transformation.* See *reflection, rotation,* and *translation.* See Section 5.6 of the Geometry essay.

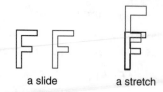

a slide   a stretch

transformations

transformation geometry The study of the geometry of transformations. See *transformation.* See Section 5.6 of the Geometry essay.

translation The motion of "sliding" an object or picture along a line segment. Same as slide. See *transformation.* See Section 5.6 of the Geometry essay.

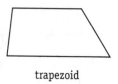

preimage

translation

trapezoid A quadrilateral that has exactly one pair of parallel sides. No two sides need be the same length. See Section 5.4 of the Geometry essay.

trapezoid

tri– A prefix meaning three, as in triangle, tricycle, or triple.

triangle A polygon with 3 sides and 3 angles. See *equilateral triangle, isosceles triangle, scalene triangle, acute triangle, right triangle,* and *obtuse triangle.* See Section 5.4 of the Geometry essay.

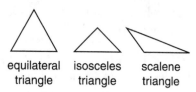

equilateral   isosceles   scalene
triangle   triangle   triangle

triangular numbers Figurate numbers that can be shown by a triangular arrangement of dots. The triangular numbers are {1, 3, 6, 10, 15, 21, 28, 36, 45, . . .}. See *figurate numbers.*

triangular numbers

triangular prism A prism whose bases are triangles. See Section 5.5 of the Geometry essay.

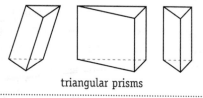

triangular prisms

triangular pyramid A pyramid in which all faces are triangles, any one of which can be called the base. If all of the faces are equilateral triangles, the pyramid is a regular tetrahedron and is one of the five regular polyhedra. See *tetrahedron* and *regular polyhedron.* See Section 5.5 of the Geometry essay.

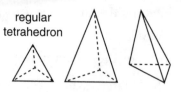

regular
tetrahedron

triangular pyramids

truncate (1) To replace all digits to the right of a particular place with 0s. For example, 3,654 can be truncated to 3,650 or 3,600 or 3,000. Truncation is similar to rounding but is easier and always makes the number smaller (unless all the truncated digits are 0s). (2) To cut off a vertex of a solid figure.

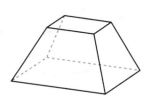

truncated pyramid

turn An informal name for a rotation transformation. See *rotation* and *transformation.* See Section 5.6 of the Geometry essay.

turn-around facts A pair of addition or multiplication (but not subtraction or division) facts in which the order of the addends or the factors is reversed. For example, $3 + 5 = 8$ and $5 + 3 = 8$ or $3 \times 9 = 27$ and $9 \times 3 = 27$. Turn-around facts illustrate the commutative properties of addition and multiplication. If a fact is known, its turn-around is also known. See Section 2.3 of the Operations and Facts essay. See *commutative property.*

turn symmetry Same as *rotational symmetry.* See Section 5.8 of the Geometry essay.

twin primes Two prime numbers that are separated by just one number. For example, 3 and 5 are twin primes; 11 and 13 are also twin primes.

2-dimensional (2-D) (1) Any figure contained completely within a plane but not entirely on a line. Objects with length and width but no thickness. (2) A figure or surface on which one can locate any point with two numbers in a coordinate system.

Compare to *1-D* and *3-D*. See Section 5.4 of the Geometry essay.

unit A label, descriptive word, or unit of measure used to put a number in context. Using units with numbers reinforces the idea that numbers refer to something. Fingers, snowballs, miles, and cents are examples of units. See Sections 2.1 and 2.3 of the Operations and Facts essay and Section 6.2 of the Measurement essay.

unit box In *Everyday Mathematics*, a box displayed alongside a set of numbers or problems. It contains the unit or label for the numbers in use.

unit box

unit fraction A fraction whose numerator is 1. For example, $\frac{1}{2}, \frac{1}{3}, \frac{1}{8}, \frac{1}{12},$ and $\frac{1}{20}$ are all unit fractions. See Sections 1.6 and 1.7 of the Number and Counting essay.

unit price The price for one item or unit of measure. For example, if a 5-ounce package of something costs $2.50, then $0.50 per ounce is the unit price. Often used to compare relative cost or value of similar things packaged in different amounts and with different prices.

unit ratio same as *n-to-1 ratio*.

unit whole Same as the whole or ONE in specifying the basis for a multiple or fraction. See Section 1.6 of the Number and Counting essay.

U.S. customary system The measuring system most frequently used in the United States. Units for linear measure (length, distance) include inch, foot, yard, and mile; units for weight include ounce and pound; units for capacity include cup, pint, quart and gallon; for temperature change , degrees Fahrenheit. See Section 6.2 of the Measurement essay.

variable A letter or other symbol that represents a number. A variable need not represent one specific number; it can stand for many different values. For example, in the expression $2\pi r$, r is a variable, and in the equation $a + 12 = 2b - 6$, a and b are variables. See Section 2.2 of the Operations and Facts essay.

Venn diagram A picture that uses circles to show relationships among sets.

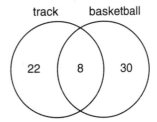

Girls on Sports Teams

Venn diagram

vertex The point at which the rays or line segments of an angle, the sides of a polygon, or the edges of a polyhedron meet. Same as *corner*. See Sections 5.3-5.5 of the Geometry essay.

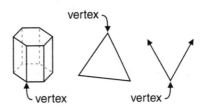

vertical Upright; perpendicular to the horizon. See *horizon*. Compare to *horizontal*.

vertical angles When two lines intersect, the angles that do not share a common side; the angles opposite each other. Vertical angles have equal measures. Same as *opposite angles*.

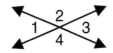

Angles 1 and 3 and Angles 2 and 4 are pairs of vertical angles.

volume A measure of the amount of space occupied by a 3-dimensional shape, generally expressed in "cubic" units, such as cm^3, cubic inches, or cubic feet. See Section 6.6 of the Measurement essay.

weight A measure of how heavy something is. Technically, weight is a measure of the force of gravity on an object, which depends on the object's mass and the strength of the gravitational field acting on it. Hence, the same object can have different weights depending on where it is. For example, a person who weighs 150 pounds in San Diego would have a different weight on the moon. Compare to *mass*. See Section 6.7 of the Measurement essay.

"What's My Rule?" In *Everyday Mathematics*, a routine that involves a set of number pairs in which the numbers in each pair are related to each other according to the same rule. "What's My Rule?" problems are usually displayed in table form in which two of the three parts (input, output, and rule) are known and the goal is to find the unknown part. See *function* and *function machine*. See Section 9.4 of the Patterns, Sequences, Functions, and Algebra essay.

in	out
4	2
7	5
12	10
8	

What's My Rule? problem

whole The entire object, collection of objects, or quantity being considered; the unit, 100%. Same as the ONE and the unit whole. See Section 1.6 of the Number and Counting essay.

whole number Any of the numbers 0, 1, 2, 3, 4, and so on. See Section 1.2 of the Number and Counting essay.

width of a rectangle Length of one side of a rectangle or rectangular object; often the shorter side.

x-by-y array An arrangement having x rows of y per row, representing x sets of y objects in each set.

yard (yd) Historically, the distance from the tip of the nose to the tip of the longest finger. In the U.S. customary system, a unit of length equivalent to 3 feet or 36 inches. See Table of Measures. See Sections 6.1 and 6.2 of the Measurement essay.

zero fact The sum of two 1-digit numbers such that one of the addends is 0, as in $0 + 5 = 5$. If 0 is added to any number, or vice versa, there is no change in the number. Also, the product of two 1-digit numbers such that one of the factors is 0, as in $4 \times 0 = 0$. The product of a number and 0 is always 0.

Index

Acre, 153
Acute angle, 129
Acute triangle, 130
Addition, 73–77
    algorithms, 101–103
    commutative property, 91–92
    fact, 89, 90
    symbols, 82–83
    turn-around rule, 89, 91–92
Add-up subtraction, 104
Algebra, 195
Algebraic expression, 88–89, 195
Algebraic order of operations, 87
Algorithms, 94–111
    addition, 101–103
        column, 101–102
        partial-sums, 101
        rename-addends, 102–103
        U.S. traditional, 103
    computational, 96–97
    division, 109–111
    focus, 99–100
    inventing, 98–99
    multiplication, 106–109
        lattice, 107–108
        modified repeated addition, 109
        modified standard U.S., 109
        partial-products, 106–107
    standard and alternative, 100–111
    subtraction, 103–106
        counting-up, 104
        European, 105–106
        left-to-right, 105
        partial differences, 106
        trade-first, 103–104
Alloy, 158

Analog clocks, 167
Angle measure, 156
Angles, 128–129
Area, 153–154
    continuous conception of, 154
    discrete conception of, 153–154
Arithmetic
    facts, 89–90
    symbols, 82–85
Arm span, 148
Arrays, 79
Arrow path, 61
Arrows, 185–186
Assessment, 38
    ongoing, 38
    periodic, 38
    portfolio, 38
    product, 38
Atomic clocks, 167
Attendance chart, 39–40
Average, 120
Axis, 143, 171

Babylonian calendar, 168
Balances, equal-arm, 151
Balance scale, 151
Ballpark estimate, 174, 178, 201
Bar graphs, 117
Bases, 136
Base-10 blocks, 35–36
Beam scale, 152
Big cube, 36
Bimetallic thermometer, 164
Binary operations, 86
Broken-line graph, 118
"Built-in" mathematics, 22–24

Calculators, 27–31, 87
  basics, 28–29
  clear keys, 29
  displaying and reading numbers, 29–30
  interpreting the display, 30–31
  introductory exercises, 29
  key sequence, 28
Calendars, 167–170
  Babylonian, 168
  Egyptian, 168
  Gregorian, 169
  Hebrew, 169
  Islamic, 169
  Julian, 168–169
  Perpetual, 169
  Roman, 168
  Thirteen-Month, 169
  World, 169
Capacity, 155
Cartesian product, 80–81
Celsius, 163–164
Center
  of a circle, 133
  of a sphere, 136
Centimeter (cm), 150
Chalk, semipermanent, 46
Chalkboard slates, 16
Chance, 121
Change diagram, 16, 74–75
Choral
  drills, 90–91
  readings, 22
Chord, 133
Circle graphs, 118
Circles, 133–135
Circumference, 133
Class calendar, 40–41
Class Data Pad, 42
Class number line, 42–44
  growing, 42–43, 64
  prefabricated, 43–44
Clocks, 166–167
  analog, 167
  atomic, 167
  digital, 167
Codes, 53
Column addition, 101–102
Communication
  home-and-school, 38–39
Commutative property, 91–92
Comparison diagram, 16, 75–77

Competition, 11–12
Complex number, 56
Concave polygon, 132
Cone, 136
Congruence, 140–141
Congruent
  figures, 139
  line segments, 140
  polygons, 140
  polyhedrons, 140
Conversion fact, 150
Convex polygon, 132
Cooperative groupings, 18
Coordinate geometry, 142–143
Coordinate grid, 143
Coordinates, 143
  map, 171–173
Corner, 126
Counting, 57–58
  backward, 60
  double, 60
  by 5s, 60
  rational, 58
  rote, 57–58
  by 10s, 59–60
  by 2s, 60
  whole numbers, 54
Counts, 53
Cube, 36, 138
  big, 36
Cubic unit, 153–154
Cubic centimeter, 150, 154–155
Cubit, 148
Cup, 155
Curriculum, managing the, 8–18
Customary system. See U.S. customary system
Cylindrical solids, 136
Cylinders, 136–137

Daily routine, 8
Daily schedule, 45
Data collection, organization, and analysis,
      114–120
Decagon, 129
Decimals, 66–69
Degree (°), 163–165
Degree Celsius (°C), 163–164
Degree Fahrenheit (°F), 163
Denomination, 158
Diagonals, 130
Diameter, 133

Dice, 23, 34–35
Digit, 148
Digital clocks, 167
Dimension, 125–126
Displays, organizing, 39–49
Distributive property, 107
Division, 77–81
   algorithms, 109–111
   measurement, 79
   partitive, 78
   quotitive, 79
   symbols, 83–85
   whole numbers, 113
Dodecahedron, 138
Double-nine dominoes, 91

Edges, 137
Egg cartons, 35
Egyptian calendar, 168
Elapsed time, 157
Electronic scale, 152
Endpoints, 127
Enlarge, 139
E Pluribus Unum, 158
Equal-grouping problems, 78–79
Equal-groups, 77
Equal-sharing, 78
Equality, 65
Equations, 86
   solving, 87–88
Equilateral
   polygons, 132
   triangles, 130, 133
Equivalence, 69
Estimates
   in calculations, 178–179
   for clarity, 176
   for consistency, 176–177
   measurements as, 150–151
   in problem solving, 177
Estimation, 174–181
   ballpark, 174
European subtraction, 105–106
Even numbers, 184
Events, 122
The Everything Math Deck, 12, 34
Expert Jigsaw, 22
Explorations, 8–9
Exponent, 85
Exponential notation, 85

Expressions, 86
Extended fact, 92
Extreme numbers, 177–178

Faces, 137, 140
Facilitator, 20
Fact extensions, 92
Fact families, 91
Fact power, 10, 91
Facts, basic, 89–92
Fact Triangles, 9–10, 91
Fahrenheit, 163
Fair, 122
Family Letters, 38–39
Fathom, 148
Flash cards, 21
Flat, 36
Flip, 139
Foot (ft), 149
Formulas, 89
Frac-Tac-Toe, 69
Fractions, 66–69
Fractions museum, 14
Frames-and-Arrows diagrams, 10, 185–186
Function Machines, 10, 190–191
Functions, 89, 189–194

Gallon (gal), 149
Games, 10–11, 90, 92–93
Gatekeeper, 20
Geometric
   solids, 32
   tools, 145
Geometry, 124–145
   computer packages, 135
   coordinate, 142–143
   dimension, 125–126
   lines, 127
   points, 126
   rays, 127
   segments, 127
   teaching, 143–145
Graphs, 117–118
Great span. See Hand span
Gregorian calendar, 169
Grouping symbols, 86
Group member duties, 20–21
Group responses, 22
Groups and partnerships, 18–19
Group structures, 21

Half-lines, 127
Hand span, 148
Hebrew calendar, 169
Heptagon, 129
Hexagon, 129
Home Links, 12, 38–39
Hundreds museum, 14

Icosahedron, 138
Image, 138
Inch (in.), 149
Inequalities, 86
In God We Trust, 158
Input, 190
Inside-outside circle, 21
Integer, 54
Intersect, 139
Intrinsic value, 158
Irrational numbers, 56
Islamic calendar, 169
Isometry transformation. *See* Transformation,
     138
Isosceles, 131
   trapezoid, 131
   triangle, 130

Jefferson, Thomas, 159
Job chart, 44–45
Jobs, classroom, 44–45
Julian calendar, 168–169
Juxtaposition, 84

Kelvin scale, 164
Key sequence, 28
Kilogram, (kg), 150
Kilometer (km), 150
Kite, 131

Landmarks, 120
Language diversity, 25–26
Lattice multiplication, 107–109
Left-to-right subtraction, 105
Length, 153
Line graphs, 118
Line plots, 117
Lines, 127
Line segment, 127
Line symmetry, 141–142
Liter (L), 149
Locations, 53
Long, 36

Magnitude estimate, 178
Maps, 170–173
   temperature, 47–48
Map
   coordinates, 171–173
   scale, 63, 173
Mass, 156
Materials/supply handler, 20
Math Boxes, 12–13
Mathematical modeling, 199–201
Math Messages, 13
Maximum, 120
Mean, 119–120
Measurement, 146–161
   division, 79
   estimates, 150–151
   personal, 147–149
   systems, 149–150
   tools and techniques, 150–152
Measuring sticks, 151
Measuring tapes, 151
Measures, 53
Median, 120
Mental arithmetic, 111–113
   strategies, 112–113
Mental Math and Reflexes, 13–14
Mercury thermometer, 164
Meteorologist, 48
Meter (m), 150
Metric system, 149–150
   converting to U.S. customary system, 150
Middle value, 120
Minimum, 120
Mode, 120
Modeling, mathematical, 199–202
Money, 157–161
   facts, 158
   history, 160
Monticello, 160
Multiplication, 77–81
   algorithms, 106–109
   symbols, 83–85
Multiplication Top-It, 11
Museums, 14

Name-collection boxes, 14, 65–66
Negative numbers, 55, 61
n-gon, 130
Nickels, 159
Nonagon, 129
Notation, 69–71

Numbered heads together, 21
Number families, 91
Number grids, 14–15, 58–61
    puzzles, 60
Number lines, 15, 62–64. *See also,* Class number
        line
    incomplete, 187–189
Number models, 81–92
Number scrolls, 61
Number sense, 174–181
    and mathematical connections, 180–181
Number sentences, 86–93
    open, 87–88
Number sequences, 184–189
Number stories, 202–204
Number systems, 53–57
Number theory, 184
Number uses, 53
Number-writing practice, 46
Numeration, 69–70

Obtuse
    angle, 129
    triangle, 130
Obverse, 159
Octagon, 129
Octahedron, 138
Odd numbers, 184
ONE, 67
1-dimensional figures, 125, 127
Open number sentences, 87
Operation diagrams. *See* Situation diagram
Operations, 72–93
    order of, 87
    symbols, 83–85
    use classes, and, 73–81
Opposite-change Rule, 102–103
Opposite of a number, 55
Ordered pairs, 171
Order of magnitude, 178
Order of operations, 87
Ordinal numbers, 56–57
Ordinates, 171
Origin, 171
Output, 190

Pairs-check, 21
Pan-balance, 88
Parallel lines, 139–140
Parallelogram, 131

Parenthesis, 86
Partial differences, 106
Partial-products multiplication, 106–107
Partial-sums addition, 101
Partitive division, 78
Parts-and-total diagram, 15, 73–74, 87
Part-whole fraction, 67
Pattern blocks, 32
Pattern-Block Templates, 31–32
Patterns
    odd and even number, 184
    visual, 182–183
Pentagon, 129
Percents, 66, 68–69
Perimeter, 153
Perpendicular lines, 139–140
Perpetual calendar, 169
Pi (π), 133–134
    digits of, 56
    mountains of, 134–135
Pie chart, 118
Place value, 69–70
Plane figures, 127–135
Plane geometry versus solid geometry, 144–145
Plastic write-on/wipe-off slates, 16
Platform scale, 152
Platonic solids, 138
Playing cards, standard, 34
Points, 126
Polygonal region, 130
Polygons, 129–133
    equilateral, 132
    regular, 132–133
Polyhedrons, 137–138
    regular, 138
Positive numbers, 55
Power, 85
Predictions, making, 122
Preimage, 138
Prisms, 136–137
    rectangular, 137
Probability, 120–122
Problem representations, 197–199
Problem solving, 37, 196–207
    strategies and solutions, sharing children's,
        204–205
    strategies for beginners, 205–206
Projects, 16
Properties, 89

Pyramids, 136, 137
   solid, 137
   triangular, 137
Pythagoras, 56

Quadrangle, 129
Quadrilateral, 129, 130–132
Quotitive division, 79

Radius, 133
Random number tables, 35
Range, 120
Rate diagram, 16
Rates, 68, 79
Rate versus ratio, 68
Ratio comparison, 53, 173
Rational numbers, 54
   negative, 55
   notation for, 71
   positive, 54, 55
   zero, 54–55
Ratios, 68, 79
Rays, 127
Reader, 20
Real numbers, 55–56
Recorder, 20
Rectangle, 131
Rectangular array, 79
Rectangular prism, 137
Reference frames, 162–173
Reflection, 139
Reflex angle, 129
Relations, 64–66, 139–141
   symbols for numerical, 64, 85
Remainder, 84
Rename-addends addition. *See* Opposite-Change
      Rule
Reverse, 159, 160
Rhombus, 131
Right angle, 129
Right triangle, 130
Rim, 159
Roman calendar, 168
Roman numerals, 44
Rotational symmetry, 142
Rotations, 128–129
Rounding, 179–180
   down, 179–180
   to nearest, 180
   up, 179

Routines, organizing, 39–49
Rubric, 38
Rulers, 31

Scalars, 68, 80
Scale factor, 80
Scalene triangle, 130
Scales, 151–152
   balance, 151
   beam, 152
   electronic, 152
   map, 63, 173
   Kelvin, 164
   platform, 152
   spring, 152
Scaling, 80
Segments, 127
Sequences, number, 184–189
Shortcuts, 92
Sides, 129–133
Similar
   polygons, 141
   polyhedrons, 141
Similarity, 140–141
Situation diagram, 16
Slates, 16
Slide, 138
Solid figures, 135–138
   cylindrical, 136
   prism, 137
   pyramid, 137
   rectangular prism, 137
   versus 3-D figures, 135–136
Solid geometry versus plane geometry, 144–145
Solution, 198
Special needs children, 24–25
Spheres, 136
Spinners, 23, 35
Spring scale, 152
Square, 131
Square array, 85
Square roots, 55–56
Square units, 153
Stem-and-leaf plots, 118–119
Straight angle, 129
Straws, 32–34
Students, organizing, 18–37
Subtraction, 73–77
   algorithms, 103–106
   symbols, 83

index

Summarizer, 20
Surface area, 153
Survey, 115
Symbols, arithmetic, 82–85
    addition, 83
    division, 83–85
    grouping, 86
    multiplication, 83–85
    relations, 85
    subtraction, 83
Symmetry, 141–142
    line, 141–142
    rotational, 142
    translation, 141
    turn, 142

Tables, 116
Tally marks, 115
Tape measures, 31
Teacher duties, 21
Teachers, substitute, 17
Team building, 19–20
Temperature, 163–165
    map, 48
    record, 47–48
Tessellation, 183
Tetrahedron, 137, 138
Thermocouple, 165
Thermometers, 162–165
    bimetallic, 164
    classroom, 47
    mercury, 164
    thermocouple, 165
Think-pair-share, 21
3-dimensional, 125
    figures, 135–141
3-D shapes museum, 14
Time, 165–170
    elapsed, 157
Timelines, 170
Tool kits, 36–37

Tools, 26–37
    geometric, 145
    measurement, 150–152
Trade-first subtraction, 103–104
Transformations, 138–139
Translation symmetry, 141
Trapezoid, 131
Triangles, 129–130
Triangular pyramid, 137
Turn-around facts. *See* Commutative property
Turn symmetry, 142
Twist-ties, 32–33
2-dimensional figures, 125–135

Unit boxes, 18
U.S. customary system, 149
    converting to metric system, 150
U.S. traditional addition, 103

van Hiele levels of geometry, 144
Variables, 88–89
Vertex, 128, 129, 130, 132, 137
Vertices, 129
Volume, 154–156
    capacity, 155
    discrete and continuous conceptions of,
        154–155
    linking area and, 155–156

Weather record, 48–49
Weight, 156
"What's My Rule?", 18, 191–192
Whole, 67
Whole numbers, 54
Wireframe, 135
World calendar, 169

Yard (yd), 148

Zero, 54, 55
    point, 162

index

K–3 Games Correlation Chart

Skill and Concept Areas

Game	K Title Page #	Grade 1 Lesson	Grade 2 Lesson	Grade 3 Lesson	Numeration	Mental Math	Basic Facts	Operations	Patterns	Geometry	Money	Time	Probability	Calculator
Addition Card Draw			12.5			■	■	■						
Addition Spin			4.2			■	■	■						
Addition Top-It		6.1	1.4	1.4		■	■	■						
Addition Top-It with Dominoes			2.5			■	■	■						
Angle Race				6.9						■				
Animal Weight Top-It		5.5				■	■	■						
Array Bingo			6.10	9.6			■	■						
Attribute Rule Game			7.2							■				
Attribute Train Game		7.2	7.2						■					
Base-10 Exchange		8.4					■							
Baseball Multiplication				4.7		■	■	■						
Basketball Addition			7.4			■	■	■						
Beat the Calculator		5.11	2.2	1.8		■	■	■						■
Before and After		3.1			■									
The Block-Drawing Game				11.6									■	
Broken Calculator			1.10	*		■	■	■						■
Buyer and Vendor Game		10.3		1.9				■			■			
Class Clock Game			1.3									■		
Clock Concentration			5.1									■		
Coin-Dice		3.12			■						■			
Coin Exchange	194	6.10	1.4		■						■			
Coin Top-It		2.10	1.4		■						■			
Concentration with Number Cards & Dominoes	89				■									
Dice-Roll and Tally Game		1.8	1.5		■								■	
Difference Game		5.7			■	■	■	■			■			
Digit Discovery			1.12		■									
Digit Game	267		3.2		■									
Dime, Nickel, Penny, Grab		3.12									■			
Disappearing Train	217					■	■	■						
Division Arrays				4.3				■						
Division Coin-Drop								■						
Dollar Rummy			3.4		■			■						
Domino Top-It		3.14			■									
Double-Digit Dice Game	268				■									
Equivalent Fractions Game			8.5	8.4	■									
Fact Power Game		6.4				■	■	■						
Fact Triangle Flip				4.6		■	■	■						
Factor Bingo				9.6	■			■						
Fraction Top-It			8.6	8.5	■									
Guess the Rule		7.2							■					
High Roller	297	2.12			■	■								
Hit the Target			7.3											■
Less Than You				1.3				■						
Magic Bag Game		5.10			■									
Making Change			3.8								■			
Matching Coin Game	40										■			
Memory Addition/Subtraction				10.9		■	■	■						■
Missing Terms				*										■
Money Exchange Game			1.6		■						■			
Monster Squeeze Game	84				■									

Number indicates first exposure at grade level. *Additional games available in *Student Reference Book*

Skill and Concept Areas

Name	K Title Page #	Grade 1 Lesson	Grade 2 Lesson	Grade 3 Lesson	Numeration	Mental Math	Basic Facts	Operations	Patterns	Geometry	Money	Time	Probability	Calculator
Multiplication Bingo				7.3		■	■	■						
Multiplication Coin-Drop						■					■			
Multiplication Draw			11.5	*		■	■							
Multiplication Top-It				10.5		■	■							
Name That Number			2.9	1.6		■		■						
Nickel/Penny Grab		2.11			■						■			
Number-Grid Game	216	9.2	1.11		■									
Number-Line Squeeze*		1.2			■									
Number Top-It				5.2	■									
One-Dollar Exchange Game		8.2									■			
One-Dollar Game	266										■			
$1, $10, $100 Exchange Game		10.3									■			
Ones, Tens, Hundreds Game	295				■			■						
Paper Money Exchange	292				■						■			
Penny-Cup		2.8	1.7		■						■			
Penny-Dice Game		1.3			■						■			
Penny-Drop Addition		2.11					■	■						
Penny Grab		2.8	6.2	2.6	■						■			
Penny Guessing		2.9			■						■			
Penny-Dime Exchange				5.8	■						■			
Penny-Nickel Exchange		2.10			■						■			
Penny-Nickel Dime Exchange		5.13			■						■			
Pick-a-Coin			10.3	*							■			
Pin the Number (Number Grid)	216		1.11		■									
Plus or Minus Game	227					■		■						
Pocket Game	201				■									
Prize Time			3.3									■		
Raft Game	221				■									
Robot Game				6.3						■				
Rolling for 50		2.1			■			■						
Scissors, Paper, Stone		1.8			■								■	
Secret Number		5.3			■									
Shaker Addition Top-It		4.12				■		■						
Shopping			4.6					■			■			
Spin a Number (1–10)	80				■									
Spinning for Money			3.2								■			
Spinning to Win				11.5									■	
Stand Up If.....		7.7							■	■				
Subtraction Top-It				3.6		■		■						
Tens-and-Ones Trading Game		5.3			■									
3, 2, 1 Game		8.5							■					
Three Addends			6.1	2.9		■		■						
Tic-Tac-Toe Addition		10.4						■						
Time Match		4.4										■		
Top-It	170	1.6			■									
Touch-and-Match Quadrangles				6.5						■				
Turn-Around Facts Game		5.10					■							
Two-Fisted Penny Addition		2.3	1.7	2.4		■					■			
"Who Am I Thinking Of?"		7.1							■					
"What's My Rule?" Fishing	99		2.11	2.3					■					
"What's My Attribute Rule?"			5.1						■	■				

Number indicates first exposure at grade level. *Additional games available in *Student Reference Book*

Tables of Measure

Metric System

Units of Length

1 kilometer (km)	=	1,000 meters (m)
1 meter (m)	=	10 decimeters (dm)
	=	100 centimeters (cm)
	=	1,000 millimeters (mm)
1 decimeter (dm)	=	10 centimeters (cm)
1 centimeter (cm)	=	10 millimeters (mm)

Units of Area

1 square meter (sq m)	=	10,000 square centimeters (sq cm)
1 square centimeter (sq cm)	=	100 square millimeters (sq mm)

Units of Volume

1 cubic meter (cu m)	=	1,000,000 cubic centimeters (cu cm)
1 cubic centimeter (cu cm)	=	1,000 cubic millimeters (cu mm)

Units of Capacity

1 kiloliter (kL)	=	1,000 liters (L)
1 liter (L)	=	1,000 milliliters (mL)

Units of Mass (Weight)

1 metric ton (t)	=	1,000 kilograms (kg)
1 kilogram (kg)	=	1,000 grams (g)
1 gram (g)	=	1,000 milligrams (mg)

U.S. Customary System

Units of Length

1 mile (mi)	=	1,760 yards (yd)
	=	5,280 feet (ft)
1 yard (yd)	=	3 feet (ft)
	=	36 inches (in.)
1 foot (ft)	=	12 inches (in.)

Units of Area

1 square yard (sq yd)	=	9 square feet (sq ft)
	=	1,296 square inches (sq in.)
1 square foot (sq ft)	=	144 square inches (sq in.)

Units of Volume

1 cubic yard (cu yd)	=	27 cubic feet (cu ft)
1 cubic foot (cu ft)	=	1,728 cubic inches (cu in.)

Units of Capacity

1 gallon (gal)	=	4 quarts (qt)
1 quart (qt)	=	2 pints (pt)
1 pint (pt)	=	2 cups (c)
1 cup (c)	=	8 fluid ounces (fl oz)
1 fluid ounce (fl oz)	=	2 tablespoons (tbs)
1 tablespoon (tbs)	=	3 teaspoons (tsp)

Units of Mass (Weight)

1 pound (lb)	=	16 ounces (oz)
1 ton (T)	=	2,000 pounds (lb)

Units of Body Measure

1 **digit** is about the width of a finger.

1 **hand** is about the width of the palm.

1 **span** is about the distance from the tip of the thumb to the tip of the little finger of outstretched hand.

1 **cubit** is about the length from the elbow to the tip of the outstretched fingers.

1 **yard** is about the distance from the tip of the nose to the tips of the fingers.

1 **fathom** is about the length from fingertip to fingertip of outstretched arms.

Units of Time

1 millennium	=	10 centuries
	=	100 decades
	=	1,000 years (yr)
1 century (cent)	=	10 decades
	=	100 years (yr)
1 year (yr)	=	12 months (mo)
	=	52 weeks (wk)
		plus 1 or 2 days
	=	365 or 366 days
1 month (mo)	=	28, 29, 30, or 31 days
1 week (wk)	=	7 days
1 day	=	24 hours (hr)
1 hour (hr)	=	60 minutes (min)
1 minute (min)	=	60 seconds (sec)

System Equivalents

1 inch is about 2.5 centimeters.

1 kilometer is about 0.6 mile.

1 mile is about 1.6 kilometers.

1 meter is about 39 inches.

1 liter is about 1.1 quarts.

1 ounce is about 28 grams.

1 kilogram is about 2.2 pounds.